1994

ACCREDITATION

MANUAL FOR

HOSPITALS

79908

Volume I • Standards

JOINT COMMISSION MISSION

The mission of the Joint Commission on Accreditation of Healthcare Organizations is to improve the quality of care provided to the public.

FOREWORD

In this era of health care reform, health care organizations should be guided by a broad vision of the past, the present, and the future to assure that patient care is effective, accessible, and affordable. The Joint Commission's vision is, in substantial measure, rooted in the beliefs of Dr Ernest A. Codman, a prominent surgeon who was a principal founder of the Hospital Standardization Program, the Joint Commission's predecessor organization. Dr Codman developed what he called the end-result system, an approach that required each hospital to track each of its patients long enough to determine whether the treatment provided was effective. If the results fell short of expectations, the hospital was to determine the underlying cause and take the actions necessary to achieve improved performance.

We use different terms today—outcomes management, continuous quality improvement, service to the patient—but the primary objectives of Dr Codman still ring true. With this 1994 *Accreditation Manual for Hospitals* (*AMH*), we launch the translation of the vision into substance. Actual performance and actual outcomes are about to become the central focus of the Joint Commission's accreditation process.

The 1994 *AMH* represents a transition in several respects. First, and most importantly, this *Manual* presents the transition of Joint Commission standards from those that focus on capability to those that focus on performance. Second, this *Manual* itself is in transition—that is, it presents phase one of a two-phase redevelopment of all Joint Commission standards around important functions. Phase two will be completed with the publication of the 1995 *AMH*.

As a result, the 1994 *AMH* may somewhat resemble the patient in the middle of surgery. Unlike previous manuals, the standards chapters are divided among four sections, three of which correspond to groups of functions that support the provision of patient care. These sections include "Care of the Patient," "Organizational Functions," and "Structures with Important Functions." These groupings of functional standards are accompanied by a fourth section, "Other Department/Service-Specific Requirements," which includes those standards that have not yet been recast into a performance mode. These standards are being revised and will be incorporated into the relevant chapters in the first three sections of the *Manual* in 1995. At that time, standards redevelopment, a major objective of the Agenda for Change, will be complete.

The Joint Commission's emphasis on outcome and performance parallels the public's rising demand for performance information. In response to this growing interest, the Joint Commission is seeking to help health care organizations better meet their public accountabilities. In the context of this *Manual*, our goal has been to reorganize the standards around important functions and to direct primary attention to patient care and organization management. With this 1994 edition of the *AMH*, the standards are framed as performance objectives. How organizations meet those objectives will be up to them. Within this new framework, general performance expectations will not be significantly increased in 1994 over 1993. Organizations whose performance would comply with the 1993 standards will, with few exceptions, also meet the 1994 requirements. However, performance expectations will begin to rise progressively in 1995 and the years that follow. These

incremental expectations will be based on careful assessments of the capabilities of accredited organizations.

This 1994 *AMH* draws on the best of both worlds—old and new, past and future. Organizations that are already being innovative and creative in their performance of important patient care functions will find support for their efforts in the new framework of this *Manual*. For those organizations seeking more explicit guidance, we offer the scoring guidelines. The scoring guidelines, particularly those for the redeveloped standards, place the standards in a context that should meet the practical needs of most users.

As always, we invite your comments and suggestions regarding this *Manual*. In particular, we ask that you let us know any concerns you may have regarding the new directions reflected by the Agenda for Change. The envisioned transition has been carefully structured to afford ample opportunities for input from, and discussion with, accredited organizations. We count on your participation in framing the expectations to be set forth in future editions of this *Manual*.

Dennis O'Leary, MD
President

CONTENTS

Standards

INTRODUCTION

With the 1994 *Accreditation Manual for Hospitals* (*AMH*), the Joint Commission completes the first phase of a two-phase transition from standards organized around a hospital's departments/services, or structure, to standards organized around functions most critical to patient care. This 1994 *Manual* also presents the change in the focus of our standards from capability to performance. In keeping with the goals of the Agenda for Change, these standards are intended to stimulate continuous, systematic, and organizationwide improvement in an organization's performance and the outcomes of care. The functions around which the standards are grouped cut across many departments/services and roles.

The transition to performance-focused accreditation, scheduled for completion with the 1995 *AMH*, will make accreditation a stronger impetus for continuous improvement. The 1994 *AMH*, a "manual in transition," will encourage hospitals to develop a new frame of reference by allowing them to see the links between the old and the new standards frameworks.

Because the shift to a functionally organized framework and performance-focused standards signifies a fundamental and substantial change, the Joint Commission recognizes that organizations need time to orient themselves to the new framework and to implement the new standards. Thus, only minimal increases in standards-compliance requirements are planned for accredited hospitals during this transition year. For example, in 1993 hospital leaders were expected to become educated in the approaches and methods of quality improvement (QA.1.1) and to develop a plan addressing how they would meet their responsibilities described in QA.1.2 through QA.1.6. The hospital needed to show evidence that its leaders were implementing at least one of the planned activities at a performance level that would result in at least a Score 2. In 1994, all six standards are relocated to the "Leadership" chapter. The performance expectations for these standards, as stated in the scoring guidelines, are that the hospital show evidence that its leaders are now acting on their plans to meet their responsibilities described in the appropriate "Leadership" standards; that is, the leaders have begun to implement the planned activities. In general, hospital performance that met 1993 standards will, with few exceptions, also meet 1994 standards.

All staff, particularly those involved in the survey process, are encouraged to read this Introduction as an orientation to the new standards framework and the use of this *Manual*.

A Framework for Improving Organizational Performance

Figure 1 (page x) depicts four critical aspects in the internal environment of any health care organization or, indeed, any organization that aspires to excellence. These aspects are

- leadership,
- management of human resources,
- management of information, and
- improving organizational performance.

Critical Aspects of a Health Care Organization's Internal Environment

- Leadership
  — Mission
  — Vision
  — Priorities
  — Resources

- Management of Human Resources
  — Education
  — Competence

- Management of Information
  — Planning
  — Aggregate Date
  — Comparative Data
  — Knowledge-Based Data

- Improving Organizational Performance
  — Collaboration
  — Process Thinking

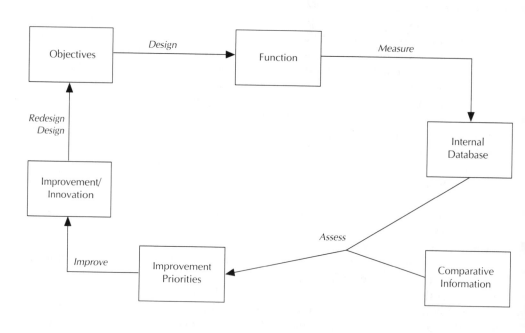

Figure 1. *This figure represents four critical aspects of the internal environment of any health care organization and a flowchart of the cycle for improving performance.*

These four important functions are also central to the Joint Commission's framework for improving performance around which this *Manual* is being reshaped. Revision of the standards is predicated on the assumption that the central purpose of health care organizations is to maximize the health of the persons served and to efficiently use the resources needed to achieve this objective.

Both patient outcomes and resource use are directly influenced by the performance of the organization: doing the right thing (the extent to which care is efficacious and appropriate), and doing these right things *well* (the extent to which care is available, timely, effective, continuous, safe, efficient, respectful, and caring). The design and operation of many important functions strongly influence whether the organization's services exhibit these qualities, or dimensions of performance. The effect of an organization's performance on its important functions or processes is reflected in its patient outcomes, the cost of its services, and the judgments made by patients, staff, purchasers, and others about the quality and value of the care provided.

The important functions identified in this *Manual* include both direct patient care activities (described in Section 1) and management and support processes and functions (addressed in Section 2). Reframing the standards in terms of these organizationwide, multidisciplinary functions emphasizes the interdependent nature of all the activities of a health care organization.

Figure 1 also includes a flowchart of the cycle for improving performance. This flowchart presents an operational model for improvement. With the recognition that patient outcomes will be improved only by increasing the effectiveness and efficiency of organizational functions, a "systems oriented" organization will turn its attention to processes that are complex, interdependent, and primarily team based. The flowchart in the diagram illustrates how components of the performance-improvement cycle are connected by the actions of an organization's leaders, managers, physicians and other clinicians, trustees, and support staff who *design, measure, assess,* and *improve* their work processes.

The performance-improvement cycle depicted in the flowchart has no beginning and no end. An organization may start its improvement effort at any point: by designing a new service, by flowcharting an existing clinical process, by measuring patient outcomes, by comparing its performance to that of other organizations, by selecting specific areas for priority attention, or even by experimenting with new ways of carrying out current functions.

This approach is valuable because it is anchored in the real work of health care professionals and in the real improvements that can be achieved to benefit patients and others. This cycle for improving performance is not new—it is the scientific method applied to making health care processes and outcomes better.

The 1994 *AMH* introduces a broader and more useful perspective on organizational improvement. This perspective, captured in Figure 1, is based on the understanding that organizational performance is the key determinant of four important results—that is, patient outcomes, costs, quality, and value. The identified functions and the cycle for improving performance included in this *Manual* are not a cookbook of required activities. They are a synthesis of important concepts and methods that health care organizations should utilize as starting points in their pursuit of excellence.

The Standards-Revision Initiative: A Focus on Outcome

The standards-revision initiative evidenced in this *Manual* is one of three initiatives of the Agenda for Change. The other two initiatives, reviewed later in this Introduction, are (1) a redesign of the survey process and (2) the development of performance measures that support ongoing improvement by allowing hospitals to track their performance in specific areas and to compare it with that of other institutions.

The standards-revision initiative emphasizes outcome more than the methods used to achieve it. This initiative, launched in response to the field's widespread interest in a more meaningful accreditation process, is founded on a recognition of each organization's uniqueness. In keeping with the goals of the Agenda for Change, the standards- revision initiative is intended to make accreditation a more powerful catalyst for continuous improvement by focusing on the organization as a complex system, by creating consistent expectations across departments/services, and by giving the organization more flexibility and choice in setting priorities and devising strategies to improve—strategies that respond more closely to the real needs of the patients and the community the organization serves.

In 1992, the standards underwent a substantial reduction in number and prescriptiveness. This streamlining continued in 1993 with a regrouping of selected standards into three new chapters: "Patient and Family Education"; "Orientation, Training, and Education of Staff"; and "Responsibilities of Department/Service Directors." This regrouping ensured that these important functions would be uniformly and consistently performed and surveyed throughout the organization.

Until their recasting in 1993, standards pertaining to these functions had varied widely across chapters relating to departments/services, producing imbalances in the survey process. For example, requirements for patient and family education appeared in some chapters and not in others when such education was clearly important throughout an organization.

This 1994 *Manual* represents a significant expansion of that effort, including both a large-scale movement toward function and performance and a continuing decrease in the prescriptiveness and detail of standards. The transition to performance-focused standards organized around important functions will be complete with the 1995 *AMH*.

Seven Chapters of Performance-Focused Standards

The 1994 *AMH* contains seven new chapters of performance-focused, functionally organized standards. Each chapter includes a preamble describing the function's role in the provision of patient care. Each chapter was developed with considerable input from focus groups, expert panels, and task forces representing a multitude of disciplines, and has been thoroughly field reviewed and tested. They are

- "Assessment of Patients,"
- "Treatment of Patients" (medication use standards only in 1994),
- "Operative and Other Invasive Procedures,"
- "Education of Patients and Family,"
- "Leadership,"
- "Management of Information," and
- "Improving Organizational Performance."

The new sets of standards partially consolidate 1993 department/service-specific standards. These 1993 standards were regrouped according to function and rewritten to stress outcome over structure and to apply evenly to many departments/services. For example, NC.1.3.4 through NC.1.3.4.6 in the "Nursing Care" chapter focused on what nursing staff members must document in each patient's medical record when the patient received nursing care. At the same time, RH.1.3 through RH.1.3.5 in the "Physical Rehabilitation Services" chapter focused on documentation requirements for all rehabilitation disciplines. NC.1.3.4.1 required that the initial assessments and reassessments be documented, whereas RH.1.2.3 required that a treatment plan be developed based on an evaluation that included an assessment of functional ability appropriate to the patient. In 1994, the "Assessment of Patients" chapter pulls together all the pieces of these discipline and department/service requirements to address the organization's responsibility to define for each patient what must be assessed, by whom, through what processes, and by what criteria.

In some cases, additional standards were developed to fill significant gaps revealed when various standards were brought together under a specific function. For example, the patient assessment standards now address an issue never before addressed in the standards, but one that has been problematic to the assessment process for many years: the provision of adequate clinical information when the report of test results is to include clinical interpretation. PE.1.5.1 in the "Assessment of Patients" chapter now requires such information.

These chapters represent the best from a variety of disciplines. While permitting standards to be applied more broadly throughout the organization, their creation also enables departments/services across the organization to benefit from advances and innovations made in other departments/services. For example, in 1993, medication preparation and storage were addressed only in the "Pharmaceutical Services" chapter. In 1994, TX.3 in the medication use section of the "Treatment of Patients" chapter calls for medication preparation and storage under proper conditions of sanitation, temperature, light, moisture, ventilation, segregation, safety, and security. Because this issue is now addressed in a cross-departmental, functional chapter, this standard (as well as the other medication use standards) now applies to all areas in the hospital where medications are prepared and stored, such as the radiology and nuclear medicine departments/services.

Much of the detail and prescriptiveness of the 1993 standards have been moved to the scoring guidelines in volume II of this *Manual*. This change gives organizations greater flexibility in choosing *how* to achieve a given outcome by providing them the opportunity to explain the rationale behind their strategy to the surveyor. Strategies other than those identified in the scoring guidelines examples are acceptable, provided the organization can clearly demonstrate how those strategies will achieve desired outcomes and meet the intent of the standards. For example, the scoring guidelines for NC.2.1.1.1 in the "Nursing Care" chapter list eight methods for objectively assessing and documenting the competence of a nursing staff member. If a hospital is using a method other than those listed that still meets the "objective assessment of competence" intent of the standard, the surveyor will accept the method as evidence of compliance.

The movement toward function and performance supports continuous improvement in many ways. With the reduction of the standards' prescriptiveness, hospitals have greater freedom to attend to those issues that matter most to their organizations and to be more innovative in addressing those issues. The removal of structural barriers fosters organizationwide awareness of the similarities among departments/services, encouraging the development of a common language. For example, by focusing on common processes to measure and improve the organization's performance of important functions, staff members are encouraged to use statistical process control techniques. When a work team is created to measure a process over time and learns how to use statistical process control procedures, all members of that team will learn the "language" or vocabulary specific to their team's activities. In sharing their findings with other staff, additional people will understand this language and begin using it relative to performance improvement.

The development of a common language in turn opens doors to new opportunities for collaboration, creating a stronger sense of shared purpose. And it enables departments/services to learn from each other and to adapt resources and systems developed elsewhere in the organization to their own needs rather than "reinvent the wheel." Such cross-fertilization of ideas boosts efficiency and fosters professional growth.

An Orientation to This *Manual*

This *Manual* is divided into four sections. The seven new chapters of performance-focused standards, located in Sections 1 and 2, apply to many departments/services across the organization. Therefore, *all hospital staff participating in the survey process should have access to the entire manual*. The matrices on pages xviii–xxi are organized according to particular departments/services and by particular roles and enable staff to locate the chapters in this *Manual* containing standards that apply to them.* For example, the hospital's president of the medical staff can find the cell on page xviii labeled "Physician" and the one on page xix labeled "President of the Medical Staff" to locate those chapters in Sections 1 through 3 that contain standards that apply to him/her. A series of discipline-specific user guides and seminars focusing on changes in the standards and the survey process are also available. For more information, call the Joint Commission Customer Service Center at (708) 916-5800.

Section 1: Care of the Patient. Section 1 addresses the primary mission of hospitals. It focuses on the functions and processes directly related to patient care.

---

*A similar matrix for the 1995 Manual *will be published when the chapters and organization of that* Manual *are finalized.*

Section 1 contains four of the seven new sets of performance-focused standards introduced in this edition of the *AMH*:

- "Assessment of Patients,"
- "Treatment of Patients" (medication use standards only in 1994),
- "Operative and Other Invasive Procedures," and
- "Education of Patients and Family."

These standards apply to many departments/services across the organization. For example, the hospital's ambulatory clinics and services assess patients, administer medications, provide education to patients, and, in outpatient surgical centers, provide operative and other invasive procedures to patients. Therefore, the standards previously located in the "Hospital-Sponsored Ambulatory Care Services" chapter have been relocated throughout all seven new functional chapters for 1994.

In 1995, Section 1 will contain four additional sets of functionally organized standards:

- "Rights of Patients and Organizational Ethics,"
- "Entry to Setting or Service,"
- "Nutritional Care," and
- "Coordination of Care."

These four chapters are listed in the 1994 Table of Contents. An explanatory page in the body of the *Manual* indicates their anticipated location in this section of the 1995 *AMH*.

Section 2: Organizational Functions. Section 2 addresses the important functions and processes that, although not directly experienced by the patient, are vital to the organization's ability to provide patient care. Section 2 contains the remaining three sets of performance-focused standards introduced in this edition of the *AMH*:

- "Leadership,"
- "Management of Information," and
- "Improving Organizational Performance."

These standards apply to most departments/services across the organization. For example, all hospital departments and services have a designated leader, a director, or a manager who is charged with at least the responsibilities covered in the standards in the "Leadership" chapter. These departments and services include those traditionally surveyed against the standards in chapters contained in Section 4 and also those departments and services that support the provision of services provided by the hospital that have never been surveyed by the Joint Commission. In 1994, surveys will be limited to only those departments and services for which standards exist in Section 4. In 1995, all departments and services, such as the business office, admissions, clergy/pastoral care, and others will be surveyed against applicable standards.

In 1995, Section 2 will contain three additional sets of functionally organized standards:

- "Management of Human Resources,"
- "Management of the Environment of Care," and
- "Surveillance, Prevention, and Control of Infection."

As with Section 1, these three chapters are listed in the 1994 Table of Contents, and an explanatory page in the body of the *Manual* indicates their anticipated location in this section of the 1995 *AMH*.

Section 3: Structures with Important Functions. Section 3 addresses four major hospital structures of sufficient complexity and overarching significance to warrant inclusion in a separate section. They are

- "Governing Body,"
- "Management and Administration,"
- "Medical Staff," and
- "Nursing."

New and/or revised functionally oriented standards for the "Governing Body," "Management and Administration," and "Nursing" chapters will appear in Section 3 of the 1995 edition of the *AMH*. The "Medical Staff" chapter has already been relocated to this section in the 1994 *AMH*.

Section 4: Other Department/Service-Specific Requirements. Section 4 serves two purposes. First, it houses those residual 1993 department/service-specific standards that have not yet been incorporated into the functional chapters in Sections 1 and 2. *Hospital departments and services are expected to comply with these standards in 1994.* Second, it identifies those department/service-specific standards that *have* made the transition to the functional chapters in Sections 1 and 2 and indicates where they can be found. These standards are printed in small italic type. Their new standard reference in the 1994 *AMH* is indicated in parentheses in bold type at the end of the standard.

It is important to note, however, that these references indicate only where the *concept* or *intent* of the old standard has been located in the new functional chapters. In most cases, the original standard has been consolidated with others and has been rewritten to stress performance and outcome and to apply more evenly to departments/services throughout the organization. For example, SP.2 in the "Special Care Units" chapter in Section 4 is addressed in LD.2.2.1 in 1994. Although the specific language of SP.2 is not found in LD.2.2.1, the concept of appropriate direction and staffing according to the needs of the patient population served by the hospital underlies the language of LD.2.2.1.

All the standards in nine department/service-specific chapters in Section 4 have already completed their transition to the functional chapters in Sections 1 and 2 or have been moved to the scoring guidelines in Volume II of this *Manual*. They are

- "Hospital-Sponsored Ambulatory Care Services,"
- "Medical Record Services,"
- "Medical Staff,"
- "Patient and Family Education,"
- "Professional Library and Health Information Services,"
- "Quality Assessment and Improvement,"
- "Responsibilities of Department/Service Directors,"
- "Surgical and Anesthesia Services," and
- "Utilization Review."

These nine chapters contain only a crosswalk in Section 4 between the old and new standards frameworks (the "Medical Staff" chapter has already been relocated to Section 3). For example, the "Surgical and Anesthesia Services" chapter has two columns of standards references crosswalking the 1993 standards to their new location in 1994. This chapter is now primarily addressed in the "Operative and Other Invasive Procedures" chapter in Section 1 as well as in other chapters in Sections 2 and 3.

All the residual department/service-specific standards will be incorporated into the functional chapters in Sections 1 and 2 of the 1995 *AMH*. New chapters for "Governing Body," "Management and Administration," and "Nursing" standards will appear in Section 3 (the "Medical Staff" chapter has already been relocated to Section 3 in the 1994 *AMH*). Thus, the 1995 *AMH* will contain three sections:

- "Care of the Patient,"
- "Organizational Functions," and
- "Structures with Important Functions."

Improving Organizational Performance

The chapter "Improving Organizational Performance" in this edition of the *AMH* replaces the 1993 chapter "Quality Assessment and Improvement." A direct outgrowth of the emphasis on systematic, continuous, and organizationwide improvement that is the hallmark of the Agenda for Change, "Improving Organizational

Performance" completes the transition from a focus on individual performance (traditional quality assurance) to a focus on the performance of the whole organization. In addition to asking organizations to measure, assess, and improve performance on a systematic basis, it also asks them to make sure processes are well designed to begin with, to use state-of-the-art information as the foundation for that design, and to incorporate design into an organizationwide, systematic plan for continuous improvement. The standards in this chapter are preceded by a comprehensive preamble that describes the Joint Commission's conception of the organizationwide, continuous improvement of performance.

Management of Information

Another significant new chapter for 1994 contains standards for the function of managing a wide variety of types and sources of information related to patient care as well as other activities and functions of an organization. This chapter was developed from a broad and visionary set of principles widely respected as setting forth clear goals for information management for all health care organizations. The chapter identifies four types of information: patient specific, aggregate, expert, and comparative. The chapter also identifies important aspects of information management such as common data definitions and linked information systems. The standards in the "Management of Information" chapter are preceded by a comprehensive preamble that describes the Joint Commission's conception of organizationwide information management.

Changes in the Survey Process

The transition from standards organized around departments/services, or structures, to those that are performance focused and organized around important functions calls for parallel changes in the survey process. Beginning in 1994, the survey process will focus more on the quality of patient care and the performance of functions across the organization and less on department/service structure. For example, in 1993, DT.4.2.1.2 in the "Dietetic Services" chapter addresses documentation of "timely and periodic assessments of the patient's nutrient intake and tolerance to the prescribed diet modification, including the effect of the patient's appetite and food habits on food intake and any substitutions made." This standard is overly prescriptive regarding the "what" of documentation. The relocated standards in the new "Assessment of Patients" chapter in Section 1 focus on developing screening criteria to determine when nutritional assessments are necessary—that is, on finding ways to readily identify patients who require nutritional assessments and interventions rather than focusing on what a nutritionist documents in the medical record of a patient undergoing such assessments.

Surveyors will begin to function more fully as a team on 1994 surveys. Rather than conducting discipline-specific surveys, all three members of the survey team (physician, nurse, and administrator) will survey the performance of important functions within departments/services across the organization.

The Joint Commission will also introduce a survey planning process in 1994. A representative from the Joint Commission will contact each organization approximately two months before the survey to develop a detailed survey agenda, and organization staff will know in advance when they will meet with surveyors.

Indicator Monitoring System

In keeping with the goals of the Agenda for Change, 1994 standards in the "Improving Organizational Performance" chapter require organizations to participate in at least one reference database, of which the Joint Commission's indicator monitoring system is one.

Data from the indicator monitoring system provide hospitals two types of valuable feedback. First, the data enable organizations to look at trends and patterns in their own performance. Second, they allow organizations to compare their performance with that of other hospitals. Both types of feedback support continuous improvement by enabling hospitals to pinpoint areas where they should be doing better. This information can assist in defining priorities and developing short- and long-range goals.

Appendix C lists indicators currently in development and which organizations are expected to consider using for 1994.

INDIVIDUAL PROFESSIONALS

1994 IMPORTANT FUNCTIONS	Alcoholism Counselor	Case Manager	Central Services Manager	Chief Operating Officer	Child Life Specialist	Clergy/Pastoral Care Provider	Dentist	Dietitian	Executive Officer/Administrator	Executive Housekeeper	Governing Body Chair	Head Nurse	Human Resources Professional	Infection Control Practitioner	Laboratorian	Licensed Independent Practitioner	Medical Affairs Director	Nuclear Medical Technologist	Nurse Anesthetist	Nurse Clinical Specialist	Nurse Executive	Nursing Director(s)	Patient Advocate	Patient Educator	Physician
SECTION 1—CARE OF THE PATIENT																									
Assessment of Patients	•	•					•	•						•	•	•	•	•	•	•	•		•	•	•
Treatment of Patients (Medication Use)	•	•					•	•						•	•	•	•	•	•	•	•		•	•	•
Operative and Other Invasive Procedures							•	•						•	•	•		•	•	•	•		•	•	•
Education of Patients and Family	•					•	•	•				•		•	•	•	•		•	•	•	•	•	•	•
SECTION 2—ORGANIZATIONAL FUNCTIONS																									
Leadership		•	•	•					•		•	•		•		•	•	•	•	•	•	•	•	•	•
Management of Information	•	•	•	•		•	•	•	•	•	•	•		•	•	•	•	•	•	•	•	•	•	•	•
Improving Organizational Performance	•	•	•	•		•	•	•	•	•	•	•		•	•	•	•	•	•	•	•	•	•	•	•
SECTION 3—STRUCTURES WITH IMPORTANT FUNCTIONS																									
Medical Staff																									
SECTION 4—OTHER DEPARTMENT/SERVICE-SPECIFIC REQUIREMENTS																									
Alcoholism and Other Drug-Dependence Services																									
Diagnostic Radiology Services																									
Dietetic Services																									
Emergency Services																									
Governing Body																									
Infection Control																									
Management and Administrative Services																									
Nuclear Medicine Services																									
Nursing Care																									
Orientation, Training, and Education of Staff																									
Pathology and Clinical Laboratory Services																									
Patient Rights																									
Pharmaceutical Services																									
Physical Rehabilitation Services																									
Plant, Technology, and Safety Management																									
Radiation Oncology Services																									

In 1994, the standards contained in these chapters will continue to be surveyed in the departments/services responsible for their implementation. Some chapters, such as "Infection Control," continue to be applicable across the organization. "Orientation, Training, and Education of Staff" contains increased expectations in keeping with the plan for the phased implementation of this chapter established when the chapter was introduced in 1993.

1994 IMPORTANT FUNCTIONS	Podiatrist	President on...	Psychiatry or...	Psychologist	Quality Imp.../Coordinato...	Radiology /...	Registered.../Administra...	Rehabilitat...	Safety Offi...	Security Pe...	Staff Educ...	Staff Nurse	Staff Phar...	Vocationa...	Volunteer...	X-Ray Tec...
INDIVIDUAL PROFESSIONALS																
SECTION 1—CARE OF THE PATIENT																
Assessment of Patients	•	•	•	•	•	•	•				•	•				
Treatment of Patients (Medication Use)	•	•	•	•	•	•	•				•	•	•			
Operative and Other Invasive Procedures	•	•	•	•	•	•	•				•	•	•	•		•
Education of Patients and Family	•	•	•	•	•	•	•				•	•				
SECTION 2—ORGANIZATIONAL FUNCTIONS																
Leadership	•	•	•	•	•	•	•	•				•				
Management of Information	•	•	•	•	•	•	•	•			•	•	•			
Improving Organizational Performance	•	•	•	•	•	•	•	•			•	•	•			
SECTION 3—STRUCTURES WITH IMPORTANT FUNCTIONS																
Medical Staff	•	•	•	•								•				
SECTION 4—OTHER DEPARTMENT/SERVICE-SPECIFIC REQUIREMENTS																
Alcoholism and Other Drug-Dependence Services																
Diagnostic Radiology Services																
Dietetic Services																
Emergency Services																
Governing Body																
Infection Control																
Management and Administrative Services																
Nuclear Medicine Services																
Nursing Care																
Orientation, Training, and Education of Staff																
Pathology and Clinical Laboratory Services																
Patient Rights																
Pharmaceutical Services																
Physical Rehabilitation Services																
Plant, Technology, and Safety Management																
Radiation Oncology Services																
Respiratory Care Services																
Social Work Services																
Special Care Units																

In 1994, the standards contained in these chapters will continue to be surveyed in the departments/services responsible for their implementation. Some chapters, such as "Infection Control," continue to be applicable across the organization. "Orientation, Training, and Education of Staff" contains increased expectations in keeping with the plan for the phased implementation of this chapter established when the chapter was introduced in 1993.

HOSPITAL DEPARTMENTS/SERVICES

Columns (Hospital Departments/Services):
Admitting Office · Alcoholism/Chemical Dependency · Ambulatory Clinics · Anesthesiology · Bioengineering · Burn Unit · Cardiac Catheterization Unit · Cardiovascular ICU · Chemical Dependency Program · Child Life Department · Dental Department · Department of Surgery · Diagnostic Radiology · Dietetic Services · Emergency Services · Employee Health Service · Finance/Accounting/Business Office · Hospital Linen/Laundry Service · Hospitalwide Training Department · ICU(s), Adult, Pediatric · Library Services · Medical and/or Surgical ICU · Medical Records Services · Neonatal ICU · Nuclear Medicine Services

1994 IMPORTANT FUNCTIONS

SECTION 1—CARE OF THE PATIENT
- Assessment of Patients
- Treatment of Patients (Medication Use)
- Operative and Other Invasive Procedures
- Education of Patients and Family

SECTION 2—ORGANIZATIONAL FUNCTIONS
- Leadership
- Management of Information
- Improving Organizational Performance

SECTION 3—STRUCTURES WITH IMPORTANT FUNCTIONS
- Medical Staff

SECTION 4—OTHER DEPARTMENT/SERVICE-SPECIFIC REQUIREMENTS
- Alcoholism and Other Drug-Dependence Services
- Diagnostic Radiology Services
- Dietetic Services
- Emergency Services
- Governing Body
- Infection Control
- Management and Administrative Services
- Nuclear Medicine Services
- Nursing Care
- Orientation, Training, and Education of Staff
- Pathology and Clinical Laboratory Services
- Patient Rights
- Pharmaceutical Services
- Physical Rehabilitation Services
- Plant, Technology, and Safety Management
- Radiation Oncology Services

In 1994, the standards contained in these chapters will continue to be surveyed in the departments/services responsible for their implementation. Some chapters, such as "Infection Control," continue to be applicable across the organization. "Orientation, Training, and Education of Staff" contains increased expectations in keeping with the plan for the phased implementation of this chapter established when the chapter was introduced in 1993.

HOSPITAL DEPARTMENTS/SERVICES

Hospital Departments/Services (columns): Nursing Care · Occupational [Therapy] · Pathology/[Laboratory] Services · Pharmacy · Physical The[rapy] · Radiation O[ncology] · Rehabilitat[ion] · Renal Dialy[sis] · Renal Dialy[sis] · Respiratory · Social Wor[k] · Speech Pa[thology] · Step-Down · Transporta[tion] · Ambulance · Utilization · Coordinatio[n] · Wellness P[rogram]

1994 IMPORTANT FUNCTIONS

SECTION 1—CARE OF THE PATIENT
- Assessment of Patients
- Treatment of Patients (Medication Use)
- Operative and Other Invasive Procedures
- Education of Patients and Family

SECTION 2—ORGANIZATIONAL FUNCTIONS
- Leadership
- Management of Information
- Improving Organizational Performance

SECTION 3—STRUCTURES WITH IMPORTANT FUNCTIONS
- Medical Staff

SECTION 4—OTHER DEPARTMENT/SERVICE-SPECIFIC REQUIREMENTS
- Alcoholism and Other Drug-Dependence Services
- Diagnostic Radiology Services
- Dietetic Services
- Emergency Services
- Governing Body
- Infection Control
- Management and Administrative Services
- Nuclear Medicine Services
- Nursing Care
- Orientation, Training, and Education of Staff
- Pathology and Clinical Laboratory Services
- Patient Rights
- Pharmaceutical Services
- Physical Rehabilitation Services
- Plant, Technology, and Safety Management
- Radiation Oncology Services
- Respiratory Care Services
- Social Work Services
- Special Care Units

In 1994, the standards contained in these chapters will continue to be surveyed in the departments/services responsible for their implementation. Some chapters, such as "Infection Control," continue to be applicable across the organization. "Orientation, Training, and Education of Staff" contains increased expectations in keeping with the plan for the phased implementation of this chapter established when the chapter was introduced in 1993.

SURVEY ELIGIBILITY CRITERIA

Any health care organization may apply for a Joint Commission accreditation survey under the standards in this *Manual** if the following eligibility requirements are met:

- The Joint Commission has applicable standards for services provided by the organization;
- The organization has a process for assessing the quality of its services that involves reviews of care by clinicians who may be integral to or separate from the organization;
- The organization is located within the United States or its territories or, if outside the United States, is operated by the United States government or under a charter of the United States Congress; and
- When applying, the organization identifies all services that it provides and advises the Joint Commission as to whether each of these services is provided directly, under contract, or through some other arrangement.

---

*The Joint Commission, working with the organization, will determine which standards from other accreditation manuals will be applied. For example, when a psychiatric/substance abuse hospital or a hospital that has a psychiatric/substance abuse department/service has demonstrated problems receiving reimbursement for its residential treatment, inpatient treatment, and/or partial-hospitalization programs for children and adolescents, the Joint Commission tailors the survey to include the appropriate standards from the Accreditation Manual for Mental Health, Chemical Dependency, and Mental Retardation/Developmental Disabilities Services.

GENERAL ADMINISTRATIVE POLICIES AND PROCEDURES

This section outlines the general administrative policies and procedures addressing the Joint Commission's accreditation process. Significant failures by an applicant or accredited organization to comply with the policies and procedures described in this section may be interpreted by the Joint Commission as a refusal to appropriately participate in the accreditation process and a withdrawal from the accreditation program.

The purpose of a Joint Commission accreditation survey is to assess the extent of a hospital's compliance with applicable Joint Commission standards. Compliance is assessed through one or more of the following means:

- Verbal information concerning the implementation of standards, or examples of their implementation, that will enable a judgment of compliance to be made;
- On-site observations by Joint Commission surveyors; and
- Documentation of compliance provided by hospital personnel.

How to Apply for Survey

Hospitals that wish to be accredited by the Joint Commission should begin by sending a request for an application for survey to the following address:

Joint Commission on Accreditation of Healthcare Organizations
Application Requests
One Renaissance Boulevard
Oakbrook Terrace, Illinois 60181

The Joint Commission sends the hospital one application for survey to complete for all applicable accreditation programs. In submitting its application, the hospital authorizes the Joint Commission to obtain official records and reports of public or publicly recognized licensing, examining, reviewing, or planning bodies. The hospital also has an obligation to furnish such documents in its possession to the Joint Commission, if requested to do so. The completed application should be returned to the Joint Commission, and the hospital should keep a copy of the application for its records. The application for survey, when accepted by the Joint Commission as reflected by notification to the hospital of the scheduling of a survey, is the primary document establishing the terms of the relationship between the hospital and the Joint Commission. The application also serves to define the entity seeking accreditation.

Surveys and Schedules

Accreditation surveys are conducted by Joint Commission surveyors. The number of days required for a survey and the composition of the survey team are based on information provided in the completed application for survey. If such information is discovered during the survey to have been inaccurate and supplied in error, any award of accreditation may be delayed, and the hospital will be responsible for paying compensation for any unnecessary expenses incurred by the Joint Commission as a result. A hospital may request a longer survey than that determined by the Joint Commission, but a fee will be charged for the additional time. Such a request should be sent to the director of the Scheduling Department.

The Joint Commission alters the composition of the survey team to meet specific hospital needs. For example, when a hospital offers an alcohol and/or other substance abuse program that has social rehabilitation as a basic element of its mission, an alcohol and substance abuse specialist is added to the survey team. Also, when a particular kind of service is provided in sufficient volume, the survey team includes surveyors who have special expertise in that service.* In addition, when a hospital has a comprehensive rehabilitation program or unit (that is, one that offers at least rehabilitation medicine, rehabilitation nursing, social work, occupational therapy, physical therapy, and speech-language pathology services) for which it wants special designation from the Joint Commission that its unit is comprehensive, a physician experienced in rehabilitation medicine is added to the usual survey team. In these cases, a fee will be charged for the addition of a physician surveyor to the team. On accreditation surveys of rehabilitation hospitals, the physician surveyor will have experience in rehabilitation medicine.

If, after mailing the application form and before the survey, the hospital undergoes a change that renders inaccurate any information entered in the application for survey, the hospital must notify the Joint Commission immediately. Changes that must be reported include a change in ownership, a significant increase or decrease in the volume of services, the addition of a new type of health service, or the deletion of an existing service. If a survey team arrives at the hospital and discovers that a change was not reported, the Joint Commission may survey, at a later date, any unreported services for which it has standards. Accreditation may not be granted if all services provided have not been surveyed.

The Joint Commission schedules a survey to renew a hospital's accreditation near the end of the three-year accreditation cycle. This is referred to as the hospital's triennial survey. Triennial surveys are ordinarily conducted no sooner than 45 days preceding an organization's survey anniversary date, unless otherwise authorized by the organization, and ordinarily no later than 45 days after the due date. The hospital is notified of the survey dates a minimum of four weeks before the survey.

To minimize the impact of a survey on a hospital's scheduled activities, the Joint Commission attempts to honor written requests that identify specific events and dates during which a hospital prefers not to be surveyed. There may be circumstances, however, that prevent the Joint Commission from honoring such requests. The Joint Commission must receive these requests no later than four months before a hospital's survey anniversary date. When possible, this request should be returned with the completed update. The Joint Commission may view a hospital's failure to accept a scheduled survey as constituting that hospital's withdrawal from the accreditation program.

Planning for Survey

A tentative survey agenda, set in collaboration between the hospital and Joint Commission staff, is constructed before the survey. Generic agendas based on the number of days required for a survey and the survey team composition have been established to promote consistency among hospital surveys. Joint Commission staff assist the hospital in customizing its survey agenda to the hospital's unique structure and characteristics, and efforts are made to make the most efficient use of hospital staff and surveyor time during the survey.

---

*For example, if an organization has 7,300 or more annual patient encounters and an average length of stay equal to or greater than 30 days for long term care, the unit is surveyed during a single tailored survey and a surveyor from the Long Term Care Accreditation Services Department participates in the survey.

The survey agenda is determined using a planning questionnaire sent to the hospital approximately four months before the survey. Other materials are provided to the hospital through the survey planning process to assist it in identifying staff who should be involved in various survey activities.

Survey Postponements and Delays

To keep survey fees to a minimum, the Joint Commission attempts to schedule surveys systematically and efficiently; therefore, hospitals are asked to accept scheduled survey dates. Nevertheless, the Joint Commission does provide for the postponement or delay of surveys. A postponement is a request to alter a survey date following notification to the hospital of the scheduled survey date(s). A delay is a request to alter the survey date prior to the scheduling of the survey. Requests for a postponement or delay should be directed to the Joint Commission. Ordinarily, the Joint Commission will not postpone or delay a survey for more than six months.

Scheduled surveys may be postponed when one or more of the following events have happened:

- A natural disaster or other major unforeseen event has occurred and has totally or substantially disrupted operations;
- The organization is involved in a major strike, has ceased admitting patients, and is transferring patients to other facilities; or
- Patients or the organization or both are being moved to another building during the scheduled survey.

It should be noted that, under the circumstances noted above, the Joint Commission reserves the right to conduct an on-site survey if the organization continues to provide patient care services. Scheduled surveys also may be postponed when the Joint Commission has provided less than four weeks advance notice in writing or by telephone of the survey date(s).

A request for a survey delay may be granted if the request is presented 60 days or more before the organization's due date or scheduled survey date and if the Joint Commission can accommodate the request without incurring direct expenses of $500 or more. A delay may also be granted to facilitate the sequential survey of organizations that are part of a multihospital system.

An organization that does not meet any of the criteria described in the previous three paragraphs still may be allowed to postpone or delay its survey if it pays a fee to defray costs. However, the Joint Commission reserves the right to deny any request for a postponement or delay, regardless of the organization's willingness to pay the fee.

If a survey is not scheduled within one year of the Joint Commission's receipt of the application for survey, the application is voided and the Joint Commission requires the submission of a new one to assure that application information is up-to-date. For initial surveys only, a nonrefundable processing fee is also required.

Scope of Accreditation Surveys

The Joint Commission has standards manuals for, and conducts surveys of, (1) hospitals, (2) nonhospital-based psychiatric and substance abuse organizations, including community mental health centers, freestanding chemical dependency providers, and organizations that serve persons with mental retardation or other developmental disabilities, (3) long term care organizations, (4) home care organizations, (5) ambulatory health care organizations, and (6) organization-based pathology and clinical laboratory services. When a hospital provides more than one of these categories of services, the Joint Commission will tailor its survey process to reflect the particular services offered by the hospital.

In the application for accreditation, the hospital is asked to indicate if certain essential services are provided by contract. When the hospital has contractual arrangements with other organizations to provide routine essential services on-site or off-site, the Joint Commission evaluates how the hospital judges the quality of services provided by the contractor. If routine essential services are provided to hospital patients, the Joint Commission reserves the right to evaluate those services as part of its survey unless the contracted organization is separately accredited or is reviewed by another accrediting body that has a written agreement with the Joint Commission and makes its findings available to the Joint Commission.

In tailoring the survey process to the nature and needs of a hospital, the Joint Commission uses the standards specifically related to each of the services provided by the hospital. Before a survey is conducted, the hospital receives a copy of each of the standards manuals to be used in the survey. The Joint Commission generally determines which manuals are applicable based on the information provided in the application for survey.

The scope of an accreditation survey is based on the services provided by the organization that submits an application for survey. In complex organizations, the parent organization and/or its subcomponents will determine the identity of the applicant organization. The Joint Commission will survey and, assuming satisfactory standards compliance, provide one accreditation award to the applicant organization for all services, programs, and related organizations that the applicant organization requests be included, provided that all such services, programs, and related organizations are judged to be organizationally* *and* functionally† integrated with the applicant organization or are publicly represented‡ as being part of the applicant organization. When the applicant organization is not the parent organization, the parent organization may request the survey of other services that are under its aegis in conjunction with the survey of the applicant organizations, provided that the services are functionally and organizationally related to the applicant organization. Organization representation of the services it provides will be assessed by examining organization letterhead, brochures used to inform the public of its services, and other available advertising media.

During the survey, the Joint Commission evaluates all health care services provided by the hospital with the objective of a single accreditation decision and a single survey report. A hospital must be prepared to provide evidence of its compliance with each standard that is applicable to its operations. To be accredited, a hospital must demonstrate that it is in substantial compliance with the standards overall, not necessarily with each applicable standard.

In the event that a Joint Commission surveyor finds that some aspect of hospital operations adversely affects patient health and safety, such findings may be considered for accreditation purposes even if the standards do not specifically address those operations. In considering any such findings, the Joint Commission may obtain other expert consultation.

If surveyors identify any condition that poses a threat to public or patient safety, the surveyors notify the hospital's chief executive officer and Joint Commis-

---

Organizational integration exists when the governing body, either directly or ultimately, controls budgetary and resource allocation decisions for the applicant organization and the service, program, or related organization being considered for inclusion within the applicant organization's survey.

†*Functional integration criteria are generally met when*
- *the organization component and its subcomponent are geographically proximate;*
- *there is an overlapping or interlocking administrative hierarchy;*
- *there are common clinical and/or administrative policies and procedures; and*
- *there are common clinical staff, such as the medical staff.*

‡*Examples of public representation may include references on letterheads, brochures, telephone book listings, or other advertising materials. Commonality of names may also be relevant.*

sion corporate office staff. The president of the Joint Commission or, in his/her absence, a vice president of the Joint Commission designated by the president to do so, is authorized, on the basis of such notification or otherwise, to decide to deny accreditation and to promptly notify the hospital's chief executive officer, as well as governmental authorities having jurisdiction, about this decision. The Accreditation Committee of the Board of Commissioners promptly reviews this decision to confirm or reverse it.

Modified Survey Process

The Joint Commission offers the option of a modified survey process to multihospital systems that own or lease at least two hospitals. This option includes four components: a corporate orientation, the same core survey team, consecutive survey of participating organizations, and a corporate summation. A system may elect to have either a corporate orientation or corporate summation or both. The orientation session provides an opportunity for corporate staff to orient the survey team to the structure and practices of the system. The survey team will also survey all centralized corporate services, documentation, and policies and procedures applicable to Joint Commission standards. After the last hospital of a system is surveyed, the survey team holds a summation for the system's corporate office staff.

Early Survey Policy

Beginning January 1, 1994, organizations will be eligible for survey under a new early survey policy. The early survey policy applies to organizations requesting Joint Commission surveys for the first time or before they have been operational for four months. Operational is defined as the point at which the organization begins to provide care to at least one patient/client. This policy also is available to, but not required for, the following:

1. Organizations that have operated for more than four months and are undergoing their first Joint Commission survey;
2. Organizations that have not participated in the accreditation process during the previous two years; and
3. Organizations that were denied accreditation during the previous two years.

Note: *Organizations in categories 1, 2, and 3 must declare during the application process that they wish to be surveyed under this policy.*

Two on-site surveys will be conducted at the applicant organization, which submits an application for survey that includes when the organization prefers the first survey to be conducted—either within the first six months of operation or before being in operation. The Joint Commission will make every effort to accommodate this preference and guarantees that the first survey will be conducted within four months of receiving the application. This first survey can be conducted as early as two months before the organization begins operating provided the following criteria are met:

- The organization is licensed or has a provisional license;
- The building in which patient care services will be provided is identified, constructed, and equipped to support those services;
- The organization has identified its chief executive officer/administrator, its chief of medical/professional staff or a medical/clinical director, and its nurse executive; and
- The organization has identified the date it will begin operations.

The Joint Commission requires written evidence of these criteria within 30 days before conducting the first survey.

The first survey normally is conducted over two days by one surveyor but may vary depending on the specific standards that are to be surveyed. Generally, the first survey assesses only the organization's physical plant, policies and procedures, plans, and related structural considerations regarding the provision of patient care. If the first survey is conducted before operations begin, the organization is required to inform the Joint Commission in writing of its operational status within 30 days of beginning operations.

The organization is placed in provisional accreditation if it complies with the selected standards assessed in the first survey. If the organization meets the decision rules for nonaccreditation, it will not qualify for provisional accreditation and will have to reapply to begin the process again. If the organization meets the decision rules for conditional accreditation, it will also be assigned provisional accreditation status. Provisional accreditation is effective the day after the survey if the organization is operating when the survey is conducted. If it is not operating, the effective date is the day after the organization begins operating, once this is confirmed in writing by the organization. Provisional accreditation status remains until the organization has completed a full survey. If operations fail to begin when the organization originally indicated or it fails to give the Joint Commission timely notice after beginning operations, provisional accreditation status will be withdrawn, forcing the organization to reapply to begin the accreditation process again.

The second survey is conducted on-site approximately six months after the first survey but at least four months after the organization has begun operating. The second survey is a full accreditation survey. Depending on the results of this survey, the organization's accreditation status will change to accreditation with commendation, accreditation with or without type I recommendations, conditional accreditation, or not accredited, according to the approved decision rules. As in any other type of survey, if the organization is assigned any type I recommendations, it is required to resolve them to remain accredited. The organization's three-year accreditation cycle begins the day after the second survey, provided that this survey did not result in a not accredited decision.

Unscheduled, Unannounced, and Random Unannounced Surveys

Either an unscheduled or unannounced survey may take place when the Joint Commission becomes aware of circumstances in an accredited organization that suggest a potentially serious standards compliance problem. For an unscheduled survey, the organization usually receives advance notice of 24 to 48 hours. Unannounced surveys are generally reserved for situations in which there is concern about a substantial deterioration in clinical care, or there is reason to believe that an immediate threat to patient health or safety exists, or when credible allegations of falsified accreditation information have been received. Advance notice of an unannounced survey is not given to an organization. Either type of survey can take place at any point in an organization's three-year accreditation cycle. The survey can either cover all the organization's services or be restricted to only those areas in which a serious standards compliance problem may exist.

In addition to conducting unscheduled or unannounced surveys for the preceding reasons, effective July 1, 1993, the Joint Commission will conduct midcycle, unannounced surveys for a 5% random sample of accredited organizations in each of the Joint Commission's accreditation programs. Random unannounced surveys are conducted for one day by one surveyor. He/she will primarily direct attention to the five performance areas that the previous year's aggregate survey data identified as being most problem filled.* Results of unannounced surveys generate appropri-

---

*In 1993 for hospitals, for example, those areas included safety management, life safety, appointment/privileging, infection control, and governance. These performance areas may change annually based on the previous year's data.

ate follow-up activities in accordance with the applicable accreditation decision rules and can affect an organization's current accreditation status. The Joint Commission absorbs all costs of conducting these unannounced surveys. The Joint Commission may view a hospital's failure to permit the accomplishment of any of these surveys as grounds for the decision to deny accreditation or constituting that hospital's withdrawal from the accreditation program. A hospital's failure to permit the accomplishment of an unannounced survey that stems from allegations of falsified information may bar that hospital from participating in the accreditation process for one year.

Falsification of Information Policy

The accuracy and veracity of information are essential to the integrity of the Joint Commission's accreditation process. Such information may be verbal in nature, may be obtained through direct observation by Joint Commission surveyors, may derive from documents supplied by the organization to the Joint Commission, or data transmitted electronically to the Joint Commission. The Joint Commission requires that each organization seeking accreditation engage in the accreditation process in good faith. Failure to participate in good faith, including, but not limited to, falsification of any information presented in the accreditation process, may be grounds for a decision to deny an organization accreditation or a decision to remove the accreditation award from an accredited organization. Falsification of information may occur in documents presented to demonstrate compliance with Joint Commission standards, in documents submitted to describe the organization's services and/or relationships with other organizations, such as those submitted through the survey application process or correspondence, and/or on diskettes submitted to transmit data. This policy also includes, in part, the following provisions:

1. Falsified information must never be provided by an organization to the Joint Commission in the accreditation process. Any efforts to do so will be construed as a violation of the organization's obligation to engage in the accreditation process in good faith.

2. For purposes of this policy, falsification is defined as the fabrication, in whole or in part, of any information provided by an applicant or accredited organization to the Joint Commission. This includes, but is not limited to, any redrafting, reformatting, or content deletion of documents.

3. Notwithstanding the foregoing, additional material prepared by the organization for the purpose of summarizing or otherwise explaining original information may be submitted to the Joint Commission, so long as these materials are properly identified and dated and are accompanied by the original documents.

4. At the time of, or within ten working days following completion of a full survey or focused survey, each organization is required to submit to the Joint Commission a signed certification that attests to the accuracy and veracity of information provided to the Joint Commission. The certification is to be signed by the chief executive officer, the chairperson of the governing body, and the chief of the medical (or professional) staff (for those accreditation programs that require such staffs). In the case of a written progress report or other submitted information, the signed certification is to accompany the submitted progress report or information.

5. No accreditation award or survey report will be released to an organization until the Joint Commission has received a properly signed certification from the organization.

6. Whenever the Joint Commission has cause to believe that an accredited organization may have provided falsified information to the Joint Commission, it shall conduct an appropriate evaluation of the situation, which shall include, except as otherwise authorized by the president, an unannounced

on-site survey of the organization. Such a survey will use special protocols designed to address the alleged falsification of information, including the degree of actual organization compliance with the standards that are the subject of the allegation, if appropriate.

7. Whenever the Joint Commission is reasonably persuaded that an organization has provided falsified information in seeking to achieve or retain accreditation, it shall immediately take appropriate action, which will, under usual circumstances, be a decision not to award accreditation or a decision to remove the accreditation award from an accredited organization.

8. Any organization that is subject to a disciplinary action in the context of item 7 shall also be the subject of appropriate notification by the Joint Commission to responsible federal and state government agencies.

9. Whenever an organization becomes not accredited on the basis of falsified information, the organization shall be prohibited from participation in the accreditation process for a period of one year, unless the president, for good cause, waives all or a portion of this waiting period.

Public Information Interviews

Anyone who has information about a hospital's compliance with the accreditation standards may request a public information interview. The Joint Commission requires the hospital to provide an opportunity during a triennial survey for the presentation of information by consumers and the public, as well as by personnel and staff of the hospital undergoing survey.

The Joint Commission requires hospitals to post in public places on their premises the official Joint Commission announcement of the date of the survey and of the opportunity for a public information interview. Public notices must be posted four weeks before the survey date; notices must indicate that requests for a public information interview are to be made in writing and that the Joint Commission must receive them at least two working days before a hospital's accreditation survey begins. Notices must remain posted until the first day of the survey. Furthermore, if anyone asks about the survey, the Joint Commission expects the hospital to inform the person of the survey dates and of the fact that a public information interview may be requested or that such an interview is already scheduled.

The hospital should promptly send any request it receives for a public information interview to the Organization Liaison Unit and retain a copy for its files. The Joint Commission acknowledges both these requests and those it receives directly and sends a copy of these acknowledgments to the hospital. The Joint Commission will coordinate scheduling the public information interview within the hospital's survey agenda. The hospital is responsible for notifying the interviewee(s) of the exact date, time, and place of the public information interview.

Surveyors are required to report whether Joint Commission policies concerning the public information interview have been carried out properly. This includes reporting the manner in which the hospital posted the notice.

Public information interviews usually are conducted during the afternoon of the first survey day. The hospital is expected to provide reasonable accommodation for the interview either within the facility or at a conveniently accessible location near the hospital. Surveyors conduct the interview session and receive the information. A representative(s) of the hospital is expected to attend.

The interview consists only of the orderly receipt of information offered verbally or in writing within the prescribed time limit. The information is considered during the survey process and is reported to Joint Commission corporate office staff with the results and recommendations of the survey. Any further participation in the survey by an outside source of information must be authorized by the hospital.

Leadership Interview

At the conclusion of the document review session on the first survey day during a hospital's triennial survey, the survey team will meet with the organization's leaders to gather information on how the organization's leaders work together to assure compliance with Joint Commission standards. Hospital participants should include, at a minimum, a representative of the hospital's governing body, the chief executive officer, the president or chief of the medical staff, the nurse executive, and the person(s) responsible for performance improvement activities, if available, or an appropriate designee. At the discretion of the chief executive officer, other senior staff of the hospital may also attend.

The purpose of the leadership interview is to provide an opportunity for surveyors to begin assessing the level of communication among the various leaders of the organization, the role that each plays in its management, and the extent to which the standards' requirements for communication and cooperation are being met by the organization. During the interview, surveyors will ask standards-based questions. Participants should be able to provide information that illustrates how the organization's leaders work together to develop, review, and revise the hospital's mission, strategic plans, budgets, bases for resource allocation, operational plans, and policies.

Chief Executive Officer Exit Conference

Joint Commission surveyors hold an exit conference with the hospital's chief executive officer at the completion of all surveys. The following individuals or their designees should also attend this conference: the chairperson of the governing body, the nurse executive, the president or chief of the medical staff, and, if applicable, the chief operating officer. The Joint Commission advises that the hospital keep attendance to a minimum.

During the conference, the surveyors present their findings regarding any significant standards compliance problems. They also indicate, to the extent possible, the potential impact these problems will *likely* have on the final accreditation decision. The final decision regarding accreditation involves the processing of surveyor findings in accordance with specific aggregation and decision rules promulgated by the Accreditation Committee of the Board of Commissioners. Because of the complexity of aggregation rules, surveyors are not expected to maintain a mastery of all such rules. In addition to presenting findings and recommendations for improvement, the surveyors discuss the underlying causes of the identified problems. Hospital representatives will be given an opportunity to respond to the surveyors' recommendations and to clarify issues raised by the surveyors' findings. Upon request, surveyors will also provide consultation on survey findings that may not be directly related to standards.

Accreditation Decision and Appeal

Accreditation decisions are made in accordance with the accreditation and appeal procedures set out in Appendix E of this *Manual*. These procedures are only briefly summarized here. Joint Commission staff evaluate the results of the survey, the recommendations of the surveyor(s), and any other relevant information, such as documentation of compliance with the standards, documentation of plans to correct deficiencies, or evidence of recent improvements. Using scoring guidelines and Accreditation Committee approved aggregation and decision rules, staff make a determination regarding accreditation. This determination can be for provisional accreditation, accreditation with commendation, accreditation with or without recommendations, conditional accreditation, or not accredited. Recommendations are of two types. A type I recommendation is a recommendation or group of recommendations that address insufficient or unsatisfactory standards compliance in a specific performance area. Resolution of type I recommendations must be achieved within stipulated time frames in order for an organization to maintain its accreditation. Supplemental recommendations do not require formal follow-up. They may, however, affect the accreditation decision if not dealt with appropriately by the next triennial survey. The hospital's progress in resolving type I recommendations will be monitored by the Joint Commission through focused surveys, written progress reports, or both, at stated times during the accreditation cycle. Various categories of staff determinations must be reviewed by the Accreditation Committee, including, among others, all determinations to deny accreditation or, if challenged by the hospital under any applicable procedures, to conditionally accredit.

The above procedures do not apply when a surveyor identifies any condition that poses a threat to public or patient safety or other information indicates the existence of such a threat. In such cases, the president of the Joint Commission or, in his/her absence, a vice president of the Joint Commission designated by the president to do so, may decide to deny accreditation to the hospital. This action by the president, or his/her designee, is reported by telephone and in writing to the hospital's chief executive officer and in writing to the relevant government authorities. The Accreditation Committee promptly reviews this decision to confirm or reverse it.

The hospital has the right to pursue and have decided an appeal of any decision of the Accreditation Committee to deny accreditation before the decision becomes the final decision of the Joint Commission.

Duration of Accreditation Award

If it is found to be in substantial compliance with Joint Commission standards, a hospital is awarded accreditation for three years*. The final decision to accredit a hospital becomes effective as of the first day after completion of the hospital's survey.

At the request of an accredited hospital, the Joint Commission will conduct a full accreditation survey more frequently than once every three years. Such requests should be sent to the Division of Accreditation Surveys.

In the process of deciding to accredit a hospital, the Joint Commission determines whether survey findings warrant accreditation with any type I recommendations. When a hospital is accredited subject to one or more type I recommendations, the Joint Commission monitors the hospital's efforts to improve the area(s) of concern identified during the accreditation survey. A hospital that receives a type I recommendation is ordinarily expected to achieve substantial or significant compliance with the relevant standard(s) within a specified time, and failure to do so can generate a decision to conditionally accredit or deny accreditation.

Monitoring by the Joint Commission and the time allotted for demonstrating improvement of an area assigned a type I recommendation depend on the nature of the concern—particularly its effect on patient care—and on the time required to satisfactorily address the concern. Hospitals that receive accreditation with type I recommendations are ordinarily required to submit a written progress report or to have their compliance reviewed during an on-site survey that focuses on only those standards identified in the report as type I recommendations. Some type I recommendations, however, may require surveyors to address issues related to other standards in order to fully address compliance with the standards related to the type I recommendations. The size of the survey team and the duration of the focused survey depend on the number and extent of concerns addressed in the type

---

Excluding provisional accreditation status, which remains until an organization has completed its full survey.

I recommendations. The Joint Commission may view a hospital's failure to permit the accomplishment of any of these surveys as grounds for the decision to deny accreditation or constituting that hospital's withdrawal from the accreditation program.

An accredited hospital is expected to be in continuous compliance with all applicable standards and may be asked to supply, in writing, information about standards compliance, or may be surveyed at any time, with or without notice to the hospital, at the discretion of the Joint Commission. Such surveys will be conducted at midcycle for 5% of accredited organizations in each accreditation program starting July 1, 1993, and are also sometimes performed in response to complaints, media coverage, or other information that may raise questions regarding compliance with standards or the adequacy of protections for patient health and safety. Additionally, if a hospital fails to provide information requested by the Joint Commission, a survey might be conducted. Failure to permit a survey to take place can be viewed by the Joint Commission as constituting an immediate withdrawal from the accreditation program. Ordinarily, no fee is charged for a survey initiated at the Joint Commission's discretion.

Continuing Accreditation

Accreditation is not automatically renewed. A hospital must undergo a full accreditation survey at least every three years, and survey findings must warrant continued accreditation. Before a hospital's accreditation is due to expire, the Joint Commission sends the hospital an application for survey. Following receipt of the completed application, a survey is scheduled. The Joint Commission ordinarily schedules the survey as near as possible to the hospital's survey anniversary date. However, to allow latitude, surveys are ordinarily scheduled within a period beginning 45 days before and ending 45 days after the hospital's anniversary date.

Following a survey, a hospital's previous accreditation status remains in effect until a final decision is made either to accredit or not to accredit the hospital.

Once an accredited organization has been surveyed, the accreditation decision-making process continues until a final accreditation decision has been reached. An organization's decision to withdraw from the accreditation process after undergoing survey and before a final accreditation decision has been made will not terminate the decision-making process; a final accreditation decision will be reached.

Accreditation is not automatically transferable, and it is not ongoing if significant changes occur in the circumstances existing at the time of the survey upon which the accreditation decision was based. If an accredited hospital changes ownership or control or undergoes a significant change in its capacity or in the categories of services offered, it must notify the Joint Commission not more than 30 days after such change. Accreditation is continued until the Joint Commission can determine whether a survey is necessary to continue accreditation. Failure to notify the Joint Commission of ownership and services changes may result in loss of accreditation.

An accredited organization must notify the Joint Commission no more than 30 days after a merger or consolidation with another organization or any other major change in services, location, or corporate structure. Under such circumstances, the Joint Commission may decide the organization must be resurveyed. Failure to notify the Joint Commission of such changes may also result in a loss of accreditation.

Each year accredited organizations will receive an annual update form that includes basic identifying data and information used by the Joint Commission to schedule surveys. Organizations will update this information and return the form to the Joint Commission. During survey years this form will serve as the application for survey. This update does not replace the need for 30-day notification to the Joint Commission of major changes within an organization.

Public Recognition

The Joint Commission provides each accredited hospital with a certificate of accreditation. A hospital is not charged for the initial certificate. Additional certificates can be purchased from the Joint Commission. Such requests should be sent to the Certificate Coordinator, Scheduling Department.

The certificate and all copies remain the property of the Joint Commission and must be returned to the Joint Commission if the hospital is issued a new certificate reflecting a change in name or if its accreditation expires or is withdrawn or denied for any reason.

Organizations accredited by the Joint Commission must be accurate in describing to the public the nature and meaning of their accreditation. Hospitals cannot engage in any false or misleading advertising with regard to their accreditation.* Any such advertising may be grounds for denial of accreditation. For example, accredited organizations cannot represent their accreditation as being awarded by the Joint Commission's corporate members (the American College of Physicians, the American College of Surgeons, the American Dental Association, the American Hospital Association, and the American Medical Association). The Joint Commission has permission to reprint the seals of its corporate members on the certificates of accreditation, but these seals must not be reproduced or displayed separately from the certificate.

The Joint Commission logo is the registered trademark of the Joint Commission. Accredited organizations may use it if these guidelines are followed:
- The logo should not be displayed any larger than an organization's own logo;
- The logo and its type can be printed in only two colors—black and PMS 201;
- The logo format cannot be changed; and
- Graphic devices such as seals, other words, or slogans cannot be added to the logo except for the words "Accredited by."

For questions on using the Joint Commission logo, contact the Department of Communications.

Survey Fees

Survey fees are related to the cost of maintaining Joint Commission operations and ordinarily are determined annually. For regular, full surveys, the survey fee includes a fixed base fee and an additional variable charge that is related to the type and volume of services provided by the applicant organization. Organizations surveyed under the early survey policy are charged the base rate for the relevant accreditation program for both surveys. For more information on how survey fees are calculated, contact the Department of Planning and Financial Affairs at the Joint Commission corporate office.

When a hospital is scheduled for survey, the Joint Commission sends the hospital an invoice and asks the hospital to pay the fees in accordance with the terms specified. Hospitals are charged at the fee rate in effect at the time of survey. For an initial survey (that is, a hospital's first survey or its first survey after two or more years without Joint Commission accreditation), a hospital must send a nonrefundable processing fee with the application for survey; this payment is credited toward the hospital's total fee.

The Joint Commission offers hospitals two payment options. The hospital can either pay the full survey fee when billed or spread the payments over a 3½-month period. Under the second option, a hospital must pay half the full survey fee at the

---

The Joint Commission's Department of Communications can supply organizations receiving accreditation with commendation with guidelines for appropriate characterizations of this status to the public.

time of billing (about four weeks before the date of the survey) and must pay the other half no later than 60 days after the date of the survey.

A hospital that has not paid its survey fee in full prior to issuance of the accreditation decision and report will have 60 days from receipt of the report to remit the outstanding balance. Failure to provide timely payment may result in termination of accreditation. Hospitals having significant standards compliance problems, as reflected by either a conditional accreditation decision or a decision to deny accreditation, are notified of such a decision as soon as possible, whether or not payment has been received.

Confidentiality and Disclosure Policy

CONFIDENTIALITY

The Joint Commission treats as confidential the following information that is received or developed during the accreditation process:

- Information obtained from a hospital before, during, and/or following the accreditation survey that relates to compliance with specific accreditation standards;
- All materials that may contribute to the accreditation decision (for example, survey report forms);
- Written staff analyses and Accreditation Committee minutes and agenda materials; and
- The official accreditation decision report.

This policy applies to all hospitals that have an accreditation history, except as provided below or as otherwise provided by law or as authorized by responsible hospital officials.

DISCLOSURE

A. Information Subject to Public Release Upon Request
The Joint Commission, upon request, will publicly release the following information:

- Current accreditation status of a hospital;
- Hospital-specific performance data,* provided that the conditions set forth under Section B are met;
- For organizations surveyed in 1994 or later, the number of type I recommendations and, at the grid element level,† the nature of these recommendations;
- Hospital accreditation history;
- The date(s) of a survey after a hospital has been notified;
- The status of a hospital in the accreditation decision process;
- Applicable standards under which an accreditation survey was conducted;
- Hospital organizational and operational components included in the accreditation survey;
- The applicable standards areas involved in a Joint Commission complaint review;
- The number and nature of substantive written complaints filed against an accredited hospital since its last triennial survey that have been substantiated by the Joint Commission;

---

*Performance data consist of
1. standards compliance data produced from triennial surveys conducted in 1994 and thereafter; and
2. data from the indicator monitoring system when it becomes an integral part of the accreditation process thereafter. During the optional participation period of the indicator monitoring system, data will not be published.

†A performance area or topic, such as infection control, that receives a discrete score on the accreditation decision grid.

- For a tailored survey, the organizational component(s) that contributed to a decision of conditional accreditation or denial of accreditation; and
- Whether, at the time a hospital withdrew from accreditation, there were any type I recommendations for which the Joint Commission had no or insufficient evidence of resolution, and, after 1993, the nature of these recommendations at the grid element level.

B. Public Release of Data by the Joint Commission

The Joint Commission reserves the prerogative to publish, or otherwise release publicly, aggregate performance data* that are not hospital specific.

The Joint Commission may also publish, or otherwise release publicly, hospital-specific performance information, provided that the following conditions are met:

- The data are accompanied by an explanation of their source(s) or derivation; their accuracy, reliability, and validity; their appropriate uses; and their limitations and potential misuses;
- The data are portrayed or described in an understandable context that includes comparisons with national or other statistically valid performance data;
- For standards compliance data, the data are to be at the grid† or grid element‡ level;
- For data from the indicator monitoring system, the data are to be a summary of the most recent 12 months (usually four data points); and
- The data may be published only after the hospital has had an opportunity to comment on them.

The public release of hospital-specific standards compliance data must include:

- The year of the hospital's most recent triennial survey;
- For summary grid scores, the score for the hospital's most recent triennial survey and the relevant national comparative summary grid score data;
- For grid element scores, the specific scores for the hospital's most recent triennial survey and the relevant national comparative grid element score data for the specific grid element scores; and
- If currently different, the hospital's updated grid element scores.

C. Information Subject to Release to Responsible Government Agencies‡

The Joint Commission provides to responsible federal, state, or local government agencies the information specified under the following circumstances:

- When a serious situation that may jeopardize the safety of patients or the public is identified in a hospital by a Joint Commission surveyor and the chief executive officer has been advised of the situation, local, state, and federal authorities having jurisdiction over the hospital will immediately be notified by the Joint Commission by telephone and in writing; and

---

The summary display of the organization's overall accreditation performance. The summary grid score is calculated from grid element scores.

†*A performance area or topic, such as monitoring and evaluation of nursing, that receives a discrete score on the accreditation decision grid.*

‡*Section 92, PL 96-499, the Omnibus Budget Reconciliation Act of 1980, requires that Medicare providers include, in all their contracts for services costing $10,000 or more in any 12-month period, a clause allowing the Secretary of the U.S. Department of Health and Human Services (DHHS), the U.S. Comptroller General, or their representatives to examine the contract and the contractor's books and records. The Joint Commission herein stipulates that if its charges to any such hospital amount to $10,000 or more in any 12-month period, the contract or any agreement on which such charges are based and any of the Joint Commission's books, documents, and records that may be necessary to verify the extent and nature of Joint Commission costs will be available to the Secretary of DHHS, the Comptroller General, or any of their duly authorized representatives for four years after the survey. The same conditions will apply to any subcontracts the Joint Commission has with related organizations if the payments under such contracts amount to $10,000 or more in any 12-month period.*

- When a hospital is certified for participation in the Medicare program as a consequence of accreditation or is licensed on the basis of its accreditation (as provided in statute or regulation) and becomes conditionally accredited or not accredited, relevant Joint Commission accreditation survey information will be provided to the Administrator of the Health Care Financing Administration and, as appropriate, to the applicable state hospital licensure agency. The information provided is to be limited to the following:

  1. All type I recommendations;
  2. A statement, if any, provided by the hospital regarding the validity of the Joint Commission survey findings; and
  3. For conditionally accredited hospitals, a copy of the approved plan of correction and subsequently the results of the plan-of-correction follow-up survey.

D. Policy Oversight and Special Information Requests

The Executive Committee of the Board of Commissioners shall provide oversight of execution of this policy and shall determine the handling of official specific information requests (for example, from government agencies).

SECTION 1
CARE OF THE PATIENT

Rights of Patients and Organizational Ethics

Assessment of Patients

Entry to Setting or Service

Nutritional Care

Treatment of Patients

Operative and Other Invasive Procedures

Education of Patients and Family

Coordination of Care

RIGHTS OF PATIENTS AND ORGANIZATIONAL ETHICS

New performance-focused standards will appear in this chapter of the 1995 *Accreditation Manual for Hospitals*. For surveys conducted during 1994, see the standards in the "Patient Rights" chapter on pages 155–157 in Section 4 of this *Manual*.

ASSESSMENT OF PATIENTS

PREAMBLE

Each patient's need for care or treatment is assessed by qualified individuals. These assessments continue throughout the patient's contact with the organization.

The goal of this important function is to determine care or treatment through assessment of each patient's needs. To achieve this goal, the following processes must be performed:

1. Data must be collected to assess the needs of the patient;
2. These data must be analyzed to create the information necessary to decide the approach to meeting care or treatment needs; and
3. Decisions must be made regarding patient care or treatment based on analysis of the information.

The care or treatment provided to each patient is based on a determination of the patient's needs. This determination is based on an assessment of the patient's relevant physical, psychologic, and social status needs. The assessment includes the collection and analysis of data about the patient to determine the need for any additional data, the patient's care or treatment needs, and the care or treatment to be provided.

ASSESSMENT

PE.1
Each patient's physical, psychologic, and social status is assessed.   1 2 3 4 5 NA

PE.1.1   There is an initial assessment/screening of each patient's physical, psychologic, and social status to determine the need for care or treatment, the type of care or treatment to be provided, and the need for any further assessment.   1 2 3 4 5 NA

PE.1.2   The scope and intensity of any further assessment are determined by

    PE.1.2.1   the patient's diagnosis,   1 2 3 4 5 NA

    PE.1.2.2   the treatment setting,   1 2 3 4 5 NA

    PE.1.2.3   the patient's desire for treatment, and   1 2 3 4 5 NA

    PE.1.2.4   the patient's response to any previous treatment.   1 2 3 4 5 NA

PE.1.3   The need for assessing the patient's nutritional status is determined.   1 2 3 4 5 NA

PE.1.4   The need for assessing the patient's functional status is determined.   1 2 3 4 5 NA

    PE.1.4.1   A functional assessment is performed for each patient referred for physical rehabilitation services.   1 2 3 4 5 NA

PE.1.5   Diagnostic testing, including laboratory and other invasive and noninvasive diagnostic and imaging procedures, relevant to the determination of the patient's health care or treatment needs and to the actual care or treatment of the patient is performed.   1 2 3 4 5 NA

PE.1.5.1   When the report of test results is to include clinical interpretation, adequate clinical information is provided with the request for the test.   1 2 3 4 5 NA

PE.1.6   The need for a discharge planning assessment of the patient is determined.   1 2 3 4 5 NA

PE.1.7   The initial assessment of each patient admitted is conducted within a time frame preceding or following admission that is specified in policy.   1 2 3 4 5 NA

PE.1.7.1   The history and the physical examination are completed within the first 24 hours of admission as an inpatient.   1 2 3 4 5 NA

PE.1.7.1.1   If a history and physical examination have been performed within 30 days before admission, such as in the office of a physician staff member or, when appropriate, the office of a qualified oral-maxillofacial surgeon staff member, a durable, legible copy of this report may be used in the patient's medical record, provided no changes have occurred or provided whatever changes have occurred are recorded in the medical record at the time of admission.   1 2 3 4 5 NA

PE.1.8   Surgery is performed only after a history, physical examination, and the preoperative diagnosis have been completed and recorded in the patient's medical record. Any indicated diagnostic tests have been completed and reported in the medical record. In unusual emergency situations in which there is inadequate time to record the history and physical examination before surgery, a brief note, including the preoperative diagnosis, is recorded before surgery.   1 2 3 4 5 NA

PE.1.8.1   There is a preanesthesia assessment of each patient for whom anesthesia* is contemplated.   1 2 3 4 5 NA

PE.1.8.2   Before anesthesia is administered, there is a determination that the patient is an appropriate candidate to undergo the planned anesthesia.   1 2 3 4 5 NA

PE.1.8.2.1   This determination is made by a licensed independent practitioner with appropriate clinical privileges and is based on the results of the preanesthesia assessment.   1 2 3 4 5 NA

PE.1.8.3   Immediately before the induction of anesthesia,* the patient is reevaluated.   1 2 3 4 5 NA

PE.1.8.4   The postoperative status of the patient is assessed on admission to and discharge from the postanesthesia recovery area.   1 2 3 4 5 NA

PE.1.9   Possible victims of abuse are identified using criteria developed by the organization.   1 2 3 4 5 NA

Refer to the "Operative and Other Invasive Procedures" chapter of this Manual *for the scope of anesthesia to which these standards apply.*

REASSESSMENT

PE.2
Each patient is reassessed

PE.2.1	at regularly specified times related to the patient's course of treatment;	1 2 3 4 5 NA
PE.2.2	to determine the patient's response to treatment;	1 2 3 4 5 NA
PE.2.3	when a significant change occurs in the patient's condition; and	1 2 3 4 5 NA
PE.2.4	when a significant change occurs in the patient's diagnosis.	1 2 3 4 5 NA

CARE OR TREATMENT DECISIONS

PE.3
The information generated through the analysis of assessment data is integrated to identify and prioritize the patient's needs for care or treatment. 1 2 3 4 5 NA

PE.3.1	Care or treatment decisions are based on the identified patient needs and on care or treatment priorities.	1 2 3 4 5 NA

STRUCTURES SUPPORTING THE PATIENT ASSESSMENT FUNCTION

PE.4
The activities that comprise the patient assessment function are defined in writing. 1 2 3 4 5 NA

PE.4.1	Each discipline's scope of assessment is defined by the organization.	1 2 3 4 5 NA
PE.4.2	A licensed independent practitioner with appropriate clinical privileges is responsible for determining the degree of assessment and care or treatment provided to any patient who comes or is brought to the emergency care area.	1 2 3 4 5 NA
PE.4.3	A registered nurse assesses the patient's need for nursing care in all settings in which nursing care is to be provided.	1 2 3 4 5 NA

ADDITIONAL REQUIREMENTS FOR SPECIFIC PATIENT POPULATIONS

PE.5
The assessment and/or reassessment of patients receiving treatment for alcoholism or other drug dependencies specifically include

PE.5.1	a history of the use of alcohol and other drugs, including age of onset, duration, patterns, and consequences of use;	1 2 3 4 5 NA
PE.5.2	the history of physical problems associated with dependence;	1 2 3 4 5 NA
PE.5.3	use of alcohol and other drugs by family members;	1 2 3 4 5 NA

PE.5.4   the spiritual orientation of the patient;   1 2 3 4 5 NA

PE.5.5   types of previous treatment and responses to that treatment;   1 2 3 4 5 NA

PE.5.6   any history of physical abuse; and   1 2 3 4 5 NA

PE.5.7   the patient's sexual history, including sexual abuse (either as the abuser or the abused) and orientation.   1 2 3 4 5 NA

PE.6
The assessment of victims of alleged or suspected abuse or neglect

PE.6.1   is conducted with the consent of the patient or parent or legal guardian, or as otherwise provided by law;   1 2 3 4 5 NA

PE.6.2   is conducted in accordance with the organization's responsibility for the collection, retention, and safeguarding of evidentiary material released by the patient; and   1 2 3 4 5 NA

PE.6.3   includes, as legally required, the notification of and release of information to the proper authorities.   1 2 3 4 5 NA

PE.7
The assessment and/or reassessment of infants, children, and adolescents specifically includes, as appropriate,

PE.7.1   the patient's developmental age, length/height, head circumference, and weight;   1 2 3 4 5 NA

PE.7.2   consideration of educational needs and daily activities;   1 2 3 4 5 NA

PE.7.3   the patient's immunization status; and   1 2 3 4 5 NA

PE.7.4   the family's and/or guardian's expectations for, and involvement in, the assessment, treatment, and continuous care or treatment of the patient.   1 2 3 4 5 NA

NOTES AND COMMENTS:

ENTRY TO SETTING OR SERVICE

New performance-focused standards will appear in this chapter of the 1995 *Accreditation Manual for Hospitals.* Standards for this function appear in several chapters found in Section 4 (for example, "Alcoholism and Other Drug-Dependence Services," "Emergency Services").

NUTRITIONAL CARE

New performance-focused standards will appear in this chapter of the 1995 *Accreditation Manual for Hospitals.* For surveys conducted during 1994, see the standards in the "Dietetic Services" chapter on pages 99–104 in Section 4 of this *Manual.*

TREATMENT OF PATIENTS

New standards for medication use are found in this chapter; additional new performance-focused standards will appear in this chapter in the 1995 edition of the *Accreditation Manual for Hospitals, Volume I.* For surveys conducted during 1994, see the standards for patient treatment issues in the various department/service-specific chapters in Section 4 of this *Manual.*

Medication Use

PREAMBLE

Medications are an essential component of the care provided to most patients. They are potent agents for curing illness and often for moderating symptoms. To achieve these benefits, four groups of processes must be performed well: (1) prescription/ordering; (2) preparation and dispensing; (3) administration; and (4) patient monitoring for medication effects. The following standards address significant risk points in performing these processes and, when fully implemented, describe an optimal system.

CROSS-REFERENCES

Medication use involves multiple departments/services and disciplines. For this reason, significant linkages occur among the departments/services and disciplines responsible for performing each process. Linkages occur with the "Management of Information" chapter (when prescriptions/orders for medication and responses to the medication regimen are documented), the "Assessment of Patients" chapter (when the use of a medication is based on the assessment process), the "Medical Staff" chapter (when clinical privilege issues arise), and the "Education of Patients and Family" chapter (when education and orientation to a patient's medication regimen are an issue). In addition, the performance-improvement framework in the "Improving Organizational Performance" chapter will be used to design, measure, assess, and improve the organization's performance of the medication use function.

AVAILABILITY AND PRESCRIPTION/ORDERING OF MEDICATION(S)

TX.1
A formulary lists medications readily available for prescribing/ordering.   1 2 3 4 5 NA

TX.1.1   Appropriate organization staff, including the pharmacy department/service, develop and maintain the formulary.   1 2 3 4 5 NA

TX.1.2   In selecting medications for formulary inclusion, products are assessed on the basis of need, effectiveness, risk, and cost.

1 2 3 4 5 NA

TX.1.3   A process addresses the prescribing/ordering and procuring of medications not in the formulary.

1 2 3 4 5 NA

TX.2
Individuals who prescribe/order medications are authorized legally and through the granting of clinical privileges to do so.

1 2 3 4 5 NA

PREPARATION AND DISPENSING OF MEDICATION(S)

TX.3
Medications are prepared and stored under proper conditions of sanitation, temperature, light, moisture, ventilation, segregation, safety, and security.

1 2 3 4 5 NA

TX.4
Medications are dispensed safely and accurately for the patient for whom they are prescribed/ordered.

1 2 3 4 5 NA

TX.4.1   All medications are appropriately labeled, including any applicable accessory or cautionary statements and expiration dates.

1 2 3 4 5 NA

TX.4.2   The pharmacist reviews each prescription/order prior to dispensing the medication, with the exception of situations in which a licensed independent practitioner with appropriate clinical privileges controls prescription/ordering, preparation, and administration of medication.

1 2 3 4 5 NA

TX.4.3   The prescription/order is verified with the prescriber/orderer when there is a question.

1 2 3 4 5 NA

TX.4.4   Quantities of dispensed medications are consistent with the patient's needs and designed to minimize errors and diversion.

1 2 3 4 5 NA

TX.5
The preparation and dispensing of medications are consistent with

TX.5.1   applicable law or regulation governing professional licensure and operation of pharmacies, and

1 2 3 4 5 NA

TX.5.2   professional standards of pharmacy practice.

1 2 3 4 5 NA

TX.6
The pharmacy department/service develops and maintains a medication profile for each patient that includes, at least, the patient's name, birth date, and sex; pertinent problems/diagnosis(es); current medication therapy, including prescription and nonprescription drugs; medication allergies or sensitivities; and potential drug/food interactions.

1 2 3 4 5 NA

TX.6.1   The medication profile is available to staff responsible for the patient's care.

1 2 3 4 5 NA

TX.7
When the pharmacy is closed, there is a process for providing medications that is designed to assure adequate control, accountability, and appropriate use of the medications.

1 2 3 4 5 NA

TX.8
A stock of medical staff–approved emergency drugs is maintained and readily available in the pharmacy department/service and in designated patient care areas.

1 2 3 4 5 NA

TX.9
Records of dispensed medications are maintained as required by applicable law to assure adequate control and accountability.

1 2 3 4 5 NA

TX.10
There is a system for recalling medications that can

TX.10.1 identify the manufacturer of each patient's medications;

1 2 3 4 5 NA

TX.10.2 retrieve and safely dispose of discontinued, expired, or recalled medications; and

1 2 3 4 5 NA

TX.10.3 provide for extramural reporting of medication product defects.

1 2 3 4 5 NA

MEDICATION ADMINISTRATION

TX.11
Medications are administered to patients safely and efficiently.

1 2 3 4 5 NA

TX.11.1 Medications to be administered are verified with the prescriber's/orderer's orders and are properly prepared for administration.

1 2 3 4 5 NA

TX.11.2 The patient is identified prior to administration of medication.

1 2 3 4 5 NA

TX.11.3 Medications are administered by, or under the supervision of, appropriately licensed personnel, in accordance with applicable law and regulation governing such acts and in accordance with approved medical staff rules and regulations.

1 2 3 4 5 NA

TX.11.4 Medications brought into the organization by patients are administered only in response to written medication orders.

1 2 3 4 5 NA

TX.11.5 Self-administration of medications by patients is permitted by a specific written order from the prescriber/orderer and in accordance with established organization policy.

1 2 3 4 5 NA

TX.11.6 Investigational medications and medications in clinical trial are used only in accordance with a specific organization mechanism that addresses at least

1 2 3 4 5 NA

TX.11.6.1   review and approval by an appropriate organization committee of the organization's participation in studies of investigational medications and medications in clinical trial;

1 2 3 4 5 NA

TX.11.6.2   requirements for informed consent;   1 2 3 4 5 NA

TX.11.6.3   administration of investigational medications and medications in clinical trial in accordance with an approved protocol;   1 2 3 4 5 NA

TX.11.6.4   administration of investigational medications and medications in clinical trial by those approved by the principal investigator to do so, and only after they have been given and have demonstrated an understanding of basic pharmacologic information about the medications; and   1 2 3 4 5 NA

TX.11.6.5   documentation of doses dispensed, administered, and destroyed.   1 2 3 4 5 NA

PATIENT MEDICATION MONITORING

TX.12
Each patient's medication is monitored on an ongoing basis for effectiveness and actual or potential adverse effects or toxicity.
                                                                    1 2 3 4 5 NA

TX.12.1   Ongoing patient medication monitoring includes a collaborative assessment of the medication's effect on the patient, based on observation and information gathered and maintained in the patient's medical record and medication profile.   1 2 3 4 5 NA

TX.12.2   Significant medication errors and significant adverse drug reactions are reported in a timely manner, in accordance with written procedures.   1 2 3 4 5 NA

TX.12.2.1   The medical staff, in collaboration with the pharmacy department/service and other appropriate departments/services, develops and maintains a process for defining, identifying, and reviewing significant medication errors.   1 2 3 4 5 NA

TX.12.2.2   The medical staff, in collaboration with the pharmacy department/service and other appropriate departments/services, develops and maintains a process for defining, identifying, and reviewing significant adverse drug reactions.   1 2 3 4 5 NA

TX.12.2.2.1   Significant adverse drug reactions are reported promptly to the Food and Drug Administration.   1 2 3 4 5 NA

TX.12.3   Information from the patient's medication monitoring is used to assess the continued administration of the medication to the patient.   1 2 3 4 5 NA

TX.12.4   The conclusions and findings of patient medication monitoring are communicated, when appropriate, to health care professionals involved in the patient's care.   1 2 3 4 5 NA

POLICIES AND PROCEDURES

TX.13
Appropriate staff develop, maintain, and enforce written policies and procedures about selecting, procuring, distributing, and administering medications as well as about the safety of overall medication use.
                                                                    1 2 3 4 5 NA

PARENTERAL NUTRITION

TX.14
When parenteral nutrition services are provided, mechanisms are designed, implemented, and maintained that address

TX.14.1   the determination of the therapeutic requirement for parenteral nutrition, based on the patient assessment;   1 2 3 4 5 NA

TX.14.2   the initial and ongoing medication orders for parenteral nutrition;   1 2 3 4 5 NA

TX.14.3   preparation and dispensing;   1 2 3 4 5 NA

TX.14.4   administration, including implications for patient care; and   1 2 3 4 5 NA

TX.14.5   assessment of the parenteral nutrition's effects on the patient.   1 2 3 4 5 NA

NOTES AND COMMENTS:

OPERATIVE AND OTHER INVASIVE PROCEDURES

PREAMBLE

Operative and other invasive procedures are an essential component of care provided to many hospital patients. Such procedures are often useful for diagnosis, symptom relief, and moderation or cure of disease. To achieve these benefits, four activities (sets of processes) must be performed well:

1. Selecting appropriate procedures;
2. Preparing the patient;
3. Monitoring the patient during and after the procedures; and
4. Discharging the patient from the service or setting.

The standards in this chapter apply when any patient, in any setting, receives, for any purpose, by any route,

1. general, spinal, or other major regional anesthesia; or
2. sedation (with or without analgesia) for which there is a reasonable expectation that in the manner used, the sedation/analgesia will result in the loss of protective reflexes for a significant percentage of a group of patients.

In addition, this chapter has some important links to other chapters in this *Accreditation Manual for Hospitals* and, therefore, to other important functions of a health care organization. In particular,

- processes of operative and other invasive procedures are among the priorities for assessment and improvement by the organization, as identified in the "Improving Organizational Performance" chapter;
- decisions regarding the selection of an appropriate procedure are based on an analysis of the patient's health care or treatment needs, as described by the standards in the "Assessment of Patients" chapter;
- patients presenting for operative and other invasive procedures are assessed and treated by individuals who have been determined to be qualified in accordance with the standards on clinical privileges in the "Medical Staff" chapter and the standards on competence assessment in the "Governing Body" and "Management and Administration" chapters;
- operative and other invasive procedures are conducted in a manner to prevent and control infections in patients and personnel in accordance with the standards in the "Surveillance, Prevention, and Control of Infection" chapter;
- procedures are conducted in accordance with the standards addressing plant, technology, and safety management programs in the "Management of the Environment of Care" chapter; and
- patients receive education specific to the appropriate procedures and to their relevant health care needs, in accordance with the standards in the "Education of Patients and Family" chapter.

DEFINITION

invasive procedures Procedures involving puncture or incision of the skin or insertion of an instrument or foreign material into the body, including, but not limited to, percutaneous aspirations and biopsies, cardiac and vascular catheterizations, endoscopies, angioplasties, and implantations, and excluding venipuncture and intravenous therapy.

SELECTING APPROPRIATE PROCEDURES

OP.1
The medical staff defines the scope of an appropriate assessment for both emergent and nonemergent operative and other invasive procedures in accordance with "Assessment of Patients" standards requirements.

1 2 3 4 5 NA

OP.1.1 Determining the appropriateness of the procedure(s) for a patient is based at least on

OP.1.1.1 the patient's medical, anesthetic, and drug history;

1 2 3 4 5 NA

OP.1.1.2 the patient's physical status;

1 2 3 4 5 NA

OP.1.1.3 diagnostic data;

1 2 3 4 5 NA

OP.1.1.4 the risks/benefits of the procedure(s); and

1 2 3 4 5 NA

OP.1.1.5 the need to administer blood or blood components.

1 2 3 4 5 NA

PREPARING THE PATIENT

OP.1.2 The risks/benefits associated with the procedure(s) are discussed with the patient before documenting informed consent and include consideration, as appropriate, of at least

OP.1.2.1 alternative options if they exist;

1 2 3 4 5 NA

OP.1.2.2 the need for and risk of blood transfusion and available alternatives; and

1 2 3 4 5 NA

OP.1.2.3 anesthesia* options with attendant risks.

1 2 3 4 5 NA

OP.2
A preanesthesia patient assessment is performed before the operative and other invasive procedure(s).

1 2 3 4 5 NA

OP.3
The plans of care for the patient are formulated and documented in his/her medical record before the procedure(s) is performed and include at least

---

*Anesthesia *is defined as the administration (in any setting, by any route, for any purpose) of general, spinal, or other major regional anesthesia or sedation (with or without analgesia) for which there is a reasonable expectation that, in the manner used, the sedation/analgesia will result in the loss of protective reflexes for a significant percentage of a group of patients.*

OP.3.1	a plan for anesthesia;	1 2 3 4 5 NA
OP.3.2	a plan for nursing care;	1 2 3 4 5 NA
OP.3.3	a plan for the operative or invasive procedure;	1 2 3 4 5 NA
OP.3.4	a plan for the level of postprocedure care;	1 2 3 4 5 NA
OP.3.5	an assessment of the availability of blood or blood components for administration before initiating anesthesia, when indicated;	1 2 3 4 5 NA
OP.3.6	an assessment of the need for additional diagnostic data;	1 2 3 4 5 NA
OP.3.7	an initial assessment of the patient's acuity of needs to determine the appropriate level of postprocedure care; and	1 2 3 4 5 NA
OP.3.8	an initial assessment of the patient's physical and psychologic status and needs.	1 2 3 4 5 NA

MONITORING THE PATIENT

OP.4
The patient's physiologic status is measured and assessed during

OP.4.1	anesthesia administration and	1 2 3 4 5 NA
OP.4.2	the operative/invasive procedure.	1 2 3 4 5 NA

OP.5
The postprocedure status of the patient is measured, assessed, and documented including

OP.5.1	the patient's physiologic and psychologic status;	1 2 3 4 5 NA
OP.5.2	pathologic findings (when indicated);	1 2 3 4 5 NA
OP.5.3	intravenous fluids and drugs administered, including blood and blood components; and	1 2 3 4 5 NA
OP.5.4	any unusual events or postoperative complications and their management.	1 2 3 4 5 NA

DISCHARGING THE PATIENT

OP.6
The patient's postprocedure status is assessed on admission to the postanesthesia recovery area and before discharge from the postanesthesia recovery area or setting.

1 2 3 4 5 NA

OP.6.1	The patient is discharged either by a qualified licensed independent practitioner or by using medical staff–approved criteria.	1 2 3 4 5 NA
	OP.6.1.1 When medical staff–approved criteria are used, the patient status indicating compliance with those criteria is fully documented in his/her medical record.	1 2 3 4 5 NA

NOTES AND COMMENTS:

EDUCATION OF PATIENTS AND FAMILY*

PREAMBLE

The goal of educating the patient and family is to improve patient health outcomes by promoting recovery, speeding return to function, promoting healthy behavior, and appropriately involving patients in their care and care decisions. Patient and family education should

- facilitate the patient's/family's understanding of the patient's health status, health care options, and consequences of options selected;
- encourage participation in decision making about health care options;
- increase the patient's/family's potential to follow the therapeutic health care plan;
- maximize care skills;
- increase the patient's/family's ability to cope with the patient's health status/prognosis/outcome;
- enhance the patient's/family's role in continuing care; and
- promote a healthy life-style.

The "Education of Patients and Family" standards address the need for a systematic approach to education throughout the organization. However, they do not require any specific structure for providing education, such as an education department, a patient education committee, or employment of an educator. The standards allow the organization to focus on its current processes and how these processes are implemented in relation to the patient's plan of care, the level of care, the setting in which teaching occurs, and continuity of care.

The performance-improvement framework in the "Improving Organizational Performance" chapter will be used to design, measure, assess, and improve the organization's performance of the patient and family education function.

PF.1

The patient and/or his/her family are provided with appropriate education and training to expand their knowledge of the patient's illness and treatment needs and to learn skills and behaviors that promote recovery and improve function.

1 2 3 4 5 NA

PF.2

The patient and/or, when appropriate, his/her family receive education specific to the patient's assessed needs, abilities, and readiness, as appropriate to the patient's length of stay.

1 2 3 4 5 NA

PF.2.1 The patient and/or, when appropriate, his/her family have their learning needs, abilities, and readiness to learn assessed.

1 2 3 4 5 NA

---

*Family *refers to the person(s) who plays a significant role in the patient's life. This includes an individual(s) who may or may not be legally related to the patient.*

PF.2.1.1   When indicated, the assessment includes cultural and religious practices, emotional barriers, desire and motivation to learn, physical and/or cognitive limitations, and language barriers.   1 2 3 4 5 NA

PF.2.2   The patient and/or, when appropriate, his/her family are provided with the specific knowledge and/or skills required to meet the patient's ongoing health care needs. Such instruction is presented in ways understandable to the patient and/or his/her family and includes, but is not limited to,

PF.2.2.1   the safe and effective use of medication, when applicable, in accordance with legal requirements and patient needs;   1 2 3 4 5 NA

PF.2.2.2   the safe and effective use of medical equipment, when applicable;   1 2 3 4 5 NA

PF.2.2.3   instruction on potential drug-food interactions and counseling on nutrition intervention and/or modified diets, as appropriate;   1 2 3 4 5 NA

PF.2.2.4   instruction in rehabilitation techniques to facilitate adaptation to and/or functional independence in the environment, if needed;   1 2 3 4 5 NA

PF.2.2.5   access to available community resources, if needed;   1 2 3 4 5 NA

PF.2.2.6   when and how to obtain further treatment, if needed; and   1 2 3 4 5 NA

PF.2.2.7   the patient's and family's responsibilities in the patient's care.   1 2 3 4 5 NA

PF.3
Any discharge instructions given to the patient and/or, when appropriate, his/her family are provided to the organization or individual responsible for the patient's continuing care.   1 2 3 4 5 NA

PF.4
The organization plans and supports the provision and coordination of patient and family education activities and resources.   1 2 3 4 5 NA

PF.4.1   The organization identifies and provides the educational resources required to achieve its educational objectives.   1 2 3 4 5 NA

PF.4.2   The patient and family educational process is interdisciplinary, as appropriate to the plan of care.   1 2 3 4 5 NA

NOTES AND COMMENTS:

COORDINATION OF CARE

New performance-focused standards will appear in this chapter of the 1995 *Accreditation Manual for Hospitals*. For surveys conducted during 1994, see the standards regarding discharge planning found in the "Management and Administrative Services" chapter and in several additional chapters in the department/ service-specific chapters in Section 4 of this *Manual*.

SECTION 2
ORGANIZATIONAL FUNCTIONS

Leadership

Management of Information

Management of Human Resources

Management of the Environment of Care

Surveillance, Prevention, and Control of Infection

Improving Organizational Performance

LEADERSHIP

PREAMBLE

The goal of the leadership function is for the organization's leaders* to provide the framework for planning, directing, coordinating, providing, and improving health care services that are responsive to community and patient needs and that improve patient health outcomes.

KEY CHARACTERISTICS OF LEADERSHIP

The process of leadership starts with establishing and promulgating the organization's mission and renewing and revising it as necessary. Building on the mission, effective leadership defines and establishes a clear vision for what the organization can and resolves to become, encouraging staff participation in its development. Effective leadership develops other leaders at every level of the organization who help fulfill the organization's mission and vision. Effective leadership accurately assesses the needs of the organization's patients and other users of the organization's services and develops an organizational culture that focuses on improving performance to meet these needs.

Effective leadership

- defines a strategic plan that is consistent with the organization's mission and vision;
- clearly communicates the mission, vision, and plan throughout the organization; and
- fulfills the organization's vision by providing the framework to accomplish the goals of the strategic plan.

Developing this framework is accomplished through the proper direction, implementation, coordination, and, ultimately, improvement of services throughout the organization. In order to realize the organization's vision, leadership must have a role in teaching and coaching staff. This role is inherent to leadership.

THE PROCESS OF LEADERSHIP

To achieve the goal of the leadership function, four processes must be performed:

1. **planning services** Leadership establishes a mission statement that is reflected in long-range, strategic, and operational plans; resource allocation; and organization policies.
2. **directing services** Leadership organizes, directs, and staffs patient care and support services in a manner that is commensurate with the scope of services offered.
3. **implementing and coordinating services** Leadership integrates patient care and support services throughout the organization.

The leaders described in the leadership function include at least the leaders of the governing body; the chief executive officer and other senior managers; the elected and/or appointed leaders of the medical staff and the clinical departments and other medical staff members in hospital administrative positions; and the nurse executive and other senior nursing leaders.

4. **improving services** Leadership establishes expectations and plans and manages processes to measure, assess, and improve the performance of the organization's governance, management, clinical, and support processes.

LD.1
The leadership provides for organizational planning.

1 2 3 4 5 NA

LD.1.1 Planning includes setting a mission and vision for the organization and providing the strategic, operational, programmatic, and other plans and policies to achieve the mission and vision.

1 2 3 4 5 NA

LD.1.1.1 Planning addresses at least those important patient care and organizationwide functions identified in this *Manual*.

1 2 3 4 5 NA

LD.1.1.2 When the organization is part of a multihospital system, there is a mechanism(s) for the leaders of an individual organization to participate in policy decisions affecting their organization.

1 2 3 4 5 NA

LD.1.2 The leaders communicate the organization's plan(s) throughout the organization.

1 2 3 4 5 NA

LD.1.3 The plan(s) includes patient care services in response to identified patient needs and is consistent with the organization's mission.

1 2 3 4 5 NA

LD.1.3.1 The organization's leaders, and, as appropriate, community leaders and organizations, collaborate to design services.

1 2 3 4 5 NA

LD.1.3.2 The design of patient care services to be provided throughout the organization is appropriate to the scope and level of care required by the patients served.

1 2 3 4 5 NA

LD.1.3.3 Services are designed to be responsive to the needs and expectations of patients and/or their families/decision makers.

1 2 3 4 5 NA

LD.1.3.3.1 The organization gathers, assesses, and takes appropriate action on information that relates to the patient's satisfaction with the services provided.

1 2 3 4 5 NA

LD.1.3.4 Services are available in a timely manner to meet the needs of patients.

1 2 3 4 5 NA

LD.1.3.4.1 Such patient care services are provided either directly or through referral, consultation, or contractual arrangements and/or agreements.

1 2 3 4 5 NA

LD.1.3.4.1.1 When patient care services are performed outside the organization by another source(s), the other source(s) is approved by the medical staff through its designated mechanism, and written agreements require that the source(s) meet applicable standards contained elsewhere in this *Manual*.

1 2 3 4 5 NA

LD.1.4 The planning process provides for setting the organization's priorities for performance improvement, including mechanisms designed to reprioritize in response to unusual or urgent events.

1 2 3 4 5 NA

LD.1.5 The leaders collaborate with representatives from the appropriate disciplines and departments/services to develop an annual operating budget and, at least as required by applicable law and regulation, a long-term capital expenditure plan and to monitor implementation of the plan. 1 2 3 4 5 NA

LD.1.5.1 The governing body approves the annual operating budget and long-term capital expenditure plan. 1 2 3 4 5 NA

LD.1.5.2 The budget review process includes consideration of the appropriateness of the organization's plan for providing care to meet patient needs. 1 2 3 4 5 NA

LD.1.5.3 An annual audit of the financial statements of the organization is conducted by an independent public accountant, unless otherwise provided by law. 1 2 3 4 5 NA

LD.1.6 The leaders develop and implement mechanisms designed to assure the uniform performance of patient care processes throughout the organization. 1 2 3 4 5 NA

LD.1.7 The scope of services provided by each department/service is defined in writing and is approved by either the organization's administration, medical staff, or both, as appropriate. 1 2 3 4 5 NA

LD.1.7.1 Patient care services provided by a department/service are described in a specific written statement of the goals of patient care services and scope of services planned. 1 2 3 4 5 NA

LD.1.8 The leaders and other representatives from the organization, as appropriate, participate in the organization's decision-making structures and processes. 1 2 3 4 5 NA

LD.1.9 The organization's leaders develop programs to promote the recruitment, retention, development, and continuing education of all staff members. 1 2 3 4 5 NA

LD.1.9.1 The programs include mechanisms for promoting at least job-related educational and advancement goals of organization staff members. 1 2 3 4 5 NA

LD.2
There is effective leadership of each department/service of the organization. 1 2 3 4 5 NA

LD.2.1 Department/service directors are responsible, either personally or through delegation, for

LD.2.1.1 integrating the department/service into the organization's primary functions; 1 2 3 4 5 NA

LD.2.1.2 coordinating and integrating interdepartmental and intradepartmental services; 1 2 3 4 5 NA

LD.2.1.3 developing and implementing policies and procedures that guide and support the provision of services; 1 2 3 4 5 NA

LD.2.1.4 recommending a sufficient number of qualified and competent persons to provide care/service; 1 2 3 4 5 NA

LD.2.1.5 the determination of the qualifications and competence of department/service personnel who provide patient care services and who are not licensed independent practitioners*;

1 2 3 4 5 NA

LD.2.1.6 continuously assessing and improving the performance of care and services provided;

1 2 3 4 5 NA

LD.2.1.7 maintaining quality control programs, as appropriate;

1 2 3 4 5 NA

LD.2.1.8 orienting and providing in-service training and continuing education of all persons in the department/service;

1 2 3 4 5 NA

LD.2.1.9 recommending space and other resources needed by the department/service; and

1 2 3 4 5 NA

LD.2.1.10 participating in the selection of sources for needed services not provided by the department/service or the organization.

1 2 3 4 5 NA

LD.2.2 Patient care services are organized, directed, and staffed in a manner commensurate with the scope of services offered.

1 2 3 4 5 NA

LD.2.2.1 Directors of medical staff departments/services fulfill the responsibilities described in MS.4.6.1.1.1, MS.4.6.1.1.2, and MS.4.6.1.1.7 through MS.4.6.1.1.9 in the "Medical Staff" chapter of this *Manual*.

1 2 3 4 5 NA

LD.2.2.2 Departments/services providing patient care that are not medical staff departments/services are directed by one or more individuals whose qualifications, authority, and duties are defined in writing.

1 2 3 4 5 NA

LD.2.2.2.1 Responsibility for administrative direction and clinical direction is defined.

1 2 3 4 5 NA

LD.2.2.2.1.1 Clinical direction of patient care and treatment services is the responsibility of a qualified professional with appropriate clinical training and experience.

1 2 3 4 5 NA

LD.2.2.2.1.2 When there is more than one director of a single department/service, the responsibilities of each director are defined.

1 2 3 4 5 NA

LD.3
Patient care services are appropriately integrated throughout the organization.

1 2 3 4 5 NA

LD.3.1 The organizational and functional relationships of departments/services are specified within the organization's plan for the provision of patient care services.

1 2 3 4 5 NA

LD.3.2 The leaders individually and jointly develop and participate in systematic and effective mechanisms for

LD.3.2.1 fostering communication between and among individuals and components of the organization and coordinating internal activities; and

1 2 3 4 5 NA

---

licensed independent practitioner Any individual who is permitted by law and by the hospital to provide patient care services without direction or supervision, within the scope of the individual's license and in accordance with individually granted clinical privileges.

LD.3.2.2 communicating with the leaders of any health care delivery organization(s) that is corporately or functionally related to the organization seeking accreditation.

1 2 3 4 5 NA

LD.3.3 All department/service policies and procedures are developed in collaboration with associated departments/services and are approved by the organization's administration and medical staff, as appropriate.

1 2 3 4 5 NA

LD.3.4 All staff assigned managerial responsibility participate in cross-organizational activities to improve organizational performance, as appropriate to their responsibilities.

1 2 3 4 5 NA

LD.3.4.1 Relevant information is forwarded to the appropriate leaders and the person(s) responsible for coordinating organizationwide performance improvement activities.

1 2 3 4 5 NA

LD.3.4.1.1 The responsibility for taking action on recommendations generated through performance improvement activities is assigned and defined in writing.

1 2 3 4 5 NA

LD.4
The organization's leaders set expectations, develop plans, and manage processes to assess, improve, and maintain the quality of the organization's governance, management, clinical, and support activities.

1 2 3 4 5 NA

LD.4.1 The leaders understand the approaches and methods of performance improvement.

1 2 3 4 5 NA

LD.4.2 The leaders adopt an approach to performance improvement that includes at least the following:

LD.4.2.1 Planning the process of improvement;

1 2 3 4 5 NA

LD.4.2.2 Setting priorities for improvement;

1 2 3 4 5 NA

LD.4.2.3 Assessing performance systematically;

1 2 3 4 5 NA

LD.4.2.4 Implementing improvement activities on the basis of assessment; and

1 2 3 4 5 NA

LD.4.2.5 Maintaining achieved improvements.

1 2 3 4 5 NA

LD.4.3 The leaders assure that important internal processes and activities (those that affect patient outcomes most significantly) throughout the organization are continuously and systematically assessed and improved.

1 2 3 4 5 NA

LD.4.4 The leaders allocate adequate resources for assessing and improving the organization's governance, managerial, clinical, and support processes by

1 2 3 4 5 NA

LD.4.4.1 assigning personnel, as needed, to participate in performance-improvement activities;

1 2 3 4 5 NA

LD.4.4.2 providing adequate time for personnel to participate in performance-improvement activities;

1 2 3 4 5 NA

LD.4.4.3 creating and maintaining information systems and appropriate data management processes to support collecting, managing, and analyzing data needed to facilitate ongoing improvement in performance; and

1 2 3 4 5 NA

LD.4.4.4 providing for staff training in the approaches and methods of performance improvement.

1 2 3 4 5 NA

LD.4.5 The leaders analyze and assess the effectiveness of their contributions to improving performance.

1 2 3 4 5 NA

NOTES AND COMMENTS:

MANAGEMENT OF INFORMATION

PREAMBLE

An organization's provision of health care is a complex endeavor that is highly dependent on information. This includes information about the science of care, the individual patient, the care provided, the results of care, and the performance of the organization itself. Furthermore, many individuals, departments, and services within the organization are providing care, and their work must be coordinated and integrated. Because of this dependency on information and the need to coordinate and integrate services, health care organizations must treat information as an important resource to be effectively and efficiently managed. The management of information is an active, planned activity. The organization's leaders have overall responsibility for this activity—just as they do for managing the organization's human, material, and financial resources.

Information management is a function—a set of processes—focused on meeting the organization's information needs. Its goal is to obtain, manage, and use information to enhance and improve individual and organizational performance in patient care, governance, management, and support processes. While the efficiency and effectiveness of information management processes may be affected by the technologies employed (for example, computerization), the principles of good information management (as reflected in these standards) are relevant regardless of the technology used. Thus, while these standards are compatible with current, cutting-edge technologies (and, it is hoped, with future technologies), they are intended to be equally applicable in organizations that are not computerized.

These standards describe a vision of effective and continuously improving information management in health care organizations. The objectives related to achieving this vision are

- more timely and easier access to complete information throughout the organization;
- improved data accuracy;
- demonstrated balance of proper levels of security versus ease of access;
- use of compiled data, along with external knowledge bases and comparative data, to pursue opportunities for improvement;
- redesign of important information-related processes to improve efficiency; and
- greater collaboration and information sharing to enhance patient care.

For most organizations, achieving all these goals will take varying periods of time, up to five years. Thus, the scoring guidelines for this chapter will accommodate the time needed for this transition to effective organizationwide information management.

The standards focus on the key information management processes of organizationwide planning to meet internal and external information needs. The standards also focus on management of patient-specific data/information, aggregate data/information, expert knowledge-based information, and comparative performance data/information. Specifically, the standards address

- identification of the organization's information needs;
- structural design of the information management system;
- definition and capture of data/information;

- data analysis and transformation of data into information;
- transmission and reporting of data/information; and
- assimilation and use of information.

The organization's leaders have important roles and responsibilities if an organizationwide approach to information management will be achieved, maintained, and improved. Also, staff at many levels must be educated and trained in managing and using information.

The performance-improvement framework in the "Improving Organizational Performance" chapter of this *Accreditation Manual for Hospitals* will be used to design, measure, assess, and improve the organization's performance of the information management function.

PLANNING

IM.1
Information management processes are planned and designed to meet the health care organization's internal and external information needs.

1 2 3 4 5 NA

IM.1.1 The information management processes within and among organization departments/services, the medical staff, the administration, and the governing body and with outside services and agencies are appropriate for the organization's size and complexity.

1 2 3 4 5 NA

IM.1.1.1 Direction, staffing, and material resource allocations are based on the organization's scope and complexity of services provided.

1 2 3 4 5 NA

IM.1.1.2 Based on the organization's information needs, appropriate staff participate in assessing, selecting, and integrating health care information technology and, as appropriate, the use of efficient interactive information management systems for clinical and organizational information.

1 2 3 4 5 NA

IM.2
The information management function provides for information confidentiality, security, and integrity.

1 2 3 4 5 NA

IM.2.1 The organization determines the need for and appropriate levels of security and confidentiality of data/information.

1 2 3 4 5 NA

IM.2.2 The organization determines how data/information can be retrieved on a timely and easy basis without compromising the data's/information's security and confidentiality.

1 2 3 4 5 NA

IM.2.2.1 A written organizational and medical staff policy requires that medical records may be removed from the organization's jurisdiction and safekeeping only in accordance with a court order, subpoena, or statute.

1 2 3 4 5 NA

IM.2.2.2 The organization has a functioning mechanism designed to preserve the confidentiality of data/information identified as sensitive or requiring extraordinary means to preserve patient privacy.

1 2 3 4 5 NA

IM.2.3 The organization has a functioning mechanism designed to safeguard records/information against loss, destruction, tampering, and unauthorized access or use.

1 2 3 4 5 NA

IM.3
Uniform data definitions and methods for capturing data are in place when feasible.

1 2 3 4 5 NA

IM.3.1 Whenever possible, minimum data sets, data definitions, codes, classifications, and terminology are standardized throughout the organization.

1 2 3 4 5 NA

IM.3.1.1 Externally standardized sets, definitions, codes, classifications, and terminology (when available) are referenced when developing organization standards.

1 2 3 4 5 NA

IM.3.2 Data are collected in a timely, economical, and efficient manner and with the degree of accuracy, completeness, and discrimination necessary for their intended use.

1 2 3 4 5 NA

IM.3.3 The organization implements mechanisms designed to ascertain that bias in the data is minimized and to assess the data's reliability, validity, and accuracy on an ongoing basis.

1 2 3 4 5 NA

IM.3.3.1 The completeness, accuracy, and timely completion of information in medical records are reviewed by the organization at least quarterly.

1 2 3 4 5 NA

IM.3.3.1.1 The review is performed by, at a minimum, the medical staff in cooperation with nursing, the health information management (medical record) department/service, management and administrative services, and representatives of other departments/services as appropriate.

1 2 3 4 5 NA

IM.3.3.1.2 The review determines that each medical record, or a representative sample of records, reflects the diagnosis, diagnostic test results, therapy, the patient's condition and in-hospital progress, and the patient's condition at discharge.

1 2 3 4 5 NA

IM.4
Decision makers and other individuals in the organization who generate, collect, and analyze data/information are educated and trained in the principles of information management.

1 2 3 4 5 NA

IM.5
Transmission of data/information is timely and accurate.

1 2 3 4 5 NA

IM.5.1 The format and methods for disseminating data/information are standardized, whenever possible.

1 2 3 4 5 NA

IM.6
The information management function enables the combination of data/information; makes information from one system (clinical and/or organizational) available to another; provides reports; clarifies and interprets data/information; and enables linkage of patient-care and non-patient-care data/information over time among the organization's departments and provider resources for all care modes.

1 2 3 4 5 NA

IM.6.1   The length of time that medical record information is retained is determined based on law and regulation and by its use for patient care, legal,
research, or educational purposes.   1 2 3 4 5 NA

IM.6.2   There are internal linkages among information management processes
related to the important patient care and organizational functions described in this *Manual*.   1 2 3 4 5 NA

IM.6.3   Linkage to external databases and bodies of expert health-related, administrative, and research knowledge are provided as required by the
organization's information management needs.   1 2 3 4 5 NA

PATIENT-SPECIFIC DATA/INFORMATION

IM.7
**The information management function provides for the definition, capture,
analysis, transformation, transmission, and reporting of individual patient-
specific data/information related to the process(es) and/or outcome(s) of
the patient's care.**   1 2 3 4 5 NA

IM.7.1   A medical record is initiated and maintained for every individual assessed
or treated. The medical record incorporates information from subsequent
contacts between the patient and the organization.   1 2 3 4 5 NA

IM.7.1.1   Entries in medical records are made only by individuals authorized to do so as specified in organization and medical staff policies. 1 2 3 4 5 NA

IM.7.2   The medical record contains sufficient information to identify the patient,
support the diagnosis, justify the treatment, document the course and
results accurately, and facilitate continuity of care among health care
providers. Each medical record contains at least the following: 1 2 3 4 5 NA

IM.7.2.1   The patient's name, address, date of birth, and the name of
any legally authorized representative;   1 2 3 4 5 NA

IM.7.2.2   The patient's legal status, for patients receiving mental health
services;   1 2 3 4 5 NA

IM.7.2.3   Emergency care provided to the patient prior to arrival, if any; 1 2 3 4 5 NA

IM.7.2.4   The record and findings of the patient's assessment (see the
"Assessment of Patients" chapter of this *Manual*);   1 2 3 4 5 NA

IM.7.2.5   A statement of the conclusions or impressions drawn from the
medical history and physical examination;   1 2 3 4 5 NA

IM.7.2.6   The diagnosis or diagnostic impression;   1 2 3 4 5 NA

IM.7.2.7   The reason(s) for admission or treatment;   1 2 3 4 5 NA

IM.7.2.8   The goals of treatment and the treatment plan;   1 2 3 4 5 NA

IM.7.2.9   Evidence of known advance directives;   1 2 3 4 5 NA

IM.7.2.10   Evidence of informed consent for procedures and treatments
for which informed consent is required by organizational policy;   1 2 3 4 5 NA

IM.7.2.11   Diagnostic and therapeutic orders, if any;   1 2 3 4 5 NA

IM.7.2.12 All diagnostic and therapeutic procedures and tests performed and the results;

1 2 3 4 5 NA

IM.7.2.13 All operative and other invasive procedures performed, using acceptable disease and operative terminology that includes etiology, as appropriate;

1 2 3 4 5 NA

IM.7.2.14 Progress notes made by the medical staff and other authorized individuals;

1 2 3 4 5 NA

IM.7.2.15 All reassessments, when necessary;

1 2 3 4 5 NA

IM.7.2.16 Clinical observations;

1 2 3 4 5 NA

IM.7.2.17 The response to the care provided;

1 2 3 4 5 NA

IM.7.2.18 Consultation reports;

1 2 3 4 5 NA

IM.7.2.19 Every medication ordered or prescribed for an inpatient;

1 2 3 4 5 NA

IM.7.2.20 Every dose of medication administered and any adverse drug reaction;

1 2 3 4 5 NA

IM.7.2.21 Each medication dispensed to or prescribed for an ambulatory patient or an inpatient on discharge;

1 2 3 4 5 NA

IM.7.2.22 All relevant diagnoses established during the course of care; and

1 2 3 4 5 NA

IM.7.2.23 Any referrals/communications made to external or internal care providers and to community agencies.

1 2 3 4 5 NA

IM.7.3 At discharge from inpatient care, a clinical resume concisely summarizes the reason for hospitalization, the significant findings, the procedures performed and treatment rendered, the patient's condition on discharge, and any specific instructions given to the patient and/or family, as pertinent.

1 2 3 4 5 NA

IM.7.3.1 A final progress note is substituted for the resume only for those patients with problems and interventions of a minor nature (as defined by the medical staff) who require less than a 48-hour period of hospitalization and in the case of normal newborn infants and uncomplicated obstetric deliveries.

1 2 3 4 5 NA

IM.7.3.2 A transfer summary may be substituted for the resume in the case of the transfer of the patient to a different level of hospitalization or residential care within the organization.

1 2 3 4 5 NA

IM.7.4 The medical record of patients undergoing operative or other invasive procedures and/or anesthesia includes the additional following information:

1 2 3 4 5 NA

IM.7.4.1 The licensed independent practitioner who is responsible for the patient records a preoperative diagnosis prior to surgery.

1 2 3 4 5 NA

IM.7.4.2 Operative reports are dictated or written in the medical record immediately after surgery and describe the findings, the technical procedures used, the specimen removed, the postoperative diagnosis, and the name of the primary surgeon and any assistants.

1 2 3 4 5 NA

IM.7.4.2.1 The completed operative report is authenticated by the surgeon and filed in the medical record as soon as possible after surgery.

1 2 3 4 5 NA

IM.7.4.2.2 When the operative report is not placed in the medical record immediately after surgery (for example, there is a transcription and/or filing delay), an operative progress note is entered in the medical record immediately after surgery to provide pertinent information for any individual required to attend to the patient.

1 2 3 4 5 NA

IM.7.4.3 Postoperative documentation includes at least a record of

IM.7.4.3.1 vital signs and level of consciousness;

1 2 3 4 5 NA

IM.7.4.3.2 medications (including intravenous fluids) and blood and blood components;

1 2 3 4 5 NA

IM.7.4.3.3 any unusual events or postoperative complications, including blood transfusion reactions, and the management of those events;

1 2 3 4 5 NA

IM.7.4.3.4 identification of who provided direct patient care nursing services and who supervised that care if it was provided by someone other than a qualified registered nurse;

1 2 3 4 5 NA

IM.7.4.3.5 the patient's discharge from the postanesthesia care area by the responsible licensed independent practitioner or by the use of relevant discharge criteria; and

1 2 3 4 5 NA

IM.7.4.3.5.1 The criteria are approved by the medical staff and are rigorously applied to determine the patient's readiness for discharge.

1 2 3 4 5 NA

IM.7.4.3.6 the name of the licensed independent practitioner responsible for the discharge.

1 2 3 4 5 NA

IM.7.5 The medical record for patients receiving continuing ambulatory care services includes a list of known significant diagnoses, conditions, procedures, drug allergies, and medications.

1 2 3 4 5 NA

IM.7.5.1 The list is initiated and maintained for each patient by the third visit.

1 2 3 4 5 NA

IM.7.6 When emergency care is provided,

IM.7.6.1 the following additional information is required in the medical record:

IM.7.6.1.1 Time and means of arrival;

1 2 3 4 5 NA

IM.7.6.1.2 The patient's leaving against medical advice; and

1 2 3 4 5 NA

IM.7.6.1.3 Conclusions at termination of treatment, including final disposition, patient's condition at discharge, and any instructions for follow-up care.

1 2 3 4 5 NA

IM.7.6.2 and it is authorized by the patient or his/her legally authorized representative, a copy of the record of emergency services provided is available to the practitioner or medical organization responsible for follow-up care.

1 2 3 4 5 NA

IM.7.7 Medical record data/information are managed in a timely manner.

1 2 3 4 5 NA

IM.7.7.1   All significant clinical information pertaining to a patient is entered into the medical record as soon as possible after its occurrence.

1 2 3 4 5 NA

IM.7.7.2   Medical records of discharged patients are completed within a time period specified in medical staff rules and regulations, not to exceed 30 days.

1 2 3 4 5 NA

IM.7.8   Verbal orders of authorized individuals are accepted and transcribed by qualified personnel who are identified by title or category in the medical staff rules and regulations.

1 2 3 4 5 NA

IM.7.8.1   Verbal orders for medications are accepted only by personnel so designated in the medical staff rules and regulations and are authenticated by the prescribing practitioner within the stated period of time.

1 2 3 4 5 NA

IM.7.8.2   The medical staff defines any category of diagnostic or therapeutic verbal orders associated with any potential hazard to the patient.

1 2 3 4 5 NA

IM.7.8.2.1   Such verbal orders are authenticated by the practitioner responsible for the patient within a time frame defined in the medical staff rules and regulations.

1 2 3 4 5 NA

IM.7.9   All entries in medical records are dated and authenticated, and a method is established to identify the authors of entries.

1 2 3 4 5 NA

IM.7.9.1   Authentication may be by written signatures or initials, rubber-stamp signatures, or computer key.

1 2 3 4 5 NA

IM.7.9.2   When rubber-stamp signatures or computer key are authorized, the individual whose signature the stamp represents or whose computer key is authorized signs a statement that he/she alone will use the stamp or the code for the computer key. This statement is filed in the organization's administrative offices.

1 2 3 4 5 NA

IM.7.9.2.1   Such a stamp or code for the computer key is not used by another individual.

1 2 3 4 5 NA

IM.7.9.3   The medical practitioner authenticates the parts of the medical record that are his/her responsibility.

1 2 3 4 5 NA

IM.7.10   The organization uses a patient information system to routinely assemble all divergently located record components when a patient is admitted to the hospital or appears for a prescheduled ambulatory care appointment. The system also assures that all record components are assembled in a timely manner, as needed, for patients seen for unscheduled ambulatory and emergency services visits.

1 2 3 4 5 NA

IM.7.10.1   The medical record or computer system indicates when a portion of the record has been filed elsewhere, in order to alert authorized personnel of its existence.

1 2 3 4 5 NA

AGGREGATE DATA/INFORMATION

IM.8
The information management function provides for the definition, capture, analysis, transmission, and reporting of data/information that can be aggregated in support of managerial decisions and operations, performance-improvement activities, and patient care.

1 2 3 4 5 NA

IM.8.1　Data/information that can be aggregated include at least the following:

IM.8.1.1　Pharmacy transactions as required by applicable law, and as necessary to adequately control and account for all drugs, including　　1 2 3 4 5 NA

　IM.8.1.1.1　maintaining a means of identifying the signatures of all practitioners authorized to prescribe/order medications, and　　1 2 3 4 5 NA

　IM.8.1.1.2　a listing of practitioners' Drug Enforcement Administration numbers, where required;　　1 2 3 4 5 NA

IM.8.1.2　Information about hazards and safety practices used to identify safety management issues to be addressed by the safety committee, including　　1 2 3 4 5 NA

　IM.8.1.2.1　summaries of the deficiencies, problems, failures, and user errors in safety management, life safety management, equipment management, and utilities management, as well as relevant published reports of hazards associated with any of these areas,　　1 2 3 4 5 NA

　IM.8.1.2.2　documented surveys, at least semiannually, of all areas of the facility to identify environmental hazards and unsafe practices, and　　1 2 3 4 5 NA

　IM.8.1.2.3　reports and investigations of all incidents involving property damage, occupational illness, or patient, personnel, or visitor injury;　　1 2 3 4 5 NA

IM.8.1.3　Records of radionuclides and radiopharmaceuticals, including the radionuclide's identity, the date received, method of receipt, activity, recipient's identity, dates administered, and disposal;　　1 2 3 4 5 NA

IM.8.1.4　Records of any required reporting to proper authorities;　　1 2 3 4 5 NA

IM.8.1.5　A coding and retrieval system for medical records by diagnosis and procedure;　　1 2 3 4 5 NA

IM.8.1.6　A coding and retrieval system for patient demographic information;　　1 2 3 4 5 NA

　IM.8.1.6.1　A continuously maintained control register for emergency and outpatient services includes at least the following information for every individual seeking care: identification, such as name, age, and sex; date, time, and means of arrival; nature of complaint; disposition; and time of departure.　　1 2 3 4 5 NA

IM.8.1.7　A coding and retrieval system for financial information;　　1 2 3 4 5 NA

IM.8.1.8　Measures (that is, indicators) of processes and outcomes for assessing performance;　　1 2 3 4 5 NA

IM.8.1.9　Summaries of actions taken as the result of organizationwide performance-improvement activities, including risk management, utilization review, infection control, and safety management;　　1 2 3 4 5 NA

IM.8.1.10　Practitioner-specific information as defined in the "Medical Staff" chapter in this *Manual*, for licensed independent practitioners;　　1 2 3 4 5 NA

IM.8.1.11　The ability to gather accurate, timely information for both operational decision making and planning purposes; and　　1 2 3 4 5 NA

IM.8.1.12 Data/information to support clinical research, as desired.　　1 2 3 4 5 NA

KNOWLEDGE-BASED INFORMATION

IM.9
The management of knowledge-based information (also referred to as the "literature") provides for the identification, organization, retrieval, analysis, delivery, and reporting of the clinical and managerial journal literature, reference information, and research data for use in designing, managing, and improving patient-specific and organizational processes.

1 2 3 4 5 NA

IM.9.1 The organization provides systems, resources, and services to meet its informational, educational, and, when appropriate, research-related needs for knowledge-based information/literature.

1 2 3 4 5 NA

IM.9.2 The extent of knowledge-based information services, resources, and systems (for example, professional library and health information services) is related not only to the organizational services provided but also to the needs of the medical and nursing staffs, administrators and managers, other health professional staff, other staff in the organization, students, patients and their families, and researchers.

1 2 3 4 5 NA

IM.9.2.1 The assessment of the organizational needs for knowledge-based information considers

IM.9.2.1.1 the need for accessibility and timeliness;

1 2 3 4 5 NA

IM.9.2.1.2 the need to link with the organization's internal information systems; and

1 2 3 4 5 NA

IM.9.2.1.3 the need to link with appropriate external databases and information networks.

1 2 3 4 5 NA

IM.9.3 Systems and structures (electronic or paper based) provide for the appropriate identification, organization, retrieval, analysis, delivery, and reporting of knowledge-based information/literature to meet identified needs.

1 2 3 4 5 NA

IM.9.4 Accessible knowledge-based information resources include clinical and management literature (in appropriate formats, including paper or electronic journals, books, technical reports, and audiovisuals); externally produced databases; practice guidelines; and information in multiple formats for patient education (brochures, articles, pamphlets, audiovisual materials, and models).

1 2 3 4 5 NA

IM.9.4.1 The organization's knowledge-based information resources are authoritative and up-to-date.

1 2 3 4 5 NA

IM.9.5 The pharmacy, medical, and nursing staff have access to poison-control information.

1 2 3 4 5 NA

IM.9.6 A hospital formulary or drug list is readily available to the staff who use it.

1 2 3 4 5 NA

COMPARATIVE DATA/INFORMATION

IM.10
The information management function provides for the definition, capture, analysis, transmission, and reporting and/or use of comparative performance data/information, the comparability of which is based on national and state guidelines for data set parity and connectivity.

1 2 3 4 5 NA

IM.10.1 The organization uses external reference databases for comparative purposes.

1 2 3 4 5 NA

IM.10.2 The organization contributes to external reference databases when required by law or regulation and/or when appropriate to the organization.

1 2 3 4 5 NA

IM.10.3 The information management function maintains the security and confidentiality of data/information when contributing to or using external databases.

1 2 3 4 5 NA

NOTES AND COMMENTS:

MANAGEMENT OF HUMAN RESOURCES

New functionally focused standards will appear in this chapter of the 1995 *Accreditation Manual for Hospitals*. For surveys conducted during 1994, see standards in various department/service-specific chapters that address the requirements for "qualified staff members" and their competence assessment and performance appraisal. There are additional standards found in the "Orientation, Training, and Education of Staff" chapter on pages 149–150 in Section 4 of this *Manual.*

MANAGEMENT OF THE ENVIRONMENT OF CARE

New functionally focused standards will appear in this chapter of the 1995 *Accreditation Manual for Hospitals.* For surveys conducted during 1994, see the standards in the "Plant, Technology, and Safety Management" chapter on pages 179–185 in Section 4 of this *Manual.*

SURVEILLANCE, PREVENTION, AND CONTROL OF INFECTION

New functionally focused standards will appear in this chapter of the 1995 *Accreditation Manual for Hospitals*. For surveys conducted during 1994, see the standards in the "Infection Control" chapter on pages 121–124 in Section 4 of this *Manual*.

IMPROVING ORGANIZATIONAL PERFORMANCE

PREAMBLE

This chapter represents a significant evolution in understanding quality improvement in health care organizations. It identifies the connection between organizational performance and judgments about quality. It shifts the primary focus from the performance of individuals to the performance of the organization's systems and processes,* while continuing to recognize the importance of the individual competence of medical staff members and other staff. Last, it provides flexibility to organizations in how they go about their design, measurement, assessment, and improvement activities. Thus, this chapter describes the essential activities common to a wide variety of improvement approaches.

Improving performance has been at the heart of the Joint Commission's Agenda for Change since its inception. This *Accreditation Manual for Hospitals* focuses on the important functions of an organization, and this chapter focuses on a framework for improving those functions. It should now be evident that

- performance is *what* is done and *how well* it is done to provide health care.
- the level of performance in health care is
  - the degree to which *what* is done is *efficacious* and *appropriate* for the individual patient, and
  - the degree to which *how* it is done makes it *available* in a *timely* manner to patients who need it, *effective*, *continuous* with other care and care providers, *safe*, *efficient*, and *caring and respectful* of the patient.

  These characteristics of *what* is done and *how* it is done are called the "dimensions of performance."
- the degree to which an organization does the right things and does them well is influenced strongly by the way it designs and carries out a number of important functions—many of which are described in this *Manual.*
- the effect of an organization's performance of these functions is reflected in patient outcomes and in the cost of its services.
- patients and others judge the quality of health care based on patient health outcomes (and sometimes on their perceptions of what was done and how it was done).
- patients and others may also judge the value of the health care by comparing their judgments of quality with the cost of the health care.

Table 1 provides definitions for the dimensions of performance.

This chapter, indeed this entire *Manual,* is being issued at a time when the health care field is redesigning its performance improvement mechanisms to incorporate concepts and methods developed by other fields. Such concepts and methods include total quality management (TQM), continuous quality improvement (CQI), and systems thinking. The health care field is also incorporating into its performance-improvement mechanisms concepts and methods developed by the health service research community, such as reference databases, clinical practice guidelines/parameters, and functional status and quality-of-life mea-

---

Throughout the remainder of this chapter, process means a single process and/or a system of integrated processes.

Table 1. Definitions of Dimensions of Performance

I. Doing the Right Thing

The **efficacy** of the procedure or treatment in relation to the patient's condition

> The degree to which the care/intervention for the patient has been shown to accomplish the desired/projected outcome(s)

The **appropriateness** of a specific test, procedure, or service to meet the patient's needs

> The degree to which the care/intervention provided is relevant to the patient's clinical needs, given the current state of knowledge

II. Doing the Right Thing Well

The **availability** of a needed test, procedure, treatment, or service to the patient who needs it

> The degree to which appropriate care/intervention is available to meet the patient's needs

The **timeliness** with which a needed test, procedure, treatment, or service is provided to the patient

> The degree to which the care/intervention is provided to the patient at the most beneficial or necessary time

The **effectiveness** with which tests, procedures, treatments, and services are provided

> The degree to which the care/intervention is provided in the correct manner, given the current state of knowledge, in order to achieve the desired/projected outcome for the patient

The **continuity** of the services provided to the patient with respect to other services, practitioners, and providers and over time

> The degree to which the care/intervention for the patient is coordinated among practitioners, among organizations, and over time

The **safety** of the patient (and others) to whom the services are provided

> The degree to which the risk of an intervention and the risk in the care environment are reduced for the patient and others, including the health care provider

The **efficiency** with which services are provided

> The relationship between the outcomes (results of care) and the resources used to deliver patient care

The **respect and caring** with which services are provided

> The degree to which the patient or a designee is involved in his/her own care decisions and to which those providing services do so with sensitivity and respect for the patient's needs, expectations, and individual differences

sures. These standards combine many of these useful concepts and methods with the best of current hospital quality assurance activities.

Health care organizations have begun to adopt some of the many approaches to CQI or TQM that have been successful in industry. Most of these approaches give health care organizations' leaders and staffs many powerful methods and tools that are useful additions to those already used in health care. Also, most of these approaches highlight the pivotal role of organizations' leaders and the importance of assessing patients' needs and expectations and listening to their feedback.

Although the standards in this chapter (as well as elsewhere in this *Manual*) do not require that an organization specifically adopt a CQI or TQM program, they selectively incorporate several core concepts of CQI/TQM. Examples of CQI/TQM concepts in the standards include the key role that leaders (individually and collectively) play in enabling the systematic assessment and improvement of performance; the fact that most problems/opportunities for improvement derive from process weaknesses, not individual incompetence; the need for careful coordination of work and collaboration among departments and professional groups; the importance of seeking judgments about quality from patients and others and using such judgments to identify areas for improvement; the importance of carefully setting priorities for improvement; and the need for both systematically improving the performance of important functions and maintaining the stability of these functions.

The standards do not require adoption of any particular management style, subscription to any specified "school" of CQI or TQM, use of specific quality improvement tools (for example, Hoshin planning), or adherence to any specific process for improvement (for example, the Joint Commission's "Ten-Step Model").

The standards in this chapter reflect the need for

- measurement on a continuing basis to understand and maintain the stability of systems and processes (for example, statistical quality control);
- measurement of outcomes to help determine priorities for improving systems and processes; and
- assessment of individual competence and performance (including by peer review), when appropriate.

This chapter has some important links to the other chapters in this *Manual* and, therefore, to other important functions of a health care organization. In particular,

- the chapter presents the performance-improvement framework for use in designing, measuring, assessing, and improving the patient care and organizational functions identified by all the chapters—including this chapter—in this *Manual*. The standards in this chapter point organizations to those functions and processes most directly related to good patient outcomes (PI.3.2 through PI.3.4.2.4) and help organizations set criteria for identifying and prioritizing their improvement efforts.
- the organization's leaders must provide the stimulus, vision, and resources to permit the activities described in this chapter to be successfully implemented. Standards in the "Leadership" chapter identify their role.
- managing the data required to design, measure, assess, and improve patient care and organizational functions requires an organizationwide approach. The standards in the "Management of Information" chapter describe this approach.
- to lead and participate effectively in improvement activities, leaders and staff must acquire the necessary new knowledge. The standards in the "Orientation, Training, and Education of Staff" chapter and the "Medical Staff" chapter set the expectations for education and address this continuing knowledge acquisition process.

Finally, the scoring guidelines for this chapter have been designed expressly to help organizations envision the long-term goals of the standards and make progress toward those goals. The activities described in this chapter will take varying periods of time to implement fully, require varying types and levels of change, and may require resource acquisition or reallocation. Thus, expectations for full compliance with many of these standards will be phased into the survey and scoring process at a pace consistent with the field's readiness.

PLAN

If an organization is to initiate and maintain improvement, leadership and planning are essential. This is especially critical for coalescing existing and new improvement activities into a systematic, organizationwide approach. These standards point to the importance of a planned approach to improvement and to the need to have all units (for example, departments/services) and all disciplines (for example, professional groups) collaborating to carry out that approach.

PI.1

The organization has a planned, systematic, organizationwide approach to designing, measuring, assessing, and improving its performance.　　1 2 3 4 5 NA

PI.1.1　　The activities described in this chapter are carried out collaboratively and include the appropriate department(s)/service(s) and discipline(s) involved.　　1 2 3 4 5 NA

DESIGN

New processes can be designed well if at least the four essential information sources listed in PI.2.1 through PI.2.1.4 are considered. Each of these sources can identify design specifications/expectations against which success can be measured.

PI.2

New processes are designed well.　　1 2 3 4 5 NA

PI.2.1　　The design is based on

　　PI.2.1.1　the organization's mission, vision, and plans;　　1 2 3 4 5 NA

　　PI.2.1.2　the needs and expectations of patients, staff, and others;　　1 2 3 4 5 NA

　　PI.2.1.3　up-to-date sources of information about designing processes (such as practice guidelines/parameters); and　　1 2 3 4 5 NA

　　PI.2.1.4　the performance of the processes and their outcomes in organizations (such as information from reference databases).　　1 2 3 4 5 NA

MEASURE

Measurement (that is, the collection of data) is the basis for determining the level of performance of existing processes and the outcomes resulting from these processes. To provide useful data, measurement must be systematic, relate to relevant dimensions of performance, and be of appropriate breadth and frequency.

　　The standards in this section address issues such as the purposes of measurement; the selection criteria for functions, processes, and outcomes to be measured; the important sources of data; and the continued role of measuring.

PI.3
The organization has a systematic process in place to collect data needed to
- *design and assess new processes;*
- *assess the dimensions of performance relevant to functions, processes, and outcomes;*
- *measure the level of performance and stability of important existing processes;*
- *identify areas for possible improvement of existing processes; and*
- *determine whether changes improved the processes.*   1 2 3 4 5 NA

PI.3.1   The collected data include measures of both processes and outcomes.   1 2 3 4 5 NA

PI.3.2   Data are collected both for the priority issues chosen for improvement and as part of continuing measurement.   1 2 3 4 5 NA

PI.3.3   The organization collects data about

PI.3.3.1 the needs and expectations of patients and others and the degree to which these needs and expectations have been met; and   1 2 3 4 5 NA

PI.3.3.1.1   These data relate to the relevant dimensions of performance.   1 2 3 4 5 NA

PI.3.3.2   its staff's views regarding current performance and opportunities for improvement.   1 2 3 4 5 NA

PI.3.4   The organization measures the performance of processes in all the patient care and organizational functions identified in this *Manual*.   1 2 3 4 5 NA

PI.3.4.1   Processes that are measured on a continuing basis include those that

PI.3.4.1.1   affect a large percentage of patients; and/or   1 2 3 4 5 NA

PI.3.4.1.2   place patients at serious risk if not performed well, or performed when not indicated, or not performed when indicated; and/or   1 2 3 4 5 NA

PI.3.4.1.3   have been or are likely to be problem prone.   1 2 3 4 5 NA

PI.3.4.2   Processes measured encompass at least

PI.3.4.2.1   those related to the use of surgical and other invasive procedures, including (1) selecting appropriate procedures, (2) preparing the patient for the procedure, (3) performing the procedure and monitoring the patient, and (4) providing postprocedure care;   1 2 3 4 5 NA

PI.3.4.2.2   those related to the use of medications, including (1) prescribing/ordering, (2) preparation and dispensing, (3) administration, and (4) monitoring the medications' effects on patients;   1 2 3 4 5 NA

PI.3.4.2.3   those related to the use of blood and blood components, including (1) ordering, (2) distributing, handling, and dispensing, (3) administration, and (4) monitoring the blood and blood components' effects on patients; and   1 2 3 4 5 NA

PI.3.4.2.4   those related to determining the appropriateness of admissions and continued hospitalization (that is, utilization review activities).   1 2 3 4 5 NA

PI.3.5   The organization collects data about

     PI.3.5.1   autopsy results,   1 2 3 4 5 NA

     PI.3.5.2   risk management activities, and   1 2 3 4 5 NA

     PI.3.5.3   quality control activities in at least the following areas:

         PI.3.5.3.1   Clinical laboratory services,   1 2 3 4 5 NA

         PI.3.5.3.2   Diagnostic radiology services,   1 2 3 4 5 NA

         PI.3.5.3.3   Dietetic services,   1 2 3 4 5 NA

         PI.3.5.3.4   Nuclear medicine services, and   1 2 3 4 5 NA

         PI.3.5.3.5   Radiation oncology services.   1 2 3 4 5 NA

ASSESS

Interpretation of the collected data provides information about the organization's level of performance along many dimensions and over time. Assessment questions include, for example,

- What is the degree of conformance to process and outcome objectives?
- How stable is a process, or how consistent is an outcome?
- Where might a stable process be improved?
- Was the undesirable variation in a process or outcome reduced or eliminated?

In addition to assessing performance over time, further information is gained from comparing data among organizations when relevant reference databases exist.

The standards in this section address the elements of a systematic assessment process and emphasize the importance of asking the right assessment questions and using the right processes and mechanisms to answer these questions.

PI.4

The organization has a systematic process to assess collected data in order to determine

- *whether design specifications for new processes were met;*
- *the level of performance and stability of important existing processes;*
- *priorities for possible improvement of existing processes;*
- *actions to improve the performance of processes; and*
- *whether changes in the processes resulted in improvement.*   1 2 3 4 5 NA

PI.4.1   The assessment process includes

     PI.4.1.1   using statistical quality control techniques, as appropriate.   1 2 3 4 5 NA

     PI.4.1.2   comparing data about

         PI.4.1.2.1   the organization's processes and outcomes over time;   1 2 3 4 5 NA

         PI.4.1.2.2   the organization's processes with information from up-to-date sources about the design and performance of processes (such as practice guidelines/parameters); and   1 2 3 4 5 NA

         PI.4.1.2.3   the organization's performance of processes and their outcomes to that of other organizations, including using reference databases.   1 2 3 4 5 NA

PI.4.1.3   intensive assessment when undesirable variation in performance may have occurred or is occurring. Such intensive assessments are initiated   1 2 3 4 5 NA

PI.4.1.3.1   by important single events and by absolute levels and/or patterns/trends that significantly and undesirably vary from those expected, based on appropriate statistical analysis;   1 2 3 4 5 NA

PI.4.1.3.2   when the organization's performance significantly and undesirably varies from that of other organizations;   1 2 3 4 5 NA

PI.4.1.3.3   when the organization's performance significantly and undesirably varies from recognized standards;   1 2 3 4 5 NA

PI.4.1.3.4   when the organization wishes to improve already good performance;   1 2 3 4 5 NA

PI.4.1.3.5   in response to all major discrepancies, or patterns of discrepancies, between preoperative and postoperative (including pathologic) diagnoses, including those identified during the pathologic review of specimens removed during surgical or invasive procedures;   1 2 3 4 5 NA

PI.4.1.3.6   by all confirmed transfusion reactions; and   1 2 3 4 5 NA

PI.4.1.3.7   by all significant adverse drug reactions.   1 2 3 4 5 NA

PI.4.2   When the findings of the assessment process are relevant to an individual's performance,   1 2 3 4 5 NA

PI.4.2.1   the medical staff is responsible for determining their use in peer review and/or the periodic evaluations of a licensed independent practitioner's competence, in accordance with the standards on renewing/revising clinical privileges delineated in the "Medical Staff" chapter; and/or   1 2 3 4 5 NA

PI.4.2.2   the department/service director is responsible for determining the competence of individuals who are not licensed independent practitioners, in accordance with LD.2.1.2.5.   1 2 3 4 5 NA

IMPROVE

The activities described in PI.3 and PI.4 identify a variety of opportunities for improvement. These include improving already well-performing processes, designing new processes, and/or reducing variation or eliminating undesirable variation in processes or outcomes.

The standards in this section address the elements of a systematic approach to improvement: planning the change, testing it, studying its effect, and implementing changes that are worthwhile improvements.

PI.5
The organization systematically improves its performance by improving existing processes.   1 2 3 4 5 NA

PI.5.1   Existing processes are improved when an organization decides to act on an opportunity for improvement or when the measurement of an existing process identifies that an undesirable change in performance may have occurred or is occurring.   1 2 3 4 5 NA

PI.5.1.1 These decisions consider

PI.5.1.1.1 opportunities to improve processes within the important functions described in this *Manual*; 1 2 3 4 5 NA

PI.5.1.1.2 the factors listed in PI.3.3 through PI.3.5.3.5; 1 2 3 4 5 NA

PI.5.1.1.3 the resources required to make the improvement; and 1 2 3 4 5 NA

PI.5.1.1.4 the organization's mission and priorities. 1 2 3 4 5 NA

PI.5.2 The design or improvement activities

PI.5.2.1 specifically consider the expected impact of the design or improvement on the relevant dimensions of performance; 1 2 3 4 5 NA

PI.5.2.2 set performance expectations for the design or improvement of the processes; 1 2 3 4 5 NA

PI.5.2.3 include adopting, adapting, or creating measures of the performance; and 1 2 3 4 5 NA

PI.5.2.4 involve those individuals, professions, and departments/services closest to the design or improvement activity. 1 2 3 4 5 NA

PI.5.3 When action is taken to improve a process,

PI.5.3.1 the action may be tested on a trial basis; 1 2 3 4 5 NA

PI.5.3.1.1 When the initial action is not effective, a new action is planned and tested. 1 2 3 4 5 NA

PI.5.3.2 the action's effect is assessed; and 1 2 3 4 5 NA

PI.5.3.3 successful actions are implemented. 1 2 3 4 5 NA

PI.5.4 Action is directed primarily at improving processes. 1 2 3 4 5 NA

PI.5.4.1 Pursuant to PI.4.2, when improvement activities lead to a determination that an individual has performance problems that he/she is unable or unwilling to improve, his/her clinical privileges or job assignment are modified (in accordance with the standards in this *Manual* on renewing/revising clinical privileges in the "Medical Staff" chapter and on determining competence in GB.1.14 in 1994 and in the "Human Resources" chapter in 1995), as indicated, or some other appropriate action is taken. 1 2 3 4 5 NA

NOTES AND COMMENTS:

SECTION 3
STRUCTURES WITH IMPORTANT FUNCTIONS

Governing Body

Managment and Administration

Medical Staff

Nursing

GOVERNING BODY

New and/or revised functionally focused standards will appear in this chapter of the 1995 *Accreditation Manual for Hospitals*. For surveys conducted during 1994, see the standards in the "Governing Body" chapter on pages 113–116 in Section 4 of this *Manual*.

MANAGEMENT AND ADMINISTRATION

New and/or revised functionally focused standards will appear in this chapter of the 1995 *Accreditation Manual for Hospitals*. For surveys conducted during 1994, see the standards in the "Management and Administrative Services" chapter on pages 125–129 in Section 4 of this *Manual*.

MEDICAL STAFF

Some standards from this chapter have been moved. Standards addressing medical staff monitoring functions have been moved to the chapter titled "Improving Organizational Performance" in Section 2. Nine standards addressing leadership functions have been moved to the chapter titled "Leadership" in Section 2. To help you identify these standards, we have printed them here in small italic type with their new standard references in bold type in parentheses. Organizations are expected to demonstrate compliance with these standards in their new context. For example, MS.4.6.1.1.3 in this chapter has been moved to the "Leadership" chapter as LD.2.1.1. This standard appears in small italic type, and the new standard reference, LD.2.1.1, appears in bold type at the end of the standard. Organizations are expected to comply with LD.2.1.1 and will be scored for compliance in the "Leadership" chapter. Standards scored in this chapter are in normal type and have accompanying scoring scales (1 2 3 4 5 NA). The exact location of these standards is also in the cross-reference in the "Medical Staff" chapter in Section 4 of this *Accreditation Manual for Hospitals* (*AMH*). Otherwise, this chapter is the same as it appeared in the 1993 *AMH*.

MS.1
There is a single organized medical staff that has overall responsibility for the quality of the professional services provided by individuals with clinical privileges,* as well as the responsibility of accounting therefor to the governing body.

1 2 3 4 5 NA

MS.1.1   The medical staff has the following characteristics:

MS.1.1.1   It includes fully licensed physicians and may include other licensed individuals permitted by law and by the hospital to provide patient care services independently† in the hospital.

1 2 3 4 5 NA

MS.1.1.2   All its members have delineated clinical privileges that allow them to provide patient care services independently† within the scope of their clinical privileges.

1 2 3 4 5 NA

MS.1.1.3   All members of the medical staff and all others with individual clinical privileges are subject to medical staff and departmental bylaws, rules and regulations, and policies and are subject to review as part of the hospital's quality assessment and improvement program.

1 2 3 4 5 NA

***clinical privileges**   *Permission to provide medical or other patient care services in the granting institution, within well-defined limits, based on the individual's professional license and his/her experience, competence, ability, and judgment.*

†**individual permitted to provide patient care services independently**   *Any individual who is permitted by law and who is also permitted by the hospital to provide patient care services without direction or supervision, within the scope of his/her license and in accordance with individually granted clinical privileges. Clinical privileges are based on criteria established by the hospital.*

MS.2

The organization establishes hospital-specific mechanisms for the appointment and reappointment of medical staff members and the granting and renewal/revision of clinical privileges.

1 2 3 4 5 NA

MS.2.1 Medical staff membership and delineated clinical privileges are granted by the governing body, based on medical staff recommendations, in accordance with the bylaws, rules and regulations, and policies of the medical staff and of the hospital.

1 2 3 4 5 NA

MS.2.1.1 Each applicant for medical staff membership is oriented to these bylaws, rules and regulations, and policies and agrees in writing that his/her activities as a member of the medical staff will be bound by them.

1 2 3 4 5 NA

MS.2.1.2 Individuals in administrative positions who desire medical staff membership or clinical privileges are subject to the same procedures as all other applicants for membership or privileges.

1 2 3 4 5 NA

MS.2.2 All individuals who are permitted by law and by the hospital to provide patient care services independently in the hospital have delineated clinical privileges, whether or not they are members of the medical staff.

1 2 3 4 5 NA

MS.2.2.1 There is a mechanism designed to assure that all individuals with clinical privileges provide services within the scope of privileges granted.

1 2 3 4 5 NA

MS.2.3 The mechanisms for appointment/reappointment and initial granting or renewal/revision of clinical privileges are

MS.2.3.1 approved and implemented by the medical staff and the governing body;

1 2 3 4 5 NA

MS.2.3.2 fully documented in the medical staff bylaws, rules and regulations, and policies; and

1 2 3 4 5 NA

MS.2.3.3 described to each applicant.

1 2 3 4 5 NA

MS.2.4 The mechanisms provide for, but need not be limited to, the following:

MS.2.4.1 Professional criteria specified in the medical staff bylaws and uniformly applied to all applicants for medical staff membership, medical staff members, or applicants for delineated clinical privileges constitute the basis for granting initial or continuing staff membership and for granting initial or renewed/revised clinical privileges.

1 2 3 4 5 NA

MS.2.4.1.1 Each clinical department develops its own criteria for recommending such privileges.

1 2 3 4 5 NA

MS.2.4.1.2 The criteria are designed to assure the medical staff and governing body that patients will receive quality care.

1 2 3 4 5 NA

MS.2.4.1.3 The criteria pertain to, at the least, evidence of current licensure, relevant training and/or experience, current competence, and health status.

1 2 3 4 5 NA

MS.2.4.1.3.1   For an applicant for initial appointment to the medical staff and for initial granting of clinical privileges, the hospital verifies information about the applicant's licensure, specific training, experience, and current competence provided by the applicant with information from the primary source(s) whenever feasible.   1 2 3 4 5 NA

MS.2.4.1.3.2   The hospital is also encouraged to consider additional information concerning the applicant from other sources, including the American Medical Association Physician Masterfile and the Federation of State Medical Boards Physician Disciplinary Data Bank. These databases and other sources may provide the hospital with information that is new or that may flag an inconsistency when compared with the individual's application.   1 2 3 4 5 NA

MS.2.4.1.3.3   Action on an individual's application for appointment or for initial clinical privileges is withheld until such information is made available and is verified.   1 2 3 4 5 NA

MS.2.5   The medical staff bylaws, rules and regulations, or policies define the information to be provided by each applicant for appointment or reappointment to the medical staff and initial or renewed/revised clinical privileges, including at least   1 2 3 4 5 NA

MS.2.5.1   previously successful or currently pending challenges to any licensure or registration (state or district, Drug Enforcement Administration) or the voluntary relinquishment of such licensure or registration;   1 2 3 4 5 NA

MS.2.5.2   voluntary or involuntary termination of medical staff membership or voluntary or involuntary limitation, reduction, or loss of clinical privileges at another hospital; and   1 2 3 4 5 NA

MS.2.5.3   involvement in a professional liability action under circumstances specified in the medical staff bylaws, rules and regulations, and policies.   1 2 3 4 5 NA

MS.2.5.3.1   At a minimum, final judgments or settlements involving the individual are reported.   1 2 3 4 5 NA

MS.2.6   Appointment or reappointment to the medical staff and the initial granting and renewal/revision of clinical privileges is also based on information regarding the applicant's competence.   1 2 3 4 5 NA

MS.2.7   In addition, reappraisal for reappointment to the medical staff or renewal/revision of clinical privileges is based on information concerning the individual's

MS.2.7.1   professional performance;   1 2 3 4 5 NA

MS.2.7.2   judgment; and   1 2 3 4 5 NA

MS.2.7.3   clinical and/or technical skills, as indicated in part by the results of quality assessment and improvement activities.   1 2 3 4 5 NA

MS.2.8   Peer recommendations are part of the basis for the development of recommendations for appointment or reappointment to the medical staff and the initial granting or renewal/revision of clinical privileges.   1 2 3 4 5 NA

MS.2.9   A structured procedure is used for the expeditious processing of complete applications for appointment, reappointment, and initial or renewed/revised clinical privileges.   1 2 3 4 5 NA

MS.2.9.1 Complete applications are acted on within a reasonable period of time, as specified in the bylaws of the medical staff and governing body.

1 2 3 4 5 NA

MS.2.9.1.1 The medical staff bylaws or rules and regulations define the characteristics of a complete application.

1 2 3 4 5 NA

MS.2.10 Sex, race, creed, and/or national origin are not used in making decisions regarding the granting or denying of medical staff membership or clinical privileges.

1 2 3 4 5 NA

MS.2.11 Each applicant

MS.2.11.1 consents to the inspection of records and documents pertinent to his/her licensure, specific training, experience, current competence, and health status and, if requested, appears for an interview;

1 2 3 4 5 NA

MS.2.11.1.1 The bylaws, rules and regulations, and policies of the medical staff and of the governing body indicate that the applicant for reappointment and/or renewal of clinical privileges is required to submit any reasonable evidence of current health status that may be requested by the executive committee of the medical staff.

1 2 3 4 5 NA

MS.2.11.2 pledges to provide for continuous care for his/her patients; and

1 2 3 4 5 NA

MS.2.11.3 acknowledges any provisions in the medical staff bylaws for release and immunity from civil liability.

1 2 3 4 5 NA

MS.2.12 The governing body is responsible for the final decision, based on medical staff recommendations, regarding an individual's appointment or reappointment to the medical staff and granting of initial or renewed/revised clinical privileges.

1 2 3 4 5 NA

MS.2.12.1 There are mechanisms, which include a fair hearing and appeal process, for addressing adverse decisions for the applicant regarding medical staff appointment or reappointment and granting of initial or renewed/revised clinical privileges.

1 2 3 4 5 NA

MS.2.13 Appointment or reappointment to the medical staff and the granting or renewal/revision of clinical privileges are made for a period of not more than two years.

1 2 3 4 5 NA

MS.2.13.1 A separate record is maintained for each individual requesting medical staff membership and/or clinical privileges.

1 2 3 4 5 NA

MS.2.14 Reappointment and/or the renewal or revision of clinical privileges is based on a reappraisal of the individual at the time of reappointment and/or the renewal or revision of clinical privileges.

1 2 3 4 5 NA

MS.2.14.1 Departmental and/or major clinical service recommendations are part of the basis for the development of recommendations for continued membership on the medical staff and/or for the delineation of individual clinical privileges.

1 2 3 4 5 NA

MS.2.15 Whatever mechanism for granting or renewal/revision of clinical privileges is used, there is evidence that the granting of clinical privileges is hospital specific and based on the individual's demonstrated current competence.

1 2 3 4 5 NA

MS.2.15.1   Privileges are related to

MS.2.15.1.1   an individual's documented experience in categories of treatment areas or procedures;

1 2 3 4 5 NA

MS.2.15.1.2   the results of treatment; and

1 2 3 4 5 NA

MS.2.15.1.3   the conclusions drawn from quality assessment and improvement activities when available.

1 2 3 4 5 NA

MS.2.15.2   Board certification is an excellent benchmark and is considered when delineating clinical privileges.

1 2 3 4 5 NA

MS.2.15.3   When privilege delineation is based primarily on experience, the individual's credentials record reflects the specific experience and successful results that form the basis for the granting of privileges.

1 2 3 4 5 NA

MS.2.15.4   When the medical staff uses a system involving classification or categorization of privileges, the scope of each level of privileges is well defined and the standards to be met by the applicant are stated clearly for each category.

1 2 3 4 5 NA

MS.2.15.4.1   This is a satisfactory method when an individual currently holding clinical privileges or applying for clinical privileges requests privileges in more than one department or clinical specialty area.

1 2 3 4 5 NA

MS.2.16   The delineation of an individual's clinical privileges includes the limitations, if any, on an individual's privileges to admit and treat patients or direct the course of treatment for the conditions for which the patients were admitted.

1 2 3 4 5 NA

MS.2.16.1   Individuals granted the privilege to admit patients to inpatient services are members of the medical staff.

1 2 3 4 5 NA

MS.2.16.2   Individuals are granted the privilege to admit patients to inpatient services in accordance with state law and criteria for standards of medical care established by the individual medical staff.

1 2 3 4 5 NA

MS.2.16.2.1   When nonphysician members of the medical staff are granted privileges to admit patients to inpatient services, provision is made for prompt* medical evaluation of these patients by a qualified physician.†

1 2 3 4 5 NA

MS.2.16.2.1.1   This requirement for prompt medical evaluation by a qualified physician does not apply to qualified oral-maxillofacial surgeons‡ who have been granted the clinical privileges to perform a history and physical examination.

1 2 3 4 5 NA

---

prompt   *Performed expeditiously.*

†**qualified physician**   *A doctor of medicine or doctor of osteopathy who, by virtue of education, training, and demonstrated competence, is granted clinical privileges by the hospital to perform a specific diagnostic or therapeutic procedure.*

‡**qualified oral-maxillofacial surgeon**   *An individual who has successfully completed a postgraduate program in oral-maxillofacial surgery accredited by a nationally recognized accrediting body approved by the U.S. Office of Education. As determined by the medical staff, the individual is also currently competent to perform a complete history and physical examination to determine the ability of each of his/her patients to undergo the oral-maxillofacial surgical procedure the oral-maxillofacial surgeon proposes to perform.*

MS.2.16.3   A patient admitted for inpatient care has a medical history taken and an appropriate physical examination performed by a physician who has such privileges.

1 2 3 4 5 NA

MS.2.16.3.1   Qualified oral-maxillofacial surgeons who admit patients without medical problems may perform the medical history and physical examination on those patients, if they have such privileges, and may assess the medical risks of the proposed surgical and/or other invasive procedure(s).

1 2 3 4 5 NA

MS.2.16.3.2   Other individuals who are permitted to provide patient care services independently may perform the medical history and physical examination, if granted such privileges and if the findings, conclusions, and assessment of risk are confirmed or endorsed by a qualified physician prior to major (as defined by the medical staff) diagnostic or therapeutic intervention or within 24 hours, whichever occurs first.

1 2 3 4 5 NA

MS.2.16.3.3   Dentists are responsible for the part of their patients' history and physical examination that relates to dentistry.

1 2 3 4 5 NA

MS.2.16.3.4   Podiatrists are responsible for the part of their patients' history and physical examination that relates to podiatry.

1 2 3 4 5 NA

MS.2.16.4   Individuals provide treatment and perform surgical and/or other invasive procedures within those areas of competence indicated by the scope of their delineated clinical privileges.

1 2 3 4 5 NA

MS.2.16.5   Each patient's general medical condition is the responsibility of a qualified physician member of the medical staff.

1 2 3 4 5 NA

MS.2.16.6   When physicians or other individuals eligible for delineated clinical privileges are engaged by the hospital to provide patient care services pursuant to a contract, their clinical privileges to admit and/or treat patients are defined through medical staff mechanisms.

1 2 3 4 5 NA

MS.2.16.7   When appropriate, temporary clinical privileges may be granted for a limited period of time by the chief executive officer on the recommendation of the chairperson of the applicable clinical department/service or the president of the medical staff.

1 2 3 4 5 NA

MS.3
The medical staff develops and adopts bylaws and rules and regulations to establish a framework for self-governance of medical staff activities and accountability to the governing body.

1 2 3 4 5 NA

MS.3.1   The bylaws and rules and regulations of the medical staff are adopted by the medical staff and approved by the governing body prior to becoming effective. Neither body may unilaterally amend the medical staff bylaws.

1 2 3 4 5 NA

MS.3.2   The bylaws and rules and regulations of the medical staff create a framework within which medical staff members can act with a reasonable degree of freedom and confidence.

1 2 3 4 5 NA

MS.3.3   Medical staff bylaws include provisions for at least the following:

MS.3.3.1   An executive committee of the medical staff that is empowered to act for the medical staff in the intervals between medical staff meetings;

1 2 3 4 5 NA

MS.3.3.1.1 The function, size, and composition of the committee and the method of selecting its members are defined, and the requirements for composition stated in MS.4.1 through MS.4.1.2.1.7 are met.

1 2 3 4 5 NA

MS.3.3.1.2 The chief executive officer of the hospital or his/her designee attends each executive committee meeting on an ex-officio basis, with or without vote.

1 2 3 4 5 NA

MS.3.3.2 Fair hearing and appellate review mechanisms, which may differ for medical staff members and other individuals holding clinical privileges and for applicants for such membership or privileges;

1 2 3 4 5 NA

MS.3.3.3 Mechanisms for corrective action, including indications and procedures for automatic and summary suspension of an individual's medical staff membership and/or clinical privileges;

1 2 3 4 5 NA

MS.3.3.4 A description of the organization of the medical staff, including categories of medical staff membership, when such exist, and appropriate officer positions, with the stipulation that each officer is a member of the medical staff;

1 2 3 4 5 NA

MS.3.3.4.1 The bylaws define

MS.3.3.4.1.1 the method of selecting officers;

1 2 3 4 5 NA

MS.3.3.4.1.2 the qualifications, responsibilities, and tenures of officers; and

1 2 3 4 5 NA

MS.3.3.4.1.3 the conditions and mechanisms for removing officers from their positions.

1 2 3 4 5 NA

MS.3.3.5 Requirements for frequency of meetings and for attendance;

1 2 3 4 5 NA

MS.3.3.6 A mechanism designed to assure effective communication among the medical staff, hospital administration, and governing body;

1 2 3 4 5 NA

MS.3.3.6.1 If there are multiple levels of governance, there is an established mechanism for the medical staff to communicate with all levels of governance involved in policy decisions affecting patient care services in the hospital.

1 2 3 4 5 NA

MS.3.3.7 A mechanism for adopting and amending the bylaws, rules and regulations, and policies of the medical staff; and

1 2 3 4 5 NA

MS.3.3.8 Medical staff representation and participation in any hospital deliberation affecting the discharge of medical staff responsibilities.

1 2 3 4 5 NA

MS.3.4 The medical staff bylaws, the rules and regulations of the medical staff, or departmental policies and procedures provide for, and require documentation in medical records of, the use of special treatment procedures.

1 2 3 4 5 NA

MS.3.4.1 Special treatment procedures that require special justification include at least the following:

MS.3.4.1.1 Restraint or seclusion;

1 2 3 4 5 NA

MS.3.4.1.1.1 A physician's verbal or written time-limited order is obtained for each use of restraint or seclusion.

1 2 3 4 5 NA

MS.3.4.1.1.1.1 The time within which the order must be obtained after each use of restraint or seclusion and the maximum time for use of either intervention are established in hospital policy.

1 2 3 4 5 NA

MS.3.4.1.1.2 There is documentation that the needs of the patient are attended to, as described in hospital policy.

1 2 3 4 5 NA

MS.3.4.1.1.2.1 Hospital policy addresses the periodic observation of the patient, including a maximum time between observations.

1 2 3 4 5 NA

MS.3.4.1.2 Electroconvulsive and other forms of convulsive therapy;

1 2 3 4 5 NA

MS.3.4.1.3 Psychosurgery or other surgical procedures to alter or intervene in an emotional, a mental, or a behavioral disorder; and

1 2 3 4 5 NA

MS.3.4.1.4 Behavior modification procedures that use aversive conditioning.

1 2 3 4 5 NA

MS.3.5 When a hospital that has a psychiatric/substance abuse department/ service determines that multidisciplinary treatment plans are appropriate, and when a hospital that provides only psychiatric/substance abuse services determines that multidisciplinary treatment plans are appropriate, there are written policies that address multidisciplinary treatment plans.

1 2 3 4 5 NA

MS.3.5.1 The written policies assure appropriate physician involvement in and approval of the multidisciplinary treatment plan.

1 2 3 4 5 NA

MS.3.6 When necessary, the medical staff bylaws and rules and regulations are revised to reflect the hospital's current practices with respect to medical staff organization and functions.

1 2 3 4 5 NA

MS.3.6.1 The bylaws, rules and regulations, and policies of the medical staff and the bylaws of the governing body do not conflict with each other.

1 2 3 4 5 NA

MS.3.6.2 If significant changes are made in the bylaws, rules and regulations, or policies of the medical staff, members of the medical staff and other individuals who have delineated clinical privileges are provided with revised texts of the written materials.

1 2 3 4 5 NA

MS.3.7 In hospitals participating in professional graduate education programs, the rules and regulations and policies specify the mechanisms by which house staff are supervised by members of the medical staff in carrying out their patient care responsibilities.

1 2 3 4 5 NA

MS.4
The medical staff is organized to accomplish its required functions.

1 2 3 4 5 NA

MS.4.1 There is an executive committee of the medical staff whose members are selected by the medical staff or appointed in accordance with governing body bylaws.

1 2 3 4 5 NA

MS.4.1.1 All members of the medical staff are eligible for membership on the executive committee.

1 2 3 4 5 NA

MS.4.1.1.1 A majority of executive committee members are fully licensed physician members of the medical staff actively practicing in the hospital.

1 2 3 4 5 NA

MS.4.1.2 The executive committee is responsible for making recommendations directly to the governing body for its approval.　　1 2 3 4 5 NA

MS.4.1.2.1　Such recommendations pertain to at least the following:

MS.4.1.2.1.1　The structure of the medical staff;　　1 2 3 4 5 NA

MS.4.1.2.1.2　The mechanism used to review credentials and to delineate individual clinical privileges;　　1 2 3 4 5 NA

MS.4.1.2.1.3　Recommendations of individuals for medical staff membership;　　1 2 3 4 5 NA

MS.4.1.2.1.4　Recommendations for delineated clinical privileges for each eligible individual;　　1 2 3 4 5 NA

MS.4.1.2.1.5　The organization of the quality assessment and improvement activities of the medical staff as well as the mechanism used to conduct, evaluate, and revise such activities;　　1 2 3 4 5 NA

MS.4.1.2.1.6　The mechanism by which membership on the medical staff may be terminated; and　　1 2 3 4 5 NA

MS.4.1.2.1.7　The mechanism for fair-hearing procedures.　　1 2 3 4 5 NA

MS.4.2　The executive committee receives and acts on reports and recommendations from medical staff committees, clinical departments/services, and assigned activity groups.　　1 2 3 4 5 NA

MS.4.3　Each clinical department or major clinical service (or medical staff, for a nondepartmentalized medical staff) has in place mechanisms designed to

MS.4.3.1　involve the members of the department/service (or medical staff) in monitoring and evaluation activities including the identification of the important aspects of the care provided by the department/service, the identification of indicators to be used to monitor the quality of care, and the evaluation of the care provided;　　1 2 3 4 5 NA

MS.4.3.2　periodically review care to draw conclusions, formulate recommendations, and initiate actions; and　　1 2 3 4 5 NA

MS.4.3.3　communicate to appropriate members of the department/service (or medical staff) the findings, conclusions, recommendations, and actions taken.　　1 2 3 4 5 NA

MS.4.4　When medical staff clinical departments/services exist, all individuals with delineated clinical privileges are assigned to and have clinical privileges in one clinical department/service and may be granted clinical privileges in other clinical departments/services.　　1 2 3 4 5 NA

MS.4.4.1　The exercise of clinical privileges within any department is subject to the rules and regulations of that department and to the authority of the department's chairperson.　　1 2 3 4 5 NA

MS.4.5　When medical staff clinical departments/services exist, the director of each medical staff department/service is certified by an appropriate specialty board, or affirmatively establishes, through the privilege delineation process, that he/she is possessed of comparable competence.　　1 2 3 4 5 NA

MS.4.6　There is effective leadership of each department/service of the medical staff.　　1 2 3 4 5 NA

MS.4.6.1   Responsibilities of the medical staff department/service director (or chairperson) are specified in the medical staff bylaws and rules and regulations.   1 2 3 4 5 NA

MS.4.6.1.1   The director of the department/service is responsible for the following:

MS.4.6.1.1.1   All clinically related activities of the department/service;   1 2 3 4 5 NA

MS.4.6.1.1.2   All administratively related activities of the department/service, unless otherwise provided for by the hospital;   1 2 3 4 5 NA

MS.4.6.1.1.3   The integration of the department/service into the primary functions of the organization; *(LD.2.1.1)*

MS.4.6.1.1.4   The coordination and integration of interdepartmental and intradepartmental services; *(LD.2.1.2)*

MS.4.6.1.1.5   The development and implementation of policies and procedures that guide and support the provision of services; *(LD.2.1.3)*

MS.4.6.1.1.6   The recommendations for a sufficient number of qualified and competent persons to provide care/service; *(LD.2.1.4)*

MS.4.6.1.1.7   Continuing surveillance of the professional performance of all individuals who have delineated clinical privileges in the department;   1 2 3 4 5 NA

MS.4.6.1.1.8   Recommending to the medical staff the criteria for clinical privileges in the department;   1 2 3 4 5 NA

MS.4.6.1.1.9   Recommending clinical privileges for each member of the department;   1 2 3 4 5 NA

MS.4.6.1.1.10   The determination of the qualifications and competence of department/service personnel who are not licensed independent practitioners and who provide patient care services; *(LD.2.1.5)*

MS.4.6.1.1.11   The continuous assessment and improvement of the quality of care and services provided; *(LD.2.1.6)*

MS.4.6.1.1.12   The maintenance of quality control programs, as appropriate; *(LD.2.1.7)*

MS.4.6.1.1.13   The orientation and continuing education of all persons in the department/service; and *(LD.2.1.8)*

MS.4.6.1.1.14   Recommendations for space and other resources needed by the department/service. *(LD.2.1.9)*

MS.4.7   The director of the department/service assesses and recommends to the relevant hospital authority off-site sources for needed patient care services not provided by the department/service or the organization.   1 2 3 4 5 NA

MS.4.8   When there are no medical staff clinical departments/services, all individuals with clinical privileges have their privileges recommended and the quality of their care reviewed through designated medical staff mechanisms.   1 2 3 4 5 NA

MS.4.8.1   These mechanisms are described in the medical staff and/or governing body bylaws and rules and regulations.   1 2 3 4 5 NA

MS.4.9 There is a mechanism designed to assure the same level of quality of patient care by all individuals with delineated clinical privileges, within medical staff departments, across departments/services, and between members and nonmembers of the medical staff who have delineated clinical privileges.   1 2 3 4 5 NA

MS.5
As part of the hospital's assessment and improvement activities, the medical staff strives to continuously improve the quality of patient care.   1 2 3 4 5 NA

MS.5.1 The medical staff provides effective mechanisms designed to monitor and evaluate the quality of patient care and the clinical performance of individuals with delineated clinical privileges, as a component of the organization's process for the assessment and improvement of performance.   1 2 3 4 5 NA

*MS.5.1.1   Monitoring and Evaluation of the Quality of Patient Care Provided by Individuals with Clinical Privileges. (**PI.4.2**)*

*MS.5.1.1.1   The quality of patient care in each department/service is evaluated in accordance with the requirements found in the "Quality Assessment and Improvement" chapter of this Manual. (**PI.4.2.1**)*

*MS.5.1.2   Review of Surgical and Other Invasive Procedures. (**PI.3.4.2**)*

*MS.5.1.2.1   Review of surgical and other invasive procedures is conducted on an ongoing basis by those departments/services performing such procedures or by a medical staff committee(s). (**PI.3.4.2.1**)*

*MS.5.1.2.2   The purpose of such review is to continuously improve the selection (appropriateness) and performance (effectiveness) of surgical and other invasive procedures. (**PI.3.4.2.1**)*

*MS.5.1.2.3   Categories of procedures are reviewed through the use of screening criteria to identify single cases or patterns of cases that require more intensive evaluation, and/or through intensive evaluation of a single case or group of cases. (**PI.3.4.2.1**)*

*MS.5.1.2.3.1   In identifying categories of procedures for review, priority is given to those categories that are performed in high volume, and/or are of high risk to patients, and/or are suspected or known to be problem prone. (**PI.3.4.1.1–PI.3.4.1.3**)*

*MS.5.1.2.3.2   Screening criteria are predetermined and may apply either to one specific category of procedure or to several categories of procedures. (**PI.3**)*

*MS.5.1.2.3.2.1   When the review of specimens removed during a surgical or other invasive procedure (described in PA.6.1.1 through PA.6.1.1.3) identifies a major discrepancy, or a pattern of discrepancies, between preoperative and postoperative (including pathologic) diagnoses, intensive evaluation is performed. (**PI.3**)*

*MS.5.1.2.3.3   When screening or intensively evaluating any category of procedure, an adequate number of cases is included. (**PI.3.4.2.1**)*

*MS.5.1.2.3.4   The combined use of screening mechanisms and intensive evaluation encompasses most categories of surgical and other invasive procedures performed in the hospital. (**PI.3.4.2.1**)*

MS.5.1.2.3.4.1 All categories of procedures that meet the criteria in MS.5.1.2.3.1 are encompassed by the review (except, for example, a high-volume procedure that is neither high risk nor problem prone). **(PI.3.4.2.1)**

*MS.5.1.2.4 Relevant results from the review of surgical and other invasive procedures are used primarily to study and improve processes involved in the selection and performance of these procedures. **(PI.3)***

*MS.5.1.2.5 When an individual has performance problems that he/ she is unable or unwilling to improve, modifications are made in clinical privileges or job assignments as indicated or some other appropriate action(s) is taken. **(PI.4.2, PI.4.2.1)***

*MS.5.1.2.6 Written reports of conclusions, recommendations, actions taken, and the results of actions taken are maintained and reported at specified intervals through channels established by the medical staff. **(PI.5.3–PI.5.3.3)***

The following standards were published in the 1992 and 1993 editions of the AMH to indicate the future direction of these activities. They were included for educational purposes only. These standards have now been recast to focus on performance and integrated into the 1994 AMH. See the references in bold type in parentheses at the end of the standards for their new locations in this Manual.

MSN.5.1.2 Evaluation and Improvement in the Use of Surgical and Other Invasive Procedures. **(PI.3.4.2, PI.3.4.2.1)**

Intent

Surgical and other invasive procedures are an essential component of the care provided to many patients served by hospitals. Such procedures are often useful for symptom relief and for the moderation or cure of disease. To achieve these benefits, four key sets of processes must be performed well: (1) selection of appropriate procedures, (2) preparation of patients, (3) performance of the procedures and monitoring the patients, and (4) postprocedure care. Performed properly, surgical and other invasive procedures usage evaluation can prompt effective analysis, evaluation, and continuous improvement in each of these important sets of processes.

The large number of procedures, the frequency of their use, the continuous introduction of new procedures, and the constant evolution of knowledge about existing procedures are all factors that influence the design of surgical and other invasive procedure usage evaluation activities. Specifically, such evaluation activities must

1. focus on the most important surgical and other invasive procedures used in a hospital. It is not feasible to assess all such procedures simultaneously.
2. provide a basis for selecting surgical and other invasive procedures that are to be evaluated and for identifying the key sets of processes that are to be the specific subject of evaluation.
3. seek to maximize the benefits of evaluation by using the results of review to improve the processes involved in selecting the procedure, preparing the patient for the procedure, performing the procedure, monitoring the patient during the procedure, and providing postprocedure care for surgical and other invasive procedures.

The principal goal of surgical and other invasive procedure usage evaluation is to improve the processes involved in selecting the appropriate procedures, preparing patients for the procedures, performing the procedures and monitoring the patients, and providing postprocedure care. Although it will often be impossible to encompass the surgical and other invasive procedures provided by all practitioners in these evaluation activities, there will be instances in which the results of evaluation activities identify individual professionals whose surgical and other invasive procedures practices need to be improved. In such cases, if the practitioner is unable or unwilling to improve his/her practices, the hospital acts to limit the ability of the practitioner to provide the surgical and other invasive procedures in the hospital (for example, through revision of clinical privileges).

*MSN.5.1.2.1   These quality assessment and improvement activities are designed to continuously improve the use of surgical and other invasive procedures. **(PI.4)***

*MSN.5.1.2.1.1   These quality assessment and improvement activities are a cooperative effort of the medical staff, nursing, management, and appropriate departments/services. **(PI.1.1)***

*MSN.5.1.2.1.2   These quality assessment and improvement activities are continuous. Although the specific subjects being reviewed may change, assessment and improvement activities are being performed continuously. **(PI.4.1.3.1)***

*MSN.5.1.2.1.2.1   Assessment and improvement activities are focused on the following sets of processes: (1) selecting appropriate surgical and other invasive procedures, (2) preparing the patient for the procedure, (3) performing the procedures and monitoring the patient, and (4) providing postprocedure care. **(PI.3.4.2.1)***

*MSN.5.1.2.1.3   These quality assessment and improvement activities are objective. Indicators related to the sets of processes identified in MSN.6.1.2.1.2.1 are used to monitor performance. **(PI.3.1)***

*MSN.5.1.2.1.4   The specific subjects of the assessment are carefully selected by either or both of the following methods: **(PI.3.4)***

*MSN.5.1.2.1.4.1   Specific surgical and other invasive procedures that are used in high volume, pose a substantial risk to patients, and/or are thought or known to be potentially problematic are first selected; and then one or more of the four sets of processes identified in MSN.5.1.2.1.2.1 are assessed and improved in order to improve the selected procedures. **(PI.3.4.1–PI.3.4.1.3)***

*MSN.5.1.2.1.4.2   The processes to be assessed are first selected from among those four sets of processes identified in MSN.5.1.2.1.2.1; and then specific surgical and other invasive procedures that are relevant to the assessment of the selected processes are identified. **(PI.3.4.1–PI.3.4.1.3, PI.2.4.1.3)***

*MSN.5.1.2.2   Reports of the findings of quality assessment and improvement activities prompt actions to improve the sets of processes identified in MSN.5.1.2.1.2.1. **(PI.5.3–PI.5.3.2)***

*MSN.5.1.2.2.1   The effect of the actions is assessed and, when those actions are determined to be successful, the improvements are maintained. **(PI.5.3.3)***

*MSN.5.1.2.2.2   When initial actions are not effective, new actions are designed and implemented and the effectiveness of those actions is assessed. **(PI.5.3.1.1)***

*MSN.5.1.2.2.3   When an individual has performance problems that he/she is unable or unwilling to improve, modifications are made in clinical privileges or job assignments as indicated or some other appropriate actions are taken. **(PI.4.2)***

*MS.5.1.3   Drug Usage Evaluation. **(PI.3.4.2.2)***

*MS.5.1.3.1   Drug usage evaluation is performed by the medical staff as a criteria-based, ongoing, planned, and systematic process designed to continuously improve the appropriate and effective use of drugs. **(PI.1.1)***

*MS.5.1.3.1.1   This process includes the routine collection and assessment of information in order to identify opportunities to improve the use of drugs and to resolve problems in their use. **(PI.3.4.2.2)***

*MS.5.1.3.2   There is ongoing monitoring and evaluation of selected drugs that are chosen for one or more of the following reasons: **(PI.3.4.1)***

*MS.5.1.3.2.1   The drug(s) is one of the most frequently prescribed drugs. **(PI.3.4.1.1)***

*MS.5.1.3.2.2   The drug(s) is known or suspected to present a significant risk to patients. **(PI.3.4.1.2)***

*MS.5.1.3.2.3   Use of the drug(s) is known or suspected to be problem prone. **(PI.3.4.1.3)***

*MS.5.1.3.2.4   The drug(s) is a critical component of the care provided for a specific diagnosis, condition, or procedure. **(PI.3.4.1.2)***

*MS.5.1.3.3   The process for monitoring and evaluating the use of drugs **(PI.3.4.2)***

*MS.5.1.3.3.1   is performed by the medical staff in cooperation with, as required, the pharmaceutical department/service, the nursing department/service, management and administrative staff, and other departments/services and individuals; **(PI.1.1)***

*MS.5.1.3.3.2   is based on the use of objective criteria that reflect current knowledge, clinical experience, and relevant literature; and **(PI.4.1.2.2)***

*MS.5.1.3.3.3   may include the use of screening mechanisms to identify, for more intensive evaluation, problems in or opportunities to improve the use of a specific drug or category of drugs. **(PI.3)***

*MS.5.1.3.4   Relevant results from the drug usage evaluation are used primarily to study and improve processes that affect the appropriate and effective use of drugs. **(PI.3)***

*MS.5.1.3.5   When an individual has performance problems that he/she is unable or unwilling to improve, modifications are made in clinical privileges or job assignments as indicated or some other appropriate action(s) is taken. **(PI.4.2, PI.4.2.1)***

*MS.5.1.3.6   Written reports of the conclusions, recommendations, actions taken, and results of actions taken are maintained and reported at specified intervals through channels established by the medical staff. **(PI.5.3–PI.5.3.3)***

The following standards were published in the 1992 and 1993 editions of the AMH to indicate the future direction of these activities. They were included for educational purposes only. These standards have now been recast to focus on performance and integrated into the 1994 AMH. See the references in bold type in parentheses at the end of the standards for their new locations in this Manual.

*MSN.5.1.3   Evaluation and Improvement in the Use of Medications. **(PI.3.4.2.2)***

Intent

Medications are an essential component of the care provided to nearly all patients served by hospitals. They are, singly and in combination, potent agents for symptom relief and, often, for the moderation or cure of disease. To achieve these benefits, four key sets of processes must be performed well: (1) prescription of appropriate medications, (2) preparation and dispensing, (3) administration, and (4) monitoring of medication effects so that appropriate modifications may be undertaken in a timely manner. Performed properly, medication usage evaluation can prompt effective analysis, evaluation, and continuous improvement in each of these important sets of processes.

The large number of medications, the frequency of their use, the continuous introduction of new medications, and the constant evolution of knowledge about existing medications are all factors that influence the design of medication usage evaluation activities. Specifically, such evaluation activities must

1. focus on the most important medications used in a hospital. It is not feasible to assess all medications simultaneously.
2. provide a basis for selecting medications that are to be evaluated and for identifying the key sets of processes that are to be the specific subject of evaluation.
3. seek to maximize the benefits of evaluation by using the results of review to improve the processes involved in prescribing, preparing and dispensing, administering, and monitoring the use of medications.

The principal goal of medication usage evaluation is to improve the processes involved in medication prescribing, preparation and dispensing, administration, and monitoring. Although it will often be impossible to encompass the medication use of all practitioners in these evaluation activities, there will be instances in which the results of evaluation activities identify individual professionals whose medication use practices need to be improved. In such cases, if the practitioner is unable or unwilling to improve his/her practices, the hospital acts to limit the ability of the practitioner to use medications for patient care in the hospital (for example, through revision of clinical privileges).

*MSN.5.1.3.1 These quality assessment and improvement activities are designed to continuously improve the use of medications. **(PI.3)***

*MSN.5.1.3.1.1 These quality assessment and improvement activities are a cooperative effort of the medical staff, nursing, management, pharmacy service, and other appropriate departments/ services. **(PI.1.1)***

*MSN.5.1.3.1.2 These quality assessment and improvement activities are continuous. Although the specific subjects being reviewed may change, assessment and improvement activities are being performed continuously. **(PI.3)***

*MSN.5.1.3.1.2.1 Assessment and improvement activities are focused on the following sets of processes: (1) prescription of appropriate medications, (2) preparation and dispensing of medications, (3) administration of medications, and (4) monitoring of the effects of medications on patients. **(PI.3.4.2.2)***

*MSN.5.1.3.1.3 These quality assessment and improvement activities are objective. Indicators related to the sets of processes identified in MSN.5.1.3.1.2.1 are used to monitor performance. **(PI.3.1)***

*MSN.5.1.3.1.4 The specific subjects of assessment are carefully selected by either or both of the following methods: **(PI.3.4)***

*MSN.5.1.3.1.4.1 Specific medications that are used in high volume, pose a substantial risk to the patients served by the hospital, and/or are thought or known to be potentially problematic are first selected; and then one or more of the four sets of processes identified in MSN.5.1.3.1.2.1 are assessed and improved in order to improve the selected procedures. **(PI.3.4.1–PI.3.4.1.3)***

*MSN.5.1.3.1.4.2 The process to be assessed is first selected from among four sets of processes identified in MSN.5.1.3.1.2.1; and then medications that are relevant to the assessment of the selected processes are identified. **(PI.3.4.1–PI.3.4.1.3)***

*MSN.5.1.3.2 Reports of the findings of quality assessment and improvement activities prompt actions to improve the sets of processes identified in MSN.5.1.3.1.2.1. **(PI.5.3–PI.5.3.2)***

*MSN.5.1.3.2.1 The effect of the actions is assessed and, when those actions are determined to be successful, the improvements are maintained. **(PI.5.3.3)***

*MSN.5.1.3.2.2 When initial actions are not effective, new actions are designed and implemented and the effectiveness of those actions is assessed. **(PI.5.3.1.1)***

*MSN.5.1.3.2.3 When an individual has performance problems that he/she is unable or unwilling to improve, modifications are made in clinical privileges or job assignments, or some other appropriate actions are taken. **(PI.4.2)***

*MS.5.1.4   The Medical Record Review Function. **(IM.3)***

*MS.5.1.4.1   The quality of medical records is reviewed at least quarterly for clinical pertinence or quality of documentation and timely completion. **(IM.3.3.1)***

*MS.5.1.4.2   The medical record review function **(IM.3)***

*MS.5.1.4.2.1   is performed by, at a minimum, the medical staff in cooperation with the nursing department/service, the medical record department/service, management and administrative services, and representatives of other departments/services as appropriate; **(IM.3.3.1.1)***

*MS.5.1.4.2.2   assures that each medical record, or a representative sample of records, reflects the diagnosis, results of diagnostic tests, therapy rendered, condition and in-hospital progress of the patient, and condition of the patient at discharge; and **(IM.3.3.1.2)***

*MS.5.1.4.2.3   includes a review of summary information regarding the timely completion of all medical records. **(IM.3.2)***

*MS.5.1.4.3   Written reports of conclusions, recommendations, actions taken, and the results of actions taken are maintained and reported at specified intervals through channels established by the medical staff. **(PI.5.3–PI.5.3.2)***

*MS.5.1.5   Blood Usage Review. **(PI.3.4.2.3)***

*MS.5.1.5.1   The medical staff performs blood usage review on an ongoing basis to continuously improve the appropriateness and effectiveness with which blood and blood components are used. **(PI.1.1)***

*MS.5.1.5.2   Blood usage review includes **(PI.3.4.1)***

*MS.5.1.5.2.1   the review of all categories of blood and blood components in the hospital; **(PI.3.4.2.3)***

*MS.5.1.5.2.1.1   The use of each category of blood and blood components is reviewed through the use of screening criteria to identify single cases or patterns of cases that require more intensive evaluation; and/or through intensive evaluation of a single case or of a group of cases. **(PI.3)***

*MS.5.1.5.2.1.1.1   Screening criteria are predetermined and may apply to either one specific category of blood or blood component or to several categories of blood or blood components. **(PI.3)***

*MS.5.1.5.2.1.1.2   When screening or intensively evaluating any category of blood or blood component, an adequate number of cases is included. **(PI.3)***

*MS.5.1.5.2.2   the intensive evaluation of all confirmed transfusion reactions; **(PI.4.1.3.6)***

*MS.5.1.5.2.3   the development or approval of policies and procedures regarding the distribution, handling, use, and administration of blood and blood components; **(PI.3.4.2.3)***

*MS.5.1.5.2.4   the review of the adequacy of transfusion services to meet the needs of patients; and **(PI.3.4.2.3)***

*MS.5.1.5.2.5   the review of ordering practices for blood and blood components. **(PI.3.4.2.3)***

MS.5.1.5.3 Relevant results from the blood usage review are used primarily to study and improve processes that affect the appropriate and effective use of blood and blood components. (PI.3)

MS.5.1.5.4 When an individual has performance problems that he/she is unable or unwilling to improve, modifications are made in clinical privileges or job assignments as indicated or some other appropriate action(s) is taken. (PI.4.2)

MS.5.1.5.5 Written reports of conclusions, recommendations, actions taken, and the results of actions taken are maintained and reported at specified intervals through channels established by the medical staff. (PI.5.3–PI.5.3.3)

The following standards were published in the 1992 and 1993 editions of the AMH to indicate the future direction of these activities. They were included for educational purposes only. These standards have now been recast to focus on performance and integrated into the 1994 AMH. See the references in bold type in parentheses at the end of the standards for their new locations in this Manual.

MSN.5.1.5 Evaluation and Improvement in the Use of Blood and Blood Components. (PI.3.4.2.3)

Intent

Blood and blood components are an essential part of the care provided to many patients served by hospitals. They are often potent agents for the moderation or cure of disease. To achieve these benefits, four key sets of processes must be performed well: (1) ordering of appropriate blood or blood components, (2) distribution, handling, and dispensing of blood and blood components, (3) administration of blood and blood components, and (4) monitoring of the effects of blood and blood components on patients so that appropriate modifications may be undertaken in a timely manner. Performed properly, blood and blood component usage evaluation can prompt effective analysis, evaluation, and continuous improvement in each of these important sets of processes. The types of blood and blood components, the frequency of their use, the introduction of new components, and the evolution of knowledge about existing blood and blood component usage are all factors that influence the design of blood and blood component usage evaluation activities. Specifically, such evaluation activities must

1. focus on the most important blood and blood components used in a hospital. It is not feasible to assess all blood and blood components simultaneously.
2. provide a basis for selecting blood and blood components that are to be evaluated and for identifying the key sets of processes that are to be the specific subject of evaluation.
3. seek to maximize the benefits of evaluation by using the results of review to improve the processes involved in ordering; distributing, handling, and dispensing; administration; and monitoring the use of blood and blood components.

The principal goal of blood and blood component usage evaluation is to improve the processes involved in blood and blood component ordering; distribution, handling, and dispensing; administration; and monitoring. Although it will often be impossible to encompass the blood and blood component usage of all practitioners in these evaluation activities, there will be instances in which the results of evaluation activities identify individual professionals whose blood and blood component usage practices need to be improved. In such cases, if the practitioner is unable or unwilling to improve his/her practices, the hospital acts to limit the ability of the practitioner to use blood or blood components for patient care in the hospital (for example, through revision of clinical privileges).

MSN.5.1.5.1 These quality assessment and improvement activities are designed to continuously improve the use of blood and blood components. (PI.3)

MSN.5.1.5.1.1 These quality assessment and improvement activities are a cooperative effort of the medical staff, nursing, management, clinical laboratory service, and other appropriate departments/services. (PI.1.1)

MSN.5.1.5.1.2 These quality assessment and improvement activities are continuous. Although the specific subjects being reviewed may change, assessment and improvement activities are being performed continuously. (PI.3)

MSN.5.1.5.1.2.1 Assessment and improvement activities are focused on the following sets of processes: (1) ordering of appropriate blood and blood components, (2) distribution, handling, and dispensing of blood and blood components, (3) administration of blood and blood components, and (4) monitoring of the effects of blood and blood components on patients. (PI.3.4.2.3)

MSN.5.1.5.1.3 These quality assessment and improvement activities are objective. Indicators related to sets of processes identified in MSN.5.1.5.1.2.1 are used to monitor performance. (PI.3.1)

MSN.5.1.5.1.4 The specific subjects of assessment are carefully selected by either or both of the following methods: (PI.3.4)

MSN.5.1.5.1.4.1 Specific blood or blood components that are used in high volume, pose a substantial risk to the patients served by the hospital, and/or are thought or known to be potentially problematic are first selected; and then one or more of the four sets of processes identified in MS.6.1.5.1.2.1 are assessed and improved in order to improve the selected procedure. (PI.3.4.1–PI.3.4.1.3)

MSN.5.1.5.1.4.2 The processes to be assessed are first selected from among those processes identified in MSN.5.1.5.1.2.1; and then specific blood or blood components that are relevant to the assessment of the selected process are identified. (PI.3.4.1–PI.3.4.1.3)

MSN.5.1.5.1.5 All confirmed transfusion reactions are evaluated. (PI.4.1.3.6)

MSN.5.1.5.2 Reports of the findings of the quality assessment and improvement prompt actions to improve the sets of processes identified in MSN.5.1.5.1.2.1. (PI.5.3–PI.5.3.2)

MSN.5.1.5.2.1 The effect of the actions is assessed and, when those actions are determined to be successful, the improvements are maintained. (PI.5.3.3)

MSN.5.1.5.2.2 When initial actions are not effective, new actions are designed and implemented and the effectiveness of those actions is assessed. (PI.5.3.1.1)

MSN.5.1.5.2.3 When an individual has performance problems that he/she is unable or unwilling to improve, modifications are made in clinical privileges or job assignments, or some other appropriate actions are taken. (PI.4.2)

MSN.5.1.5.3 The hospital has policies and procedures relating to the ordering; distributing, handling, and dispensing; administering; and monitoring of blood and blood components. (TX.13)

MS.5.1.6 The Pharmacy and Therapeutics Function. (PI.3.4.2.2)

MS.5.1.6.1 The pharmacy and therapeutics function is performed by the medical staff, in cooperation with the pharmaceutical department/service, the nursing department/service, management and administrative services, and, as required, other departments/services and individuals. (PI.1.1)

MS.5.1.6.2 The pharmacy and therapeutics monitoring function includes at least (PI.3.4.2.2)

*MS.5.1.6.2.1   the development or approval of policies and procedures relating to the selection, distribution, handling, use, and administration of drugs and diagnostic testing materials; **(TX.13)***

*MS.5.1.6.2.2   the development and maintenance of a drug formulary or drug list; **(TX.1)***

*MS.5.1.6.2.3   the evaluation and, when no other such mechanism exists, the approval of protocols concerned with the use of investigational or experimental drugs; and **(scoring guideline for TX.13)***

*MS.5.1.6.2.4   the definition and review of all significant untoward drug reactions. **(PI.4.1.3.7)***

*MS.5.1.7   Risk Management Activities. **(PI.3.4.1.2)***

*MS.5.1.7.1   The medical staff actively participates, as appropriate, in risk management activities related to the clinical aspects of patient care and safety, which include **(PI.3.4.1.2)***

*MS.5.1.7.1.1   the identification of general areas of potential risk in the clinical aspects of patient care and safety; **(PI.3.4.1.2)***

*MS.5.1.7.1.2   the development of criteria for identifying specific cases with potential risk in the clinical aspects of patient care and safety, and evaluation of these cases; **(PI.3.4.1.2)***

*MS.5.1.7.1.3   the correction of problems in the clinical aspects of patient care and safety identified by risk management activities; and **(PI.3.4.1.2)***

*MS.5.1.7.1.4   the design of programs to reduce risk in the clinical aspects of patient care and safety. **(PI.5.1)***

*MS.5.1.8   Other Review Functions. **(PI.1)***

*MS.5.1.8.1   The medical staff participates in other review functions, including infection control, internal and external disaster plans, hospital safety, and utilization review. **(PI.3.4.2.4)***

MS.5.1.8.2   Except in hospitals with psychiatric/substance abuse departments/services or in hospitals providing only psychiatric/substance abuse services, the role of the medical staff is clearly defined in the written plan for the care and/or appropriate referral of patients who are emotionally ill, who become emotionally ill while in the hospital, or who suffer the results of alcoholism or drug abuse.

1 2 3 4 5 NA

MS.5.1.8.3   The medical staff, with other appropriate hospital staff, develops and uses criteria that identify deaths in which an autopsy should be performed.

1 2 3 4 5 NA

MS.5.1.8.3.1   The medical staff attempts to secure autopsies in all deaths that meet the criteria adopted by the medical staff.

1 2 3 4 5 NA

MS.5.1.8.3.2   The mechanism for documenting permission to perform an autopsy is defined.

1 2 3 4 5 NA

MS.5.1.8.3.3   There is a system for notifying the medical staff, and specifically the attending practitioner, when an autopsy is being performed.

1 2 3 4 5 NA

*MS.5.1.8.3.4   Findings from autopsies are used as a source of clinical information in quality assessment and improvement activities. **(PI.3.5.1)***

MS.5.2   The effectiveness of all functions—monitoring and evaluation of the quality of patient care provided by individuals with clinical privileges, surgical case review, drug usage evaluation, medical record review function, blood usage review, pharmacy and therapeutics function, and other review functions—is evaluated as part of the annual reappraisal of the hospital's program to assess and improve quality.   1 2 3 4 5 NA

MS.6
All individuals with delineated clinical privileges participate in continuing education.

1 2 3 4 5 NA

MS.6.1   Hospital-sponsored educational activities are offered.   1 2 3 4 5 NA

MS.6.1.1   These activities relate, at least in part, to

MS.6.1.1.1   the type and nature of care offered by the hospital; and   1 2 3 4 5 NA

MS.6.1.1.2   the findings of quality assessment and improvement activities.   1 2 3 4 5 NA

MS.6.2   Each individual's participation in continuing education is   1 2 3 4 5 NA

MS.6.2.1   documented; and   1 2 3 4 5 NA

MS.6.2.2   considered at the time of reappointment to the medical staff and/or renewal or revision of individual clinical privileges.   1 2 3 4 5 NA

NOTES AND COMMENTS:

NURSING

New and/or revised functionally focused standards will appear in this chapter of the 1995 *Accreditation Manual for Hospitals*. For surveys conducted during 1994, see the standards in the "Nursing Care" chapter on pages 141–147 in Section 4 of this *Manual*.

SECTION 4
OTHER DEPARTMENT/SERVICE-SPECIFIC REQUIREMENTS

Alcoholism and Other Drug-Dependence Services

Diagnostic Radiology Services

Dietetic Services

Emergency Services

Governing Body

Hospital-Sponsored Ambulatory Care Services

Infection Control

Management and Administrative Services

Medical Record Services

Medical Staff

Nuclear Medicine Services

Nursing Care

Orientation, Training, and Education of Staff (does not apply to medical staff members)

Pathology and Clinical Laboratory Services

Patient and Family Education

Patient Rights

Pharmaceutical Services

Physical Rehabilitation Services

Plant, Technology, and Safety Management

Professional Library and Health Information Services

Quality Assessment and Improvement

Radiation Oncology Services

Respiratory Care Services

Responsibilities of Department/Service Directors

Social Work Services

Special Care Units

Surgical and Anesthesia Services

Utilization Review

ALCOHOLISM AND OTHER DRUG-DEPENDENCE SERVICES

Some of the standards in this chapter of the 1993 *Accreditation Manual for Hospitals* have been recast to focus on improving individual and organizational performance and have been moved to Sections 1 and 2 of this *Manual.* To help you identify these standards, we have printed them here in small italic type with their new standard references in bold type in parentheses. Organizations are expected to demonstrate compliance with these standards in their new context. For example, AL.1 in this chapter has been recast and moved to the "Leadership" chapter, as LD.1.3. This standard appears in small italic type, and the new standard reference, LD.1.3, appears in bold type in parentheses at the end of the standard. Organizations are expected to comply with LD.1.3 and will be scored for compliance in the "Leadership" chapter. Standards scored in this chapter are in normal type and have accompanying scoring scales (1 2 3 4 5 NA).

This chapter applies to all hospital-sponsored alcoholism and drug-dependence programs or tracks that have social rehabilitation as a basic element of their missions. Such programs may be surveyed by an alcohol/drug program specialist, who is added to the Hospital Accreditation Services survey team for this purpose.

AL.1   An organized program for alcoholism and other drug dependence provides individualized assessment and treatment in response to identified patient needs. **(LD.1.3)**

AL.1.1   The services are designed to identify and respond to the biopsychosocial antecedents, influences, and effects associated with the patient's dependence. **(LD.1.3)**

AL.1.2   These needed services are provided either directly or through referral, consultation, or contractual arrangements and/or agreements. **(LD.1.3.4.2)**

AL.1.3   Special treatment needs of patients by reason of age, gender, sexual orientation, or ethnic origin are evaluated.

1 2 3 4 5 NA

AL.1.3.1   Efforts are made to meet these treatment needs, either directly or through referral, consultation, or contractual arrangements and/or agreements, and those efforts are documented.

1 2 3 4 5 NA

AL.1.4   Services for children and adolescents (as well as for adults, if applicable) address the special needs of these age groups, including **(LD.1.3.4)**

AL.1.4.1   education and learning problems; **(LD.1.3.4)**

AL.1.4.2   family involvement; **(LD.1.3.4)**

AL.1.4.3   biopsychosocial development; **(LD.1.3.4)**

AL.1.4.4   effects of a minor's legal status; **(LD.1.3.4)**

AL.1.4.5   nutrition; and   1 2 3 4 5 NA

*AL.1.4.6   recreational and leisure activities. (**LD.1.3.4**)*

AL.1.5   Those responsible for developing the summary and treatment approach demonstrate competence in their

AL.1.5.1   ability to obtain information about, and interpret information in terms of, the dependence;   1 2 3 4 5 NA

AL.1.5.2   knowledge of the natural history of dependence;   1 2 3 4 5 NA

AL.1.5.3   understanding of the biological and sociocultural dimensions influencing dependence;   1 2 3 4 5 NA

AL.1.5.4   general understanding of the range of treatment needed by dependent patients; and   1 2 3 4 5 NA

AL.1.5.5   knowledge of available treatment resources and their appropriate utilization.   1 2 3 4 5 NA

*AL.2   A comprehensive assessment of the biopsychosocial needs and spiritual orientation of the patient is conducted. (**PE.5.4**)*

*AL.2.1   The assessment includes a history of the use of alcohol and other drugs, including age of onset, duration, patterns, and consequences of use; use of alcohol and other drugs by family members; and types of, and responses to, previous treatment. (**PE.5.1, PE.5.3, PE.5.5**)*

*AL.2.2   The physical assessment includes, but need not be limited to, the following: (**PE.1.7.1**)*

*AL.2.2.1   For inpatient and residential programs, a comprehensive medical history and physical examination; (**PE.1.7.1**)*

*AL.2.2.2   For outpatient and partial-hospitalization programs, an appropriate medical history and an appropriate physical examination; (**PE.1.7.1**)*

*AL.2.2.2.1   The history of physical problems associated with dependence is included. (**PE.5.2**)*

*AL.2.2.3   Appropriate laboratory screening tests, based on findings of the history and physical examination; (**PE.1.5**)*

*AL.2.2.3.1   These tests are interpreted in relationship to the dependence process. (**scoring guideline for PE.1.5**)*

*AL.2.2.4   Tests for communicable diseases, when indicated; and (**scoring guideline for PE.1.5**)*

*AL.2.2.5   Any history of physical abuse. (**PE.5.6**)*

*AL.2.3   The psychiatric/psychological assessment includes, but need not be limited to, the following: (**PE.1.1**)*

*AL.2.3.1   A systematic mental status examination with special emphasis on immediate recall and recent and remote memory; (**scoring guideline for PE.1.1**)*

*AL.2.3.2   A determination of current and past psychiatric/psychological abnormality; (**scoring guideline for PE.1.1**)*

*AL.2.3.3   A determination of the degree of danger to self or others; and (**scoring guideline for PE.1.1**)*

AL.2.3.4   A neuropsychological assessment, if indicated by the psychiatric/psychological assessment. (scoring guideline for PE.1.1)

AL.2.3.4.1   Special emphasis is placed on cognitive functioning, including any learning impairment that might influence diagnosis and treatment. (scoring guideline for PE.1.1)

AL.2.4   The social assessment includes, but need not be limited to, the following: (PE.1.1)

AL.2.4.1   The family's history of alcoholism and other drug dependence; (scoring guideline for PE.1.1)

AL.2.4.2   The patient's educational level, vocational status, and job performance history; (scoring guideline for PE.1.1)

AL.2.4.3   The patient's social support networks, including family and peer relationships; (scoring guideline for PE.1.1)

AL.2.4.4   The patient's sexual history, including sexual abuse (either as the abuser or the abused) and orientation; (PE.5.7)

AL.2.4.5   The patient's perception of his/her strengths and weaknesses; (scoring guideline for PE.1.1)

AL.2.4.6   The patient's leisure, recreational, and vocational interests and hobbies; (scoring guideline for PE.1.1)

AL.2.4.7   The patient's daily activity patterns, including those that support and those that are alternatives to dependence; (scoring guideline for PE.1.1)

AL.2.4.8   The social and cultural influences on the patient and the patient's identity, including values, beliefs, and spiritual orientation; (scoring guideline for PE.1.1)

AL.2.4.9   The patient's own perception of his/her dependence; (scoring guideline for PE.1.1)

AL.2.4.10   The patient's ability to participate with peers in programs and social activities; (scoring guideline for PE.1.1)

AL.2.4.11   Interviews with family members and significant others, as available, with the patient's written or verbal permission; and (scoring guideline for PE.1.1)

AL.2.4.12   Legal problems, if applicable. (scoring guideline for PE.1.1)

AL.2.5   A summary integrates the information from the history of dependence and the biopsychosocial assessments.

1 2 3 4 5 NA

AL.3
For each patient, there is a written, comprehensive, and individualized description of the treatment to be undertaken.

1 2 3 4 5 NA

AL.3.1   The treatment plan specifies the regular times at which the plan will be reassessed.

1 2 3 4 5 NA

AL.3.2   The treatment plan is based on the problems and needs identified in the assessments.

1 2 3 4 5 NA

AL.3.2.1   There is documented justification when identified clinical problems and needs are not addressed.

1 2 3 4 5 NA

AL.3.2.2   The patient's perception of his/her needs and, when appropriate and available, the family's perception of the patient's needs are
documented.   1 2 3 4 5 NA

AL.3.2.3   The patient's participation in the development of his/her
treatment plan is sought and documented.   1 2 3 4 5 NA

> AL.3.3   Each patient is reassessed to determine current clinical prob-
> lems, needs, and responses to treatment. **(PE.2, PE.2.3)**
>
> AL.3.3.1   The reassessment is conducted **(PE.2)**
>
> AL.3.3.1.1   when major clinical changes occur; and **(PE.2.1, PE.2.2)**
>
> AL.3.3.1.2   regularly at specified times that are related to the patient's
> course of treatment. **(PE.2.4)**
>
> AL.3.3.2   Such reassessment includes major family, social, or life
> events (for example, death in the family, divorce, financial difficulty)
> that may complicate treatment. **(PE.2.5)**
>
> AL.3.3.3   Changes in treatment are documented. **(IM.7.2.8)**

AL.3.4   Each individual who provides treatment services has been determined
to be competent to provide such services by reason of education, training, experience, and findings of quality assessment and improvement
activities.   1 2 3 4 5 NA

> AL.4   The quality of services provided by the program(s) is monitored
> and evaluated in accordance with standards in the "Quality Assess-
> ment and Improvement" chapter of this Manual to determine the de-
> gree to which patients **(PI.3.4–PI.3.4.1.3)**
>
> AL.4.1   are receiving accurate assessments; **(PI.3.4–PI.3.4.1.3)**
>
> AL.4.2   are receiving effective treatment; and **(PI.3.4–PI.3.4.1.3)**
>
> AL.4.3   have treatment complications, including their implications for
> continued treatment. **(PI.3.4–PI.3.4.1.3)**
>
> AL.5   At defined intervals, the physical and social environment of the
> program is assessed and modified, as needed, to support the therapeu-
> tic goals of the program. **(PI.3)**

AL.6
For each patient, before discharge, a plan for discharge is designed to provide appropriate continuity of care.   1 2 3 4 5 NA

AL.6.1   The plan for continuing treatment describes and facilitates the transfer
of the patient and of the responsibility for his/her continuing care to
another phase or modality of the program; to other programs, agencies,
or individuals; and/or to the patient and his/her personal support
system.   1 2 3 4 5 NA

AL.6.1.1   The plan is in accordance with the patient's needs as
reassessed at the time of transfer.   1 2 3 4 5 NA

AL.6.1.2   The plan is developed in collaboration with the patient and,
as appropriate and available and with the patient's written or verbal
permission, with family members.   1 2 3 4 5 NA

AL.6.1.3 The plan is implemented in a manner acceptable to the patient and in accordance with the patient's need for confidentiality.　　1 2 3 4 5 NA

AL.6.1.4 Implementation of the plan includes timely and direct communication with, and transfer of information to, the other programs, agencies, or individuals that will be providing continuing care.　　1 2 3 4 5 NA

AL.6.2　*The efficacy of the discharge planning process is evaluated, using an adequate sample of discharges, by obtaining, evaluating, and documenting information from accepting programs, agencies, or individuals.* **(PI.3.5–PI.3.5.3)**

AL.6.2.1　*The information includes, but need not be limited to, the following:* **(PI.3.5–PI.3.5.3)**

AL.6.2.1.1　*Whether patient contact occurred as planned; and* **(PI.3.5–PI.3.5.3)**

AL.6.2.1.2　*Whether the referral was appropriate, including an evaluation of the capacity of the accepting program(s) to meet the patient's needs.* **(PI.3.5–PI.3.5.3)**

Notes and Comments:

DIAGNOSTIC RADIOLOGY SERVICES

Some of the standards in this chapter of the 1993 *Accreditation Manual for Hospitals* have been recast to focus on improving individual and organizational performance and have been moved to Sections 1 and 2 of this *Manual*. To help you identify these standards, we have printed them here in small italic type with their new standard references in bold type in parentheses. Organizations are expected to demonstrate compliance with these standards in their new context. For example, DR.1 in this chapter has been recast and moved to the "Leadership" chapter, as LD.1.3.4. This standard appears in small italic type, and the new standard reference, LD.1.3.4, appears in bold type in parentheses at the end of the standard. Organizations are expected to comply with LD.1.3.4 and will be scored for compliance in the "Leadership" chapter. Standards scored in this chapter are in normal type and have accompanying scoring scales (1 2 3 4 5 NA).

DR.1   Diagnostic radiology services are regularly and conveniently available to meet the needs of patients as determined by the medical staff. **(LD.1.3.4)**

DR.1.1   All individuals who provide diagnostic radiology services independently, whether or not they are members of the department/service, have delineated clinical privileges for the services they provide.   1 2 3 4 5 NA

DR.1.2   The director of diagnostic radiology services is a physician member of the medical staff who is qualified by education and experience in radiology, is clinically competent, and possesses the administrative skills necessary to assure effective leadership of the department/service.   1 2 3 4 5 NA

DR.1.3   Comprehensive safety rules are developed by the director of the department/service in cooperation with the hospital's safety committee and the hospital's radiation safety committee, if one exists.   1 2 3 4 5 NA

DR.1.4   Work assignments are consistent with the qualifications of department/service personnel.   1 2 3 4 5 NA

DR.1.5   At least one qualified radiologic technologist is on duty or available when needed.   1 2 3 4 5 NA

DR.1.6   A radiologic technologist does not independently perform diagnostic fluoroscopic procedures for the purpose of interpretive fluoroscopy except for those localizing procedures approved by the director of the diagnostic radiology department/service.   1 2 3 4 5 NA

DR.1.7   There is a description of the means for providing diagnostic radiology services when they are not provided by the hospital. **(scoring guideline for LD.1.3.4.2.1)**

DR.1.8   When diagnostic radiology procedures are performed outside the hospital, the off-site source(s) meets the standards contained in this chapter of this Manual. (scoring guideline for LD.1.3.4.2.1)

DR.1.9   When diagnostic radiology services are not provided by the department/service, the clinical department/service providing such services is responsible for the monitoring and evaluation of the quality of the services provided in order to achieve comparable quality of care. (PI.3.4)

DR.1.10   In a hospital that provides only psychiatric/substance abuse services, but does not provide for diagnostic radiology services itself, there is a description of the means for providing such services. (scoring guideline for LD.1.3.4.2.1)

DR.2   There are policies and procedures to assure effective management, safety, proper performance of equipment, effective communication, and quality control in the diagnostic radiology department/service. (LD.2, LD.2.1.2, LD.2.1.3, LD.2.1.7)

DR.2.1   Policies and procedures are developed in cooperation with the medical staff, administration, nurse executive and other appropriate registered nurses, and, as necessary, other clinical departments/services and are implemented. (LD.3.3)

DR.2.1.1   The policies and procedures are reviewed periodically by a medical radiation physicist.

1 2 3 4 5 NA

DR.2.2   The written policies and procedures include, but need not be limited to, the following:

DR.2.2.1   Diagnostic radiology services performed at the request of individuals licensed to practice independently and authorized by the hospital to make such requests;

1 2 3 4 5 NA

DR.2.2.2   A quality control program designed to minimize patient, personnel, and public risks and to maximize the quality of diagnostic information; (PI.3.4.1–PI.3.4.1.3, PI.3.5.3.2)

DR.2.2.3   Implementation of PL.3 through PL.3.3.1.2 in the "Plant, Technology, and Safety Management" chapter of this *Manual* for all electrically and nonelectrically powered equipment used in the diagnosis, treatment, or monitoring of patients to assure that the equipment, wherever located in the hospital, performs properly;

1 2 3 4 5 NA

DR.2.2.4   Provisions that a qualified physician, qualified medical radiation physicist, or other qualified individual (PI.4.2–PI.4.2.2)

DR.2.2.4.1   monitor performance evaluations of diagnostic and treatment equipment at least annually, and (PI.4.2–PI.4.2.2)

DR.2.2.4.2   monitor doses from diagnostic radiology procedures; (PI.4.2–PI.4.2.2)

DR.2.2.5   With respect to radiation hazards from equipment, adherence to the recommendations of any currently recognized and reliable authority on radiation hazards, such as the National Council on Radiation Protection and Measurements, and any requirements of appropriate licensing agencies or other government bodies;

1 2 3 4 5 NA

DR.2.2.6   Guidelines for protecting personnel and patients from radiation;

1 2 3 4 5 NA

DR.2.2.7   The monitoring of staff and personnel for exposure to radiation;

1 2 3 4 5 NA

DR.2.2.8   Guidelines developed in consultation with the infection control committee for the protection of staff, patients, and equipment; and   1 2 3 4 5 NA

DR.2.2.9   Orientation and a safety education program for all personnel.   1 2 3 4 5 NA

*DR.3   Reports of consultations, interpretations of diagnostic radiology studies, and/or interpretations of therapeutic invasive procedures are included in the patient's medical record. (**IM.7.2.12, IM.7.2.18**)*

*DR.3.1   Requests/referrals for diagnostic and/or monitoring and/or therapeutic invasive procedures include the study or studies requested and appropriate clinical data to aid in the performance of the procedures requested. (**IM.7.2.4–IM.7.2.6, IM.7.2.11, IM.7.2.13**)*

DR.3.2   Only individuals with delineated clinical privileges to interpret diagnostic studies and/or perform therapeutic invasive procedures authenticate reports of studies and procedures.   1 2 3 4 5 NA

DR.3.2.1   Individuals authenticate only those reports of procedures for which they have been granted specific clinical privileges through the medical staff privilege delineation process.   1 2 3 4 5 NA

DR.3.3   Authenticated reports are entered in the patient's medical record and, as appropriate, are filed in the department/service.   1 2 3 4 5 NA

Note: *Refer also to the "Improving Organizational Performance" chapter of this* Manual. *For further requirements relating to medical records, see the "Management of Information" chapter of this* Manual.

NOTES AND COMMENTS:

DIETETIC SERVICES

Some of the standards in this chapter of the 1993 *Accreditation Manual for Hospitals* have been recast to focus on improving individual and organizational performance and have been moved to Sections 1 and 2 of this *Manual.* To help you identify these standards, we have printed them here in small italic type with their new standard references in bold type in parentheses. Organizations are expected to demonstrate compliance with these standards in their new context. For example, DT.1 in this chapter has been recast and moved to the "Leadership" chapter, as LD.2.1.2. This standard appears in small italic type, and the new standard reference, LD.2.1.2, appears in bold type in parentheses at the end of the standard. Organizations are expected to comply with LD.2.1.2 and will be scored for compliance in the "Leadership" chapter. Standards scored in this chapter are in normal type and have accompanying scoring scales (1 2 3 4 5 NA).

*DT.1   The dietetic department/service is organized, directed, staffed, and integrated with other units and departments/services of the hospital in a manner designed to assure the provision of optimal nutritional care and quality foodservice. (**LD.2.1.2**)*

*DT.1.1   The scope of the dietetic services provided to inpatients and, as appropriate, to ambulatory care patients and patients in a hospital-administered home care program is defined in writing. (**LD.1.7.1.2**)*

DT.1.2   The dietetic department/service is directed on a full-time basis by an individual who, by education or specialized training and experience, is knowledgeable about foodservice management.

1 2 3 4 5 NA

DT.1.3   Dietetic services are provided by a sufficient number of qualified personnel under competent supervision.

1 2 3 4 5 NA

DT.1.4   A qualified dietitian supervises the nutritional aspects of patient care and assures that quality nutritional care is provided to patients.

1 2 3 4 5 NA

DT.1.4.1   Qualified dietitians or qualified designees participate in committee activities concerned with nutritional care.

1 2 3 4 5 NA

DT.1.4.2   When the services of a qualified dietitian are used on a part-time basis, this individual provides such services on the premises on a regularly scheduled basis.

1 2 3 4 5 NA

DT.1.4.3   The regularly scheduled visits are sufficient to provide for at least the following:

DT.1.4.3.1   Approval of menus, including modified diets;

1 2 3 4 5 NA

DT.1.4.3.2   Any required nutritional assessments;

1 2 3 4 5 NA

DT.1.4.3.3   Participation in the development of policies and procedures; and

1 2 3 4 5 NA

DT.1.4.3.4   Evaluation of the dietetic services provided.   1 2 3 4 5 NA

DT.1.4.4   When a qualified dietitian serves only in a consultant capacity, this individual regularly submits written reports to the chief executive officer concerning the extent of services provided.   1 2 3 4 5 NA

DT.1.4.5   When dietetic services are provided by an off-site food management company, the company complies with all applicable requirements of this *Manual*, and the contract specifies this compliance.   1 2 3 4 5 NA

DT.2
Written policies and procedures specify the provision of dietetic services.   1 2 3 4 5 NA

DT.2.1   There are written policies and procedures concerning the scope and conduct of dietetic services.   1 2 3 4 5 NA

DT.2.1.1   Administrative policies and procedures concerning food procurement, preparation, and service are developed by the director of the dietetic department/service.   1 2 3 4 5 NA

DT.2.1.2   Nutritional care policies and procedures are developed by a qualified dietitian.   1 2 3 4 5 NA

DT.2.2   The policies and procedures are dated and enforced and relate to at least the following:

DT.2.2.1   *The responsibilities and authority of the director of the dietetic department/service and, when the director is not a qualified dietitian, of the qualified dietitian; (LD.2.1)*

DT.2.2.2   Food purchasing, storage, inventory, preparation, and service;   1 2 3 4 5 NA

DT.2.2.3   Diet orders, which are recorded in the patient's medical record by an authorized individual before the diet is served to the patient;   1 2 3 4 5 NA

DT.2.2.4   The proper use of and adherence to standards for nutritional care, as specified in the diet manual/handbook;   1 2 3 4 5 NA

DT.2.2.5   Menus;   1 2 3 4 5 NA

DT.2.2.6   The role, as appropriate, of the dietetic department/service in the preparation, storage, distribution, and administration of enteric tube feedings and total parenteral nutrition programs;   1 2 3 4 5 NA

DT.2.2.7   Alterations in diets or diet schedules, including the provision of foodservice to persons who do not receive the regular meal service;   1 2 3 4 5 NA

DT.2.2.8   Ancillary dietetic services, as appropriate, including food storage and kitchens on patient care units, formula supply, cafeterias, vending operations, and ice making;   1 2 3 4 5 NA

DT.2.2.9   An identification system designed to assure that each patient receives the appropriate diet as ordered;   1 2 3 4 5 NA

DT.2.2.10   Personal hygiene and health of dietetic personnel;   1 2 3 4 5 NA

DT.2.2.11   Infection control measures to minimize the possibility of contamination and transfer of infection;   1 2 3 4 5 NA

DT.2.2.11.1 These measures include the establishment of a monitoring procedure to assure that dietetic personnel are free from communicable infections and open skin lesions.   1 2 3 4 5 NA

DT.2.2.12 Pertinent safety practices, including the control of electrical, flammable, mechanical, and, as appropriate, radiation hazards; and   1 2 3 4 5 NA

DT.2.2.13 Compliance with applicable law and regulation.   1 2 3 4 5 NA

DT.2.3 A qualified dietitian develops or adopts a diet manual/handbook in cooperation with representatives of the medical staff and with other appropriate dietetic staff.   1 2 3 4 5 NA

DT.2.3.1 The standards for nutritional care specified in the diet manual/handbook should at least be in accordance with those of the *Recommended Dietary Allowances* (1989) of the Food and Nutrition Board of the National Research Council of the National Academy of Sciences.   1 2 3 4 5 NA

DT.2.3.2 The nutritional deficiencies of any diet that is not in compliance with the recommended dietary allowances are specified.   1 2 3 4 5 NA

DT.2.3.3 The diet manual/handbook serves as a guide to ordering diets, and the served menus should be consistent with the requirements in the diet manual/handbook.   1 2 3 4 5 NA

DT.2.3.4 The diet manual/handbook is reviewed annually and revised as necessary by a qualified dietitian, dated to identify the review and any revisions made, and approved by the medical staff through its designated mechanism.   1 2 3 4 5 NA

DT.2.3.5 A copy of the diet manual/handbook is located in each patient care unit.   1 2 3 4 5 NA

DT.2.3.6 All master menus and modified diets are approved by a qualified dietitian.   1 2 3 4 5 NA

DT.3
The dietetic department/service is designed and equipped to facilitate the safe, sanitary, and timely provision of foodservice to meet the nutritional needs of patients.   1 2 3 4 5 NA

DT.3.1 Sufficient space and equipment is provided for the dietetic department/service to accomplish the following:

DT.3.1.1 Store food and nonfood supplies under sanitary and secure conditions;   1 2 3 4 5 NA

DT.3.1.2 Store food separately from nonfood supplies;   1 2 3 4 5 NA

DT.3.1.2.1 When storage facilities are limited, paper products may be stored with food supplies.   1 2 3 4 5 NA

DT.3.1.3 Prepare and distribute food, including modified diets;   1 2 3 4 5 NA

DT.3.1.4 Clean and sanitize utensils and dishes apart from food preparation areas; and   1 2 3 4 5 NA

DT.3.1.5 Allow support personnel to perform their duties.   1 2 3 4 5 NA

DT.3.2 The facilities and equipment of the dietetic department/service are in compliance with applicable sanitation and safety law and regulation.   1 2 3 4 5 NA

DT.3.3 The following sanitation precautions are taken in the handling and preparation of food:

DT.3.3.1   Food is protected from contamination and spoilage;   1 2 3 4 5 NA

DT.3.3.2   Foods are stored at proper temperatures, utilizing appropriate thermometers and maintaining temperature records;   1 2 3 4 5 NA

DT.3.3.3   Lighting, ventilation, and humidity are controlled to prevent the condensation of moisture and growth of molds;   1 2 3 4 5 NA

DT.3.3.4   Methods to prevent contamination are used for making, storing, and dispensing ice;   1 2 3 4 5 NA

DT.3.3.5   Separate cutting boards are provided for meat, poultry, fish, raw fruits and vegetables, and cooked foods, unless boards are used that are nonabsorbent and can be cleaned and sanitized adequately between uses;   1 2 3 4 5 NA

DT.3.3.6   All working surfaces, utensils, and equipment are cleansed thoroughly and sanitized after each period of use;   1 2 3 4 5 NA

DT.3.3.7   Adequate hand-washing and hand-drying facilities are conveniently located throughout the department/service;   1 2 3 4 5 NA

DT.3.3.8   Dishwashing and utensil-washing equipment and techniques that result in sanitized serviceware and that prevent recontamination are used;   1 2 3 4 5 NA

DT.3.3.9   Plasticware, china, and glassware that have lost their glaze or are chipped or cracked are discarded;   1 2 3 4 5 NA

DT.3.3.10   Disposable containers and utensils are discarded after one use;   1 2 3 4 5 NA

DT.3.3.11   Traffic of unauthorized individuals through food preparation and service areas is controlled; and   1 2 3 4 5 NA

DT.3.3.12   Garbage is held, transferred, and disposed of in a manner that does not create a nuisance or a breeding place for insects, rodents, and vermin or otherwise permit the transmission of disease.   1 2 3 4 5 NA

DT.3.4 The following safety precautions are implemented:

DT.3.4.1   Food and nonfood supplies are clearly labeled;   1 2 3 4 5 NA

DT.3.4.2   A review is conducted of the hospital's preventive and corrective maintenance and safety programs as they relate to the dietetic department/service; and   1 2 3 4 5 NA

DT.3.4.2.1   Actions are taken based on the findings of the review.   1 2 3 4 5 NA

DT.3.4.2.2   The review and actions taken are documented.   1 2 3 4 5 NA

DT.3.4.3   All food is procured from sources that process food under regulated quality and sanitation controls.   1 2 3 4 5 NA

DT.4
Dietetic services are provided in accordance with a written order by the individual responsible for the patient, and appropriate dietetic information is recorded in the patient's medical record.

1 2 3 4 5 NA

DT.4.1 The qualified dietitian or authorized designee enters dietetic information into the medical record as specified, and in the location determined, by those performing the medical record review function. **(scoring guideline for IM.7.2)**

DT.4.2 At the request of the appropriate medical staff member, the qualified dietitian or authorized designee documents appropriate nutritional information in the medical record.

1 2 3 4 5 NA

DT.4.2.1   Such documentation includes the following:

DT.4.2.1.1   A summary of the dietary history and/or nutritional assessment when the past dietary pattern is known to have a bearing on the patient's condition or treatment;

1 2 3 4 5 NA

DT.4.2.1.2   Timely and periodic assessments of the patient's nutrient intake and tolerance to the prescribed diet modification, including the effect of the patient's appetite and food habits on food intake and any substitutions made; and **(scoring guideline for PE.1.3)**

DT.4.2.1.3   A description or copy of the diet information forwarded to another organization when a patient is discharged.

1 2 3 4 5 NA

DT.4.3 Within 24 hours of admission and within 24 hours after any subsequent orders for diet modification, the diet order is confirmed by the practitioner responsible for the patient receiving oral alimentation.

1 2 3 4 5 NA

DT.5   Appropriate quality control mechanisms are established. **(PI.3)**

DT.5.1   At least the following quality control mechanisms are implemented: **(PI.3)**

DT.5.1.1   All menus are evaluated for nutritional adequacy; **(PI.3)**

DT.5.1.2   There is a means of identifying patients who are not receiving oral intake; **(PI.3)**

DT.5.1.3   Special diets are monitored; **(PI.3)**

DT.5.1.4   As appropriate, the nutrient intake of patients is assessed and recorded; **(PI.3)**

DT.5.1.5   A maximum effort is made to assure an appetizing appearance, palatability, proper serving temperature, and retention of the nutrient value of food; **(PI.3)**

DT.5.1.5.1   Whenever possible, patient food preferences are respected and appropriate dietary substitutions are made available; and **(PI.3)**

DT.5.1.5.2   Surveys to determine patient acceptance of food are encouraged, particularly in the case of long-stay patients. **(PI.3)**

Note: *For other standards related to dietetic services, refer to the following chapters of this Manual: "Improving Organizational Performance," "Infection Control," "Manament of Information," "Pharmaceutical Services," and "Plant, Technology, and Safety Management."*

NOTES AND COMMENTS:

EMERGENCY SERVICES

Some of the standards in this chapter of the 1993 *Accreditation Manual for Hospitals* have been recast to focus on improving individual and organizational performance and have been moved to Sections 1 and 2 of this *Manual*. To help you identify these standards, we have printed them here in small italic type with their new standard references in bold type in parentheses. Organizations are expected to demonstrate compliance with these standards in their new context. For example, ES.1.1 in this chapter has been recast and moved to the "Leadership" chapter, as LD.1.3.1. This standard appears in small italic type, and the new standard reference, LD.1.3.1, appears in bold type in parentheses at the end of the standard. Organizations are expected to comply with LD.1.3.1 and will be scored for compliance in the "Leadership" chapter. Standards scored in this chapter are in normal type and have accompanying scoring scales (1 2 3 4 5 NA).

ES.1
Emergency care is provided by qualified individuals, and appropriate services are provided through a well-defined plan, based on community need and the defined capability of the hospital.
 1 2 3 4 5 NA

> *ES.1.1   Whenever feasible, all hospitals that offer emergency medical services in a community participate in community planning for emergency services.* **(scoring guideline for LD.1.3.1)**

ES.1.2   The hospital has a procedure whereby all ill or injured individuals who seek emergency care are assessed by qualified individuals and, as indicated, are either treated or referred to an appropriate organization.
 1 2 3 4 5 NA

ES.1.3   The hospital evaluates and classifies itself to indicate its capability in providing emergency medical services to the community served.*
 1 2 3 4 5 NA

ES.1.3.1   A Level I emergency department/service offers comprehensive emergency care 24 hours a day, with at least one physician experienced in emergency care on duty in the emergency care area.
 1 2 3 4 5 NA

ES.1.3.1.1   There is in-hospital physician coverage by members of the medical staff or by senior-level residents for at least medical, surgical, orthopedic, obstetric/gynecologic, pediatric, and anesthesia services.
 1 2 3 4 5 NA

ES.1.3.1.2   Other specialty consultation is available within approximately 30 minutes; initial consultation through two-way voice communication is acceptable.
 1 2 3 4 5 NA

Specific and general requirements are established for four levels of emergency services. Other comparable classifications, such as state or regional, are acceptable, and the hospital is evaluated for compliance at the appropriate level.

ES.1.3.2   A Level II emergency department/service offers emergency care 24 hours a day, with at least one physician experienced in emergency care on duty in the emergency care area, and with specialty consultation available within approximately 30 minutes by members of the medical staff or by senior-level residents.

1 2 3 4 5 NA

ES.1.3.3   A Level III emergency department/service offers emergency care 24 hours a day, with at least one physician available to the emergency care area within approximately 30 minutes through a medical staff call roster.

1 2 3 4 5 NA

ES.1.3.3.1   Specialty consultation is available by request of the attending medical staff member or by transfer to a designated hospital where definitive care can be provided.

1 2 3 4 5 NA

ES.1.3.4   A Level IV emergency department/service offers reasonable care in determining whether an emergency exists, renders lifesaving first aid, and makes appropriate referral to the nearest organizations that are capable of providing needed services.

1 2 3 4 5 NA

ES.1.3.4.1   The mechanism for providing physician coverage at all times is defined by the medical staff.

1 2 3 4 5 NA

ES.1.4   Patients are transferred in accordance with the community-based hospital emergency plan.

1 2 3 4 5 NA

ES.1.4.1   The hospital is capable of instituting essential lifesaving measures and implementing emergency procedures that will minimize further compromise of the condition of any infant, child, or adult being transported.

1 2 3 4 5 NA

ES.1.4.2   Unless extenuating circumstances are documented in the patient's record, no patient is arbitrarily transferred to another hospital if the hospital where the patient is initially seen has the means for providing adequate care.

1 2 3 4 5 NA

ES.1.4.2.1   The patient is not transferred until the receiving organization has consented to accept the patient and the patient is considered sufficiently stabilized for transport.

1 2 3 4 5 NA

ES.1.4.2.2   Responsibility for the patient during transfer is established, and all pertinent medical information accompanies the patient being transferred.

1 2 3 4 5 NA

ES.1.5   When required frequently in the emergency care area, there is a means of communicating in the languages of the predominant population groups served by the hospital's emergency department/service.

1 2 3 4 5 NA

ES.2
The emergency department/service is well organized, properly directed, and staffed according to the nature and extent of health care needs anticipated and the scope of services offered.

1 2 3 4 5 NA

*ES.2.1   The emergency department/service is directed by a physician member of the medical staff. (**scoring guideline for LD.2.2.1**)*

ES.2.1.1   The director, the deputy director, or other qualified physician in charge of a Level I or Level II emergency department/service has training and/or experience in a specialty appropriate (as determined by the medical staff) to the care and treatment of emergency patients.   1 2 3 4 5 NA

ES.2.1.2   The director of a Level I emergency department/service or the director's deputy or qualified physician designee is readily available.   1 2 3 4 5 NA

ES.2.1.3   Direction of a Level III emergency department/service may be provided by a physician member of the medical staff or by a multi-disciplinary medical staff committee, with the chairperson of the committee serving as director of the emergency department/service.   1 2 3 4 5 NA

ES.2.2   The method of providing medical staff coverage is defined.   1 2 3 4 5 NA

ES.2.2.1   When the medical staff has assumed the responsibility for coverage, its members have an obligation for emergency department/service coverage as determined by the medical staff, each in accordance with his/her clinical competence and privileges.   1 2 3 4 5 NA

ES.2.2.2   Specialists in limited practice are available on an established schedule to provide consultation on the needs of emergency patients or to provide special services to emergency patients.   1 2 3 4 5 NA

*ES.2.2.3   A physician is responsible for the degree of evaluation and treatment provided to any patient who presents himself/herself or is brought to the emergency care area. (**PE.4.2**)*

ES.2.2.4   The priority with which persons seeking emergency care will be seen by a physician may be determined by specially trained personnel using guidelines established by the emergency department/service director and approved by the medical staff.   1 2 3 4 5 NA

ES.2.2.5   Rosters designating medical staff members on duty or on call for primary coverage and specialty consultation are posted in the emergency care area.   1 2 3 4 5 NA

ES.2.3   A designated registered nurse who is qualified by relevant training, experience, and current competence in emergency care supervises the care provided by all nursing staff members within the emergency department/service.   1 2 3 4 5 NA

ES.2.3.1   The number of nursing staff members is sufficient for the types and volume of patients served.   1 2 3 4 5 NA

ES.2.3.2   Level I and Level II emergency departments/services have at least one registered nurse and a sufficient number of other nursing staff members permanently assigned and on duty within the emergency care area at all times.   1 2 3 4 5 NA

ES.2.3.3   A Level III emergency department/service has a registered nurse available on at least an on-call, in-house basis at all times.   1 2 3 4 5 NA

*ES.2.3.4   The registered nurse assigned managerial responsibility for emergency care services participates in committee activities concerned with the emergency department/service. (**LD.3.4**)*

ES.2.4   When emergency medical technicians or other allied health personnel are used, their duties and their responsibilities to physicians and nurses providing care within the emergency service area are defined in writing.   1 2 3 4 5 NA

ES.3   The emergency department/service is appropriately integrated with other units and departments/services of the hospital. (LD.2.1.2)

ES.3.1   Clinical laboratory services with the capability of performing all routine studies are readily available at all times to Level I, Level II, and Level III emergency departments/services. (LD.1.3.4)

ES.3.1.1   Laboratory services supporting Level I and Level II emergency departments/services provide arterial blood gas and pH determinations, coagulation studies, serum and urine osmolality studies, microbiologic studies, and, as required, toxicologic studies.

1 2 3 4 5 NA

ES.3.1.2   An adequate supply of blood is available at all times, either in-hospital or from an off-site source approved by the medical staff.

1 2 3 4 5 NA

ES.3.1.3   The hospital provides for blood typing and crossmatching capability and for blood-storage facilities that are readily available to the emergency department/service.

1 2 3 4 5 NA

ES.3.2   Diagnostic radiology services are readily available at all times to provide routine studies using both fixed and mobile equipment.

1 2 3 4 5 NA

ES.3.2.1   For Level I and Level II emergency departments/services, angiography of all types, sonography, and nuclear scanning are readily available, as needed.

1 2 3 4 5 NA

ES.3.3   Level I emergency departments/services have prompt access, as needed, to operating suites that have the following capabilities: cardiopulmonary bypass pump oxygenator; operating microscope; thermal-control equipment for the patient and for blood; fracture table; roentgenographic equipment, including image intensifier; endoscopes, all varieties; craniotomy equipment; electrocardiograph-oscilloscope-defibrillator; pacemaker-insertion capability; mechanical ventilator; and equipment for monitoring direct blood pressure, temperature, blood-flow rate, and respirations.

1 2 3 4 5 NA

ES.3.3.1   Appropriate surgical specialists and anesthesiology and operating room personnel are in-house and available within an appropriate time.

1 2 3 4 5 NA

ES.3.4   Level II emergency departments/services have prompt access to operating suites with the following equipment: thermal-control equipment for the patient and for blood, fracture table, appropriate endoscopic equipment, electrocardiograph-oscilloscope-defibrillator, mechanical ventilator, and temperature-monitoring equipment.

1 2 3 4 5 NA

ES.3.4.1   Roentgenographic equipment is readily available.

1 2 3 4 5 NA

ES.3.5   Depending on the emergency services provided, there is access to the obstetric suite and special care units.

1 2 3 4 5 NA

ES.4   Emergency department/service patient care is guided by written policies and procedures. (LD.2.1.3)

ES.4.1   There are written policies and procedures specifying the scope and conduct of patient care to be provided in the emergency department/service. (LD.1.7.1, LD.1.7.1.2)

ES.4.1.1   Such policies and procedures are approved by the medical staff and hospital administration. (LD.1.7)

ES.4.1.2   The policies and procedures in Level I, Level II, and Level III emergency departments/services and, as appropriate, in Level IV emergency departments/services relate to at least the following:

ES.4.1.2.1   Location, storage, and procurement of medications, blood, supplies, and equipment at all times;   1 2 3 4 5 NA

ES.4.1.2.2   Provision of care to an unemancipated minor not accompanied by a parent or guardian or to an unaccompanied, unconscious patient;   1 2 3 4 5 NA

ES.4.1.2.3   Transfer and discharge of patients;   1 2 3 4 5 NA

ES.4.1.2.4   Infection control measures;   1 2 3 4 5 NA

ES.4.1.2.5   Procedures to be followed in the event of equipment failure;   1 2 3 4 5 NA

ES.4.1.2.6   Pertinent safety practices;   1 2 3 4 5 NA

ES.4.1.2.7   Specification of the scope of treatment allowed, including the general and specific procedures that may not be performed by medical staff members in the emergency department/service, and the use of anesthesia;   1 2 3 4 5 NA

ES.4.1.2.8   Who, other than physicians, may perform special procedures, under what circumstances, and under what degree of supervision; and   1 2 3 4 5 NA

ES.4.1.2.9   The handling of adult and child victims of alleged or suspected abuse or neglect. **(PE.6)**

ES.4.1.2.9.1   Criteria are developed for identifying possible victims of abuse. **(PE.6)**

ES.4.1.2.9.1.1   The criteria address at least the following types of abuse: **(scoring guideline for PE.6)**

ES.4.1.2.9.1.1.1   Physical assault; **(scoring guideline for PE.6)**

ES.4.1.2.9.1.1.2   Rape or other sexual molestation; and **(scoring guideline for PE.6)**

ES.4.1.2.9.1.1.3   Domestic abuse of elders, spouses, partners, and children. **(scoring guideline for PE.6)**

ES.4.1.2.9.2   Procedures for the evaluation of patients who meet the criteria address **(PE.6)**

ES.4.1.2.9.2.1   patient consent; **(PE.6.1)**

ES.4.1.2.9.2.2   examination and treatment; **(PE.6)**

ES.4.1.2.9.2.3   the hospital's responsibility for the collection, retention, and safeguarding of specimens, photographs, and other evidentiary material released by the patient; and **(PE.6.2)**

ES.4.1.2.9.2.4   as legally required, notification of and release of information to the proper authorities. **(PE.6.3)**

ES.4.1.2.9.3   A list is maintained in the emergency department/service of private and public community agencies that provide, or arrange for, evaluation and care for victims of abuse, and referrals are made as appropriate. **(scoring guidelines for PE.6, PE.6.1, PE.6.2, PE.6.3)**

*ES.4.1.2.9.4   The medical record includes documentation of examinations, treatment given, any referrals made to other care providers and to community agencies, and any required reporting to the proper authorities. (**IM.7.2, IM.7.2.5, IM.7.2.8, IM.7.2.23**)*

ES.4.1.2.9.5   There is a plan for education of appropriate staff about the criteria for identifying and the procedures for handling possible victims of abuse.

1 2 3 4 5 NA

*ES.4.2   Current toxicologic reference materials and antidote information are readily available in the emergency department/service, along with the telephone number of the regional poison control information center. (**scoring guideline for IM.9.5**)*

ES.5
The emergency department/service is designed and equipped to facilitate the safe and effective care of patients.

1 2 3 4 5 NA

ES.5.1   Sufficient space is provided for the care of emergency patients, particularly those with life-threatening conditions.

1 2 3 4 5 NA

ES.5.1.1   The design of the emergency department/service area facilitates the visual and auditory privacy of patients, without compromising patient care.

1 2 3 4 5 NA

ES.5.2   When observation beds are permitted, there are written policies and procedures that address the type of patient use, the maximum time period of use, the mechanism for providing appropriate surveillance, and the type of nurse/patient system to be used.

1 2 3 4 5 NA

ES.5.3   When warranted by the size and sophistication of the emergency care area, an intercommunication/alarm system is provided between the nurses' station and any examination, treatment, or other areas from which additional personnel may need to be summoned in an emergency.

1 2 3 4 5 NA

ES.5.4   When general anesthesia is administered in the emergency department/service, the anesthesia area meets the requirements of the National Fire Protection Association (NFPA) standards, especially the standards cited in Chapter 12, "Hospital Requirements," in NFPA 99, *Standard for Health Care Facilities*, 1990, and the "Surgical and Anesthesia Services" chapter of this *Manual.*

1 2 3 4 5 NA

*ES.5.5   Equipment and supplies used in the emergency department/service are of the same quality as those used throughout the hospital and are suitable for all sizes of patients treated. (**scoring guidelines for LD.1.3.2, LD.1.6**)*

ES.5.5.1   Equipment is checked on a scheduled basis in accordance with the hospital preventive maintenance program and the requirements of the "Plant, Technology, and Safety Management" chapter of this *Manual.*

1 2 3 4 5 NA

ES.5.5.2   At least the following are readily available for use in Level I and Level II emergency departments/services and, as appropriate, in Level III and Level IV emergency departments/services:

ES.5.5.2.1   Oxygen and the means of administration;

1 2 3 4 5 NA

ES.5.5.2.2   Mechanical ventilatory assistance equipment, including airways, manual breathing bag, and ventilator;

1 2 3 4 5 NA

ES.5.5.2.3   Cardiac defibrillator with synchronization capability;   1 2 3 4 5 NA

ES.5.5.2.4   Respiratory and cardiac monitoring equipment;   1 2 3 4 5 NA

ES.5.5.2.5   Thoracentesis and closed thoracostomy sets;   1 2 3 4 5 NA

ES.5.5.2.6   Tracheostomy or cricothyrotomy set;   1 2 3 4 5 NA

ES.5.5.2.7   Tourniquets;   1 2 3 4 5 NA

ES.5.5.2.8   Vascular cutdown sets;   1 2 3 4 5 NA

ES.5.5.2.9   Laryngoscopes and endotracheal tubes;   1 2 3 4 5 NA

ES.5.5.2.10   Tracheobronchial and gastric suction equipment;   1 2 3 4 5 NA

ES.5.5.2.11   Urinary catheters with closed volume urinary systems;   1 2 3 4 5 NA

ES.5.5.2.12   Pleural and pericardial drainage set;   1 2 3 4 5 NA

ES.5.5.2.13   Minor surgical instruments;   1 2 3 4 5 NA

ES.5.5.2.14   Splinting devices; and   1 2 3 4 5 NA

ES.5.5.2.15   Emergency obstetric pack.   1 2 3 4 5 NA

ES.5.5.3   Emergency drug carts or emergency drug storage areas are checked by an appropriate individual at least once per shift and after each use to assure that all items that must be immediately available are actually in the cart and in usable condition.   1 2 3 4 5 NA

ES.5.5.3.1   This requirement may be met by a system designed to assure the continued integrity of the contents between periods of use.   1 2 3 4 5 NA

*ES.6   A medical record is maintained on every patient seeking emergency care and is incorporated into the patient's permanent hospital record. (**IM.7.1**)*

*ES.6.1   All prior pertinent inpatient and ambulatory care patient medical record documentation, including previous visits to the emergency department/service, are made available, whenever possible, when requested by the attending physician or other authorized individual. (**scoring guideline for IM.7.5**)*

*ES.6.1.1   Each time a patient visits the emergency department/service, the following information is entered in the patient's medical record: (**IM.7.6, IM.7.6.1**)*

*ES.6.1.1.1   Pertinent history of the illness or injury and physical findings, including the patient's vital signs; (**IM.7.2.5**)*

*ES.6.1.1.2   Emergency care provided to the patient prior to arrival; (**IM.7.2.3**)*

*ES.6.1.1.3   Diagnostic and therapeutic orders; (**IM.7.2.11**)*

*ES.6.1.1.4   Clinical observations, including the results of treatment; (**IM.7.2.16, IM.7.2.17**)*

*ES.6.1.1.5   Reports of procedures, tests, and results; (**IM.7.2.12**)*

*ES.6.1.1.6   Diagnostic impression; (**IM.7.2.6**)*

*ES.6.1.1.7   Conclusion at the termination of evaluation/treatment, including final disposition, of the patient's condition on discharge or transfer; and (**IM.7.6.1.3**)*

ES.6.1.1.8 A patient's leaving against medical advice. (IM.7.6.1.2)

ES.6.2 A control register is continuously maintained and includes at least the following information for every individual seeking care: identification, such as name, age, sex; date, time, and means of arrival; nature of complaint; disposition; and time of departure. (IM.8.1.6.1)

ES.6.3 The medical record is authenticated by the practitioner who is responsible for its clinical accuracy. (IM.7.1.1, IM.7.9, IM.7.9.3)

ES.7 The emergency department/service establishes appropriate quality control mechanisms. (PI.3)

ES.7.1 At least the following quality control mechanisms are established: (PI.3)

ES.7.1.1 When authorized, a copy of the record of emergency services provided is available to the practitioner or medical organization responsible for follow-up care; and (IM.7.6.2)

ES.7.1.2 The following are available to the patient's personal practitioner and to the practitioner who provides emergency care: an official interpretation of x-rays, based on a timely review; reports of laboratory tests; and an interpretation of electrocardiograms by physicians with such privileges. (IM.7.7 and IM.7.7.1)

ES.7.1.2.1 There is a mechanism for notifying and recalling those patients who require additional radiologic, laboratory, or electrocardiographic studies.

1 2 3 4 5 NA

ES.7.1.3 Patient transfer is carried out safely and in accordance with a written transfer protocol.

1 2 3 4 5 NA

Note: *For other requirements related to emergency services, refer to the following chapters of this Manual: "Alcoholism and Other Drug-Dependence Services," "Diagnostic Radiology Services," "Improving Organizational Performance," "Infection Control," "Management of Information," "Medical Staff," "Nuclear Medicine Services," "Nursing Care," "Operative and Other Invasive Procedures," "Pathology and Clinical Laboratory Services," "Patient and Family Education," "Pharmaceutical Services," "Plant, Technology, and Safety Management," "Radiation Oncology Services," "Social Work Services," and "Staff Orientation, Training, and Education."*

NOTES AND COMMENTS:

GOVERNING BODY

Some of the standards in this chapter of the 1993 *Accreditation Manual for Hospitals* have been recast to focus on improving individual and organizational performance and have been moved to Sections 1 and 2 of this *Manual.* To help you identify these standards, we have printed them here in small italic type with their new standard references in bold type in parentheses. Organizations are expected to demonstrate compliance with these standards in their new context. For example, GB.1.8 in this chapter has been recast and moved to the "Leadership" chapter, as LD.1. This standard appears in small italic type, and the new standard reference, LD.1, appears in bold type in parentheses at the end of the standard. Organizations are expected to comply with LD.1 and will be scored for compliance in the "Leadership" chapter. Standards scored in this chapter are in normal type and have accompanying scoring scales (1 2 3 4 5 NA).

GB.1
An organized governing body, or designated persons so functioning, is responsible for establishing policy, maintaining quality patient care, and providing for institutional management and planning.   1 2 3 4 5 NA

GB.1.1   The governing body adopts bylaws in accordance with its legal accountability and its responsibility to the patient population served.   1 2 3 4 5 NA

GB.1.2   The bylaws specify at least the following:

GB.1.2.1   The role and purpose of the hospital;   1 2 3 4 5 NA

GB.1.2.2   The duties and responsibilities of the governing body;   1 2 3 4 5 NA

GB.1.2.3   The process and criteria for the selection of members of the governing body;   1 2 3 4 5 NA

GB.1.2.4   The governing body's organizational structure, including at least

GB.1.2.4.1   the mechanism for selecting officers,   1 2 3 4 5 NA

GB.1.2.4.2   the responsibilities of officers,   1 2 3 4 5 NA

GB.1.2.4.3   the procedures for meetings,   1 2 3 4 5 NA

GB.1.2.4.4   the composition and responsibilities of governing body committees, if any, and   1 2 3 4 5 NA

GB.1.2.4.5   the inclusion of medical staff members on governing body committees that deliberate issues affecting the discharge of medical staff responsibilities;   1 2 3 4 5 NA

GB.1.2.5   The relationship of responsibilities of the governing body and   1 2 3 4 5 NA

GB.1.2.5.1   any authority superior to the governing body, if such exists,   1 2 3 4 5 NA

GB.1.2.5.2   the chief executive officer, and   1 2 3 4 5 NA

GB.1.2.5.3   the medical staff;   1 2 3 4 5 NA

GB.1.2.6   The requirement for the establishment of a medical staff;   1 2 3 4 5 NA

GB.1.2.7   The requirement for the establishment of auxiliary organizations, if applicable;   1 2 3 4 5 NA

GB.1.2.8   The mechanism for adopting the governing body bylaws; and   1 2 3 4 5 NA

GB.1.2.9   The mechanism for review and revision of the bylaws.   1 2 3 4 5 NA

GB.1.3   When not legally prohibited, members of the medical staff are eligible for full membership on the governing body in the same manner as other individuals.   1 2 3 4 5 NA

GB.1.4   The medical staff has the right of representation (through attendance and voice), by one or more medical staff members selected by the medical staff, at meetings of the governing body.   1 2 3 4 5 NA

> GB.1.5   *There is a systematic and effective mechanism for communication between members of the governing body, the administration, and the medical staff. (scoring guideline for LD.1.2)*

> GB.1.5.1   *In addition, there is a systematic and effective mechanism for communication between the hospital's governing body, administration, and medical staff and the governing bodies and management of any health care delivery organizations that are corporately and functionally related to the hospital. (scoring guideline for LD.3.2, LD.3.2.2)*

GB.1.6   Any auxiliary organizations and individual volunteers delineate their purpose and function for approval by the governing body.   1 2 3 4 5 NA

GB.1.7   A record of governing body proceedings is maintained.   1 2 3 4 5 NA

> GB.1.8   *The governing body provides for institutional planning. (LD.1)*

> GB.1.8.1   *The administration, the medical staff, the nursing department/service, other departments/services, and appropriate advisers participate in the planning process. (scoring guideline for LD.1)*

> GB.1.9   *The governing body approves an annual operating budget, develops a long-term capital expenditure plan as required by applicable law and regulation, and monitors implementation of the plan. (LD.1.5, LD.1.5.1)*

GB.1.10   The governing body appoints a chief executive officer.   1 2 3 4 5 NA

GB.1.10.1   The chief executive officer is qualified for his/her responsibilities through education and experience.   1 2 3 4 5 NA

GB.1.10.1.1   The governing body designates a mechanism for monitoring the chief executive officer's performance.   1 2 3 4 5 NA

GB.1.11   The medical staff executive committee makes recommendations concerning the issues listed in MS.4.1.2.1 through MS.4.1.2.1.7 directly to the governing body for its approval.   1 2 3 4 5 NA

GB.1.12 Any differences in recommendations concerning medical staff appointments, reappointments, terminations of appointments, and the granting or revision of clinical privileges are resolved within a reasonable period of time by the governing body and the medical staff.   1 2 3 4 5 NA

GB.1.13 The governing body acts on recommendations concerning medical staff appointments, reappointments, terminations of appointments, and the granting or revision of clinical privileges within a reasonable period of time, as specified in the bylaws of the medical staff.   1 2 3 4 5 NA

GB.1.14 The governing body requires a process or processes designed to assure that all individuals who provide patient care services, but who are not subject to the medical staff privilege delineation process, are competent to provide such services.   1 2 3 4 5 NA

1 2 3 4 5 NA

> GB.1.14.1 *The quality of patient care services provided by these individuals is reviewed as part of the hospital's program to assess and improve quality. (**PI.1**)*

GB.1.15 The governing body requires a process or processes designed to assure that all individuals responsible for the assessment, treatment, or care of patients are competent in the following, as appropriate to the ages of the patients served:

GB.1.15.1 Ability to obtain information and interpret information in terms of the patient's needs;   1 2 3 4 5 NA

GB.1.15.2 Knowledge of growth and development; and   1 2 3 4 5 NA

GB.1.15.3 Understanding of the range of treatment needed by these patients.   1 2 3 4 5 NA

GB.1.16 The governing body requires mechanisms to assure the provision of one level of patient care in the hospital.   1 2 3 4 5 NA

> GB.1.16.1 *The governing body requires mechanisms to assure that all patients with the same health problem are receiving the same level of care in the hospital. (**LD.1.6**)*
>
> GB.1.17 *The governing body requires the medical staff and staffs of the departments/services to implement and report on the activities and mechanisms for monitoring and evaluating the quality of patient care, for identifying opportunities to improve patient care, and for identifying and resolving problems. (**PI.1.1**)*
>
> GB.1.17.1 *The governing body, through the chief executive officer, supports these activities and mechanisms. (**PI.1.1**)*
>
> GB.1.18 *The governing body provides for resources and support systems for the quality assessment and improvement functions and risk management functions related to patient care and safety. (**PI.1.1**)*

GB.1.19 The governing body holds the medical staff responsible for the development, adoption, and periodic review of medical staff bylaws and rules and regulations that are consistent with hospital policy and with any applicable legal or other requirements.   1 2 3 4 5 NA

GB.1.19.1 The medical staff bylaws and rules and regulations that have been adopted by the medical staff are subject to, and effective on, approval by the governing body; approval is not unreasonably withheld.   1 2 3 4 5 NA

GB.1.20   The governing body requires the medical staff, staff of departments/ services, and others as appropriate to review and revise all department/ service policies and procedures when warranted. The period between reviews does not exceed three years.

1 2 3 4 5 NA

GB.1.21   The governing body evaluates its own performance.

1 2 3 4 5 NA

GB.1.22   The governing body's bylaws and/or rules and regulations specify the authority and responsibility of each level of the organization with respect to

GB.1.22.1   quality of care;

1 2 3 4 5 NA

GB.1.22.2   quality assessment and improvement mechanisms;

1 2 3 4 5 NA

GB.1.22.3   credentials review and privilege delineation;

1 2 3 4 5 NA

GB.1.22.4   selection of the hospital's governing body;

1 2 3 4 5 NA

GB.1.22.5   selection of the hospital's chief executive officer and other key management staff;

1 2 3 4 5 NA

GB.1.22.6   selection of medical staff department chairperson;

1 2 3 4 5 NA

GB.1.22.7   planning of hospital services;

1 2 3 4 5 NA

GB.1.22.8   development and approval of the hospital's budget; and

1 2 3 4 5 NA

GB.1.22.9   review of the governing body's performance.

1 2 3 4 5 NA

GB.2
The governing body avoids conflicts of interest.

1 2 3 4 5 NA

GB.2.1   The governing body provides for full disclosure of the ownership and control of the hospital and of any health care delivery organizations that are corporately and functionally related to the hospital.

1 2 3 4 5 NA

GB.3
All members of the governing body understand and fulfill their responsibilities.

1 2 3 4 5 NA

NOTES AND COMMENTS:

HOSPITAL-SPONSORED AMBULATORY CARE SERVICES

Standards in this chapter of the 1993 *Accreditation Manual for Hospitals* have been recast to focus on improving individual and organizational performance and have been moved to Sections 1 and 2 of this *Manual*. The following cross-reference is provided for your information.

1993	**1994**
HO.1	LD.1.3.4.2, LD.1.3
HO.1.1	LD.1.7.1
HO.1.1.1	LD.1.7.1
HO.1.1.1.1	LD.1.7.1.1
HO.1.1.1.2	LD.1.7.1.2
HO.1.1.2	scoring guideline for LD.1.3
HO.1.2	LD.2, LD.3
HO.1.3	LD.1.3, LD.1.7.1.2, LD.2.1.3, LD.2.1.4
HO.1.4	MS.2.16.5
HO.1.5	PI.1 and PI.1.1
HO.1.6	scoring guideline for LD.1.5.2
HO.1.7	LD.1.3.4.2
HO.1.7.1	LD.1.3.4.2.1
HO.1.7.2	LD.1.3.4.2.1
HO.1.7.3	PL.1.2.1
HO.1.7.4	LD.1.3.4.2.1
HO.1.7.5	PI.3
HO.1.7.6	LD.1.3.4.2.1
HO.1.8	LD.2.2.2
HO.1.8.1	LD.2.2.2.1
HO.1.8.2	LD.2.2.2.1.1, PE.4.2
HO.1.8.3	LD.2.2.2.1.2
HO.1.9	scoring guideline for LD.1.3
HO.1.9.1	PI.3.4
HO.1.10	LD.2.1.5
HO.1.11	LD.2.2.2.1
HO.1.11.1	NC.3.4.1
HO.1.12	LD.3.1–LD.3.2.2
HO.2	LD.1.7.1.2, LD.2.1.3
HO.2.1	LD.3.3
HO.2.2	LD.2.1.3
HO.2.2.1	LD.1.3.4
HO.2.2.2	RI.1
HO.2.2.3	MA.1.3.10
HO.2.2.3.1	PE.2, PE.2.1
HO.2.2.3.2	PE.2, PE.2.3
HO.2.2.4	IM.7.5

1993	**1994**
HO.2.2.4.1	IM.2.3
HO.2.2.5	MA.1.3.5, MA.1.3.5.1
HO.2.2.6	TX.5, TX.5.1
HO.2.2.7	TX.8
HO.2.2.8	IC.1
HO.2.2.9	PL.1.2.1
HO.2.2.10	IC.4
HO.2.2.11	PL.1.7
HO.2.2.12	TX.13
HO.2.2.13	RI.1–RI.1.1.2
HO.2.2.14	scoring guidelines for MS.3.4.1.1.2, MS.3.4.1.1.2.1
HO.2.2.14.1	ES.5.2
HO.2.2.15	PE.6
HO.2.2.15.1	scoring guideline for PE.6
HO.2.2.15.1.1	scoring guideline for PE.6
HO.2.2.15.1.1.1	scoring guideline for PE.6
HO.2.2.15.1.1.2	scoring guideline for PE.6
HO.2.2.15.1.1.3	scoring guideline for PE.6
HO.2.2.15.2	PE.6
HO.2.2.15.2.1	PE.6.1
HO.2.2.15.2.2	PE.6
HO.2.2.15.2.3	PE.6.2
HO.2.2.15.2.4	PE.6.3
HO.2.2.15.3	scoring guidelines for PE.6, PE.6.1, PE.6.2, PE.6.3
HO.2.2.15.4	IM.7.2.23
HO.2.2.15.5	SE.2.1, SE.2.1.1
HO.2.3	OP.1
HO.2.3.1	PE.1.8
HO.2.3.2	OP.1
HO.2.3.3	OP.1
HO.2.3.4	scoring guideline for OP.3.3
HO.2.3.5	RI.1.1.6
HO.3	PL.1
HO.3.1	PL.2.2, MA.1.3.4.2.1
HO.3.2	PL.4.2, PL.4.2.1.4
HO.3.3	LD.1.3.2
HO.3.4	TX.8, PH.2.5.1.6.1
HO.4	IM.7.5
HO.4.1	scoring guideline for IM.7.5
HO.4.2	IM.7.2
HO.4.2.1	IM.7.2.1
HO.4.2.2	IM.7.2.5
HO.4.2.3	IM.7.2.11
HO.4.2.4	IM.7.2.16, IM.7.2.17
HO.4.2.5	IM.7.2.12
HO.4.2.6	IM.7.2.6
HO.4.2.7	IM.7.2.12
HO.4.2.8	PE.7.3
HO.4.2.9	scoring guideline for PE.1.7.1
HO.4.2.10	PE.7.1
HO.4.2.11	IM.7.2.23

1993	**1994**
HO.4.2.12	IM.7.2.23
HO.4.3	IM.7.7.1
HO.4.4	IM.7.5
HO.4.4.1	scoring guideline for IM.7.5
HO.4.4.1.1	scoring guideline for IM.7.5
HO.4.4.1.2	scoring guideline for IM.7.5
HO.4.4.1.3	scoring guideline for IM.7.5
HO.4.4.1.4	scoring guideline for IM.7.5
HO.4.4.2	IM.7.5.1
HO.4.4.2.1	scoring guideline for IM.7.5
HO.4.4.2.2	scoring guideline for IM.7.5
HO.4.4.2.2.1	scoring guideline for IM.7.5
HO.4.4.2.2.2	IM.7.10.1
HO.4.4.3	scoring guideline for IM.7.5
HO.4.5	IM.7.4.2
HO.5	LD.4
HO.5.1	LD.1.3.4
HO.5.1.1	LD.1.3.4
HO.5.1.1.1	LD.1.3.3
HO.5.1.1.2	MA.1.3.10–MA.1.3.10.2
HO.5.1.1.3	RI.1.1.2.1
HO.5.1.2	PI.3.3–PI.3.3.2
HO.5.1.2.1	PI.3.3–PI.3.3.2
HO.5.1.3	PI.3.4
HO.5.1.3.1	PI.3.4
HO.5.1.4	IM.7.2, IM.7.2.23
HO.5.1.4.1	IM.7.2, IM.7.2.23
HO.5.1.4.1.1	IM.7.2, IM.7.2.23
HO.5.1.4.2	scoring guideline for IM.7.5
HO.5.1.5	PI.4.1.2–PI.4.1.2.3
HO.5.1.5.1	SE.4, SE.4.1

INFECTION CONTROL

Some of the standards in this chapter of the 1993 *Accreditation Manual for Hospitals* have been recast to focus on improving individual and organizational performance and have been moved to Sections 1 and 2 of this *Manual*. To help you identify these standards, we have printed them here in small italic type with their new standard references in bold type in parentheses. Organizations are expected to demonstrate compliance with these standards in their new context. For example, IC.2.3.2.1 in this chapter has been recast and moved to the "Leadership" chapter, as LD.3.4.1.1. This standard appears in small italic type, and the new standard reference, LD.3.4.1.1, appears in bold type in parentheses at the end of the standard. Organizations are expected to comply with LD.3.4.1.1 and will be scored for compliance in the "Leadership" chapter. Standards scored in this chapter are in normal type and have accompanying scoring scales (1 2 3 4 5 NA).

IC.1
There is an effective hospitalwide program for the surveillance, prevention, and control of infection.

1 2 3 4 5 NA

IC.1.1   All patient care and patient care support departments/services are included in the program.

1 2 3 4 5 NA

IC.1.2   There are written policies and procedures that describe

IC.1.2.1   the role and scope of participation of each department/service in infection prevention and control activities; and

1 2 3 4 5 NA

IC.1.2.2   the role and scope of participation of employee health activities in the program.

1 2 3 4 5 NA

IC.1.3   There are written policies and procedures that describe the types of surveillance carried out to monitor the rates of nosocomial infections, the systems used to collect and analyze data, and the activities to prevent and control infection.

1 2 3 4 5 NA

IC.1.3.1   There is ongoing review and analysis of nosocomial infection data, risk factors, and, as needed, special studies that relate to infection prevention and control.

1 2 3 4 5 NA

IC.1.3.1.1   Laboratory support, particularly microbiological and serological, is provided. (LD.1.3.4.1)

IC.1.3.1.2   Nosocomial infection data, using, as appropriate, rates stratified by infection risk or focused infection studies, are collected on an ongoing basis for the following purposes:

IC.1.3.1.2.1   To monitor the effects of intervention strategies on the infection rates; and

1 2 3 4 5 NA

IC.1.3.1.2.2 To provide feedback to selected groups of physicians, nurses, and support staff about the nosocomial infection risk of their patients.

1 2 3 4 5 NA

IC.1.3.2 Activities are conducted to prevent and control infections in patients and personnel.

1 2 3 4 5 NA

IC.1.3.2.1 Written policies define the indications for specific precautions to prevent transmission of infection, including

IC.1.3.2.1.1 adequate infection control devices and supplies to be available in patient care areas; and

1 2 3 4 5 NA

IC.1.3.2.1.2 filled infectious waste containers to be disposed of in a timely manner in accordance with the hospital's hazardous materials and waste program.

1 2 3 4 5 NA

IC.1.3.2.2 Persons qualified in infection surveillance, prevention, and control provide consultation regarding the purchase of all equipment and supplies used for sterilization, disinfection, and decontamination purposes.

1 2 3 4 5 NA

IC.1.3.2.3 Cleaning procedures, agents, and schedules in use throughout the hospital are periodically reviewed.

1 2 3 4 5 NA

IC.1.3.2.3.1 Persons qualified in infection surveillance, prevention, and control provide consultation regarding any major change in cleaning products or techniques.

1 2 3 4 5 NA

IC.2
A multidisciplinary committee oversees the program for surveillance, prevention, and control of infection.

1 2 3 4 5 NA

IC.2.1 Committee membership includes representatives from at least the medical staff, nursing, administration, and the person(s) directly responsible for management of the infection surveillance, prevention, and control program.

1 2 3 4 5 NA

IC.2.1.1 Representation from housekeeping, central services, laundry, the dietetic department/service, the engineering and maintenance department/service, pharmacy, and the operating suite is available on at least a consultative basis.

1 2 3 4 5 NA

IC.2.1.2 The infection control committee meets not less than quarterly.

1 2 3 4 5 NA

IC.2.2 The committee approves the type and scope of surveillance activities, which include at least the following:

IC.2.2.1 Review of designated microbiological reports;

1 2 3 4 5 NA

IC.2.2.2 Review of patient infections, as appropriate, to determine whether an infection is nosocomial, using definitions and criteria approved by the committee;

1 2 3 4 5 NA

IC.2.2.2.1 Review focuses on those infections that present the potential for prevention or intervention to reduce the risk of future occurrence.

1 2 3 4 5 NA

IC.2.2.2.2 Review is directed to surveillance data, when available.

1 2 3 4 5 NA

IC.2.2.3   Prevalence and incidence studies, if appropriate; and

1 2 3 4 5 NA

IC.2.2.4   Routine or special collection of other data, as approved by the committee.

1 2 3 4 5 NA

IC.2.2.4.1   Sampling of personnel or the environment for infective agents is done only at the direction of the committee, or its designee, and only in accordance with applicable law or regulation.

1 2 3 4 5 NA

IC.2.3   The committee approves actions to prevent or control infection, based on an evaluation of the surveillance reports of infections and of the infection potential among patients and hospital personnel.

1 2 3 4 5 NA

IC.2.3.1   Conclusions, recommendations, and actions are documented in the minutes of the committee meetings.

1 2 3 4 5 NA

*IC.2.3.2   The minutes are forwarded to the medical staff (through the executive committee), the chief executive officer, the nurse executive, and the person(s) responsible for hospitalwide quality assessment and improvement activities. **(scoring guideline for LD.3.4.1.1)***

*IC.2.3.2.1   The responsibility for taking action on the recommendations documented in the minutes is assigned and defined in writing. **(LD.3.4.1.1)***

IC.2.4   The committee reviews and approves, at least every two years, all policies and procedures related to the infection surveillance, prevention, and control program and to infection surveillance, prevention, and control activities in all departments/services.

1 2 3 4 5 NA

*IC.2.4.1   Reviews and approvals are documented in the minutes of the committee meetings. **(LD.3.4.1.1)***

IC.2.5   The authority of the committee, or its designee, to institute any surveillance, prevention, and control measures or studies when there is reason to believe that any patient or personnel may be in danger is defined in writing and approved by the hospital administration and medical staff.

1 2 3 4 5 NA

IC.2.5.1   The statement of authority is reviewed and authenticated every two years by the hospital administration and the medical staff.

1 2 3 4 5 NA

IC.3
Responsibility for the management of infection surveillance, prevention, and control is assigned to a qualified person(s).

1 2 3 4 5 NA

IC.3.1   The amount of time the person(s) spends in infection surveillance, prevention, and control activities is related to the needs of the hospital, as defined by the committee responsible for overseeing the infection surveillance, prevention, and control program.

1 2 3 4 5 NA

IC.4
There are written policies and procedures for infection surveillance, prevention, and control for all patient care departments/services.

1 2 3 4 5 NA

IC.4.1   All personnel are competent to participate in infection monitoring, prevention, and control activities.

1 2 3 4 5 NA

IC.5

Patient care support departments/services, such as central services, housekeeping services, and linen and laundry services, are available to assist in the prevention and control of infections and are provided with adequate direction, staffing, and facilities to perform all required infection surveillance, prevention, and control functions.

1 2 3 4 5 NA

IC.5.1 When the hospital conducts decontamination and sterilization activities, there are specific written policies and procedures for these activities.

1 2 3 4 5 NA

IC.5.1.1 The performance of all sterilizing equipment throughout the hospital is monitored.

1 2 3 4 5 NA

IC.5.1.2 There are written policies for the shelf life of all stored sterile items.

1 2 3 4 5 NA

IC.5.1.3 There are written policies and procedures for the reuse of disposable items.

1 2 3 4 5 NA

IC.5.1.3.1 These policies and procedures address the reprocessing of disposable items to be reused.

1 2 3 4 5 NA

IC.5.2 The laundry service provides, either directly or in accordance with a written agreement with an off-site source, an adequate supply of clean linen.

1 2 3 4 5 NA

IC.5.2.1 Clean linen is delivered to the user in such a way as to minimize microbial contamination from surface contact or airborne deposition.

1 2 3 4 5 NA

IC.5.2.2 Soiled linen is collected in such a manner as to minimize microbial dissemination into the environment.

1 2 3 4 5 NA

NOTES AND COMMENTS:

MANAGEMENT AND ADMINISTRATIVE SERVICES

Some of the standards in this chapter of the 1993 *Accreditation Manual for Hospitals* have been recast to focus on improving individual and organizational performance and have been moved to Sections 1 and 2 of this *Manual.* To help you identify these standards, we have printed them here in small italic type with their new standard references in bold type in parentheses. Organizations are expected to demonstrate compliance with these standards in their new context. For example, MA.1.3.4 in this chapter has been recast and moved to the "Leadership" chapter, as LD.1.3. This standard appears in small italic type, and the new standard reference, LD.1.3, appears in bold type in parentheses at the end of the standard. Organizations are expected to comply with LD.1.3 and will be scored for compliance in the "Leadership" chapter. Standards scored in this chapter are in normal type and have accompanying scoring scales (1 2 3 4 5 NA).

MA.1
The hospital is managed effectively and efficiently.

1 2 3 4 5 NA

MA.1.1   A chief executive officer appointed by the governing body is responsible for the operation of the hospital in a manner commensurate with the authority conferred by the governing body.

1 2 3 4 5 NA

MA.1.1.1 The chief executive officer is qualified by education and experience that is appropriate to the fulfillment of the responsibilities of the position.

1 2 3 4 5 NA

MA.1.2   The chief executive officer takes all reasonable steps to provide for the following:

MA.1.2.1 Hospital compliance with applicable law and regulation; and

1 2 3 4 5 NA

MA.1.2.2 Consistent with governing body policy, the review of and prompt action on reports and recommendations of authorized planning, regulatory, and inspection agencies.

1 2 3 4 5 NA

MA.1.3   The chief executive officer, through the management and administrative staff, provides for the following:

MA.1.3.1 Implementation of organized management and administrative functions throughout the hospital, including establishment of clear lines of responsibility and accountability within departments/services and between department/service heads and administrative staff;

1 2 3 4 5 NA

MA.1.3.2 Implementation of effective communication mechanisms between and among hospital departments/services, the medical staff, the administration, and the governing body; **(scoring guideline for LD.3.2.1)**

MA.1.3.3   Establishment of internal controls to safeguard physical, financial, and human resources;

1 2 3 4 5 NA

> *MA.1.3.4   Coordination of hospital services with the identified needs of the patient population served, including those for neonate, child, and adolescent patients; (**LD.1.3**)*

MA.1.3.4.1   In hospitals providing services to neonate, child, and adolescent patients, there is a mechanism for the coordination and facilitation of the family's and/or guardian's involvement throughout the course of treatment.

1 2 3 4 5 NA

MA.1.3.4.1.1   At a minimum, this mechanism is designed to

MA.1.3.4.1.1.1   facilitate family involvement in the assessment, treatment, and continuing care of the patient; and

1 2 3 4 5 NA

> *MA.1.3.4.1.1.2   aid the family in coping with illnesses that are particularly traumatic because of their duration, severity, or effect on the patient's physical or psychological development. (**PF.2**)*

MA.1.3.4.2   When a course of treatment separates the child or adolescent patient from normal daily living experience for a significant period of time, the patient's needs for activities of daily living are provided for in the physical and social environment.

1 2 3 4 5 NA

MA.1.3.4.2.1   The physical environment is designed to encourage its use and provide comfort and security.

1 2 3 4 5 NA

MA.1.3.4.2.2   Provisions are made in the social environment for

MA.1.3.4.2.2.1   activities appropriate to the age and development of patients; and

1 2 3 4 5 NA

MA.1.3.4.2.2.2   peer and group interaction.

1 2 3 4 5 NA

MA.1.3.4.3   Needed services are provided either directly or through referral, consultation, or contractual arrangements and/or agreements, including services for

1 2 3 4 5 NA

MA.1.3.4.3.1   patients who are emotionally ill, who become emotionally ill while in the hospital, or who suffer the results of alcoholism or drug abuse; and

1 2 3 4 5 NA

MA.1.3.4.3.2   emergency patients who are under the influence of drugs or alcohol or who are emotionally ill or become difficult to manage.

1 2 3 4 5 NA

MA.1.3.4.3.2.1   The role of the medical staff in providing such services is defined.

1 2 3 4 5 NA

MA.1.3.4.4   The patient's referral to services provided through referral, consultation, or contractual arrangements and/or agreements is documented.

1 2 3 4 5 NA

MA.1.3.4.5   Furniture and equipment are appropriate to the age, size, and developmental needs of the patient.

1 2 3 4 5 NA

MA.1.3.5   A hospitalwide policy on patients' rights and responsibilities;

1 2 3 4 5 NA

MA.1.3.5.1 In hospitals providing services to neonate, child, and adolescent patients, the policy addresses the rights and responsibilities of these patients and of their parents and/or guardians.

1 2 3 4 5 NA

MA.1.3.5.1.1 The policy describes the mechanism for resolving conflicts that arise concerning the care of the patient.

1 2 3 4 5 NA

MA.1.3.5.1.2 The policy is adopted by the medical staff and approved by the governing body.

1 2 3 4 5 NA

MA.1.3.6 A mechanism for receiving and responding to patients' and families' complaints concerning the quality of care;

1 2 3 4 5 NA

MA.1.3.6.1 Patients and families are informed of their right to present complaints and how to do so.

1 2 3 4 5 NA

MA.1.3.6.2 The organization analyzes the complaint, and, when indicated, takes appropriate corrective action.

1 2 3 4 5 NA

MA.1.3.6.3 Each patient or family making a significant complaint receives a response from the organization that substantively addresses the complaint.

1 2 3 4 5 NA

MA.1.3.6.4 Presentation of a complaint does not in itself serve to compromise a patient's future access to care.

1 2 3 4 5 NA

MA.1.3.7 A hospitalwide policy on the withholding of resuscitative services from patients;

1 2 3 4 5 NA

MA.1.3.8 Policies and procedures for the identification and referral of organ and tissue donors to organ procurement agencies or tissue banks;

1 2 3 4 5 NA

MA.1.3.9 Policies and procedures for notifying appropriate organ procurement agencies and tissue banks when organs and tissues become available for transplantation;

1 2 3 4 5 NA

MA.1.3.10 A plan for effectively communicating

MA.1.3.10.1 in the language(s) of the predominant population group(s) served by the hospital, and

1 2 3 4 5 NA

MA.1.3.10.2 as needed, with persons with impaired hearing or speaking skills;

1 2 3 4 5 NA

MA.1.3.11 Hospitalwide policies and procedures on discharge planning, which include, but need not be limited to,

1 2 3 4 5 NA

MA.1.3.11.1 mechanisms to

MA.1.3.11.1.1 identify patients who require discharge planning to foster continuity of medical and/or other care to meet their identified needs, and

1 2 3 4 5 NA

MA.1.3.11.1.2 initiate discharge planning on a timely basis,

1 2 3 4 5 NA

MA.1.3.11.2 the role in the initiation and implementation of the discharge planning process of the physician or other licensed independent practitioner primarily responsible for the patient, nursing staff, social work staff, other appropriate staff, the patient, and the patient's family or representative and/or guardian, and

1 2 3 4 5 NA

MA.1.3.11.3 the documentation in the medical record of the discharge plan, including an assessment of the availability of appropriate services to meet the patient's identified needs after hospitalization;

1 2 3 4 5 NA

MA.1.3.12 A policy designed to facilitate access to appropriate educational services for each child or adolescent patient when the treatment necessitates a significant absence from school;

1 2 3 4 5 NA

MA.1.3.13 Hospitalwide policies and procedures designed to assure that whenever a neonate, child, or adolescent patient is transferred from one setting to another (for example, intraorganization, interorganization, or discharge), the patient's need for continuing treatment, continuing education, and support for normal development is assessed;

1 2 3 4 5 NA

MA.1.3.14 Dissemination and enforcement of a hospitalwide smoking policy that prohibits the use of smoking materials throughout the hospital building(s); and

1 2 3 4 5 NA

MA.1.3.14.1 Any exceptions to the prohibition are authorized for a patient by a physician's written authorization, based on criteria that are defined by the medical staff.

1 2 3 4 5 NA

MA.1.3.15 A hospitalwide policy that specifies the time within which an order must be obtained after each use of restraint or seclusion and the maximum time for the use of either intervention.

1 2 3 4 5 NA

MA.1.3.15.1 This policy also addresses periodic observation of patients for whom restraint or seclusion is employed, including a maximum time between observations.

1 2 3 4 5 NA

MA.1.4 The chief executive officer, through the management and administrative staff, provides for personnel policies and practices that pertain to at least the following:

MA.1.4.1 Employment of personnel, without regard to sex, race, creed, or national origin, whose qualifications are commensurate with anticipated job responsibilities;

1 2 3 4 5 NA

MA.1.4.2 Verification of all applicable current licensure/certification;

1 2 3 4 5 NA

MA.1.4.3 Periodic performance evaluation for each employee, based on a job description, and for each person providing direct patient care or support services under a contract, who is not subject to a clinical privileging process; and

1 2 3 4 5 NA

MA.1.4.3.1 For individuals without clinical privileges who have some responsibility for the assessment, treatment, or care of patients, the job description and periodic performance appraisals address the ages of the patients served.

1 2 3 4 5 NA

MA.1.4.4 Provision of employee health services, in consultation with the medical staff.

1 2 3 4 5 NA

*MA.1.5 The chief executive officer, through the management and administrative staff, provides written plans for the implementation of financial policies and practices that pertain to at least the following: (**LD.1.5**)*

*MA.1.5.1 A formal budget that reflects the organization of the hospital and is developed with the participation of the medical staff and staff of other departments/services; and (**LD.1.5**)*

*MA.1.5.2   Unless otherwise provided by law, an annual audit, by an independent public accountant, of the financial statements of the hospital. (**LD.1.5.3**)*

*MA.1.6   The chief executive officer, through the management and administrative staff, provides support for the medical staff in the following activities: (**LD.4–LD.4.3**)*

*MA.1.6.1   Identification of general areas of potential risk in the clinical aspects of patient care and safety; (**LD.4–LD.4.3**)*

*MA.1.6.2   Development of criteria for identifying specific cases with potential risk in the clinical aspects of patient care and safety and evaluation of these cases; (**LD.4–LD.4.3**)*

*MA.1.6.3   Correction of problems in the clinical aspects of patient care and safety identified by risk management activities; and (**LD.4–LD.4.3**)*

*MA.1.6.4   Design of programs to reduce risk in the clinical aspects of patient care and safety. (**LD.4–LD.4.3**)*

NOTES AND COMMENTS:

MEDICAL RECORD SERVICES

Standards in this chapter of the 1993 *Accreditation Manual for Hospitals* have been recast to focus on improving individual and organizational performance and have been moved to Sections 1 and 2 of this *Manual.* The following cross-reference is provided for your information.

1993	1994
MR.1	scoring guideline for IM.3, IM.7, IM.8
MR.1.1	IM.7.1
MR.1.2	IM.7.7.1
MR.1.3	scoring guideline for IM.7.2
MR.1.3.1	scoring guideline for IM.7.2
MR.1.3.2	scoring guideline for IM.7.2
MR.1.3.3	scoring guideline for IM.7.2
MR.1.3.4	IM.8
MR.1.4	IM.7.10
MR.2	IM.7.2
MR.2.1	IM.7.2–IM.7.2.23
MR.2.1.1	IM.7.2–IM.7.2.23
MR.2.1.2	IM.7.2–IM.7.2.23
MR.2.1.3	IM.7.2–IM.7.2.23
MR.2.1.4	IM.7.2–IM.7.2.23
MR.2.1.5	IM.7.2–IM.7.2.23
MR.2.1.6	IM.7.2–IM.7.2.23
MR.2.1.6.1	IM.7.2–IM.7.2.23
MR.2.1.6.2	IM.7.2–IM.7.2.23
MR.2.1.7	IM.7.2–IM.7.2.23
MR.2.1.8	IM.7.2–IM.7.2.23
MR.2.1.9	IM.7.2–IM.7.2.23
MR.2.2	IM.7.2
MR.2.2.1	IM.7.2.1
MR.2.2.2	scoring guideline for PE.1.1
MR.2.2.2.1	scoring guideline for PE.1.1
MR.2.2.2.2	scoring guideline for PE.1.1
MR.2.2.2.3	scoring guideline for PE.1.1
MR.2.2.2.4	scoring guideline for PE.1.1
MR.2.2.3	PE.7
MR.2.2.3.1	PE.7.1
MR.2.2.3.2	PE.7.2
MR.2.2.3.3	PE.7.3
MR.2.2.3.4	PE.7.4
MR.2.2.4	PE.1.7.1
MR.2.2.5	IM.7.2.5
MR.2.2.5.1	IM.7.2.5

1993	**1994**
MR.2.2.5.2	PE.1.7.1
MR.2.2.5.2.1	PE.1.7.1
MR.2.2.5.3	IM.7.9.3
MR.2.2.6	IM.7.2.5
MR.2.2.7	IM.7.2.8
MR.2.2.7.1	IM.7.2.15
MR.2.2.8	IM.7.2.11
MR.2.2.8.1	IM.7.8
MR.2.2.8.2	IM.7.8.2
MR.2.2.8.2.1	IM.7.8.2.1
MR.2.2.9	IM.7.2.14
MR.2.2.10	IM.7.2.18
MR.2.2.11	IM.7.2.14
MR.2.2.12	IM.7.2.12
MR.2.2.12.1	IM.7.9
MR.2.2.12.2	IM.7.4.2.2
MR.2.2.13	IM.7.2.12
MR.2.2.14	IM.7.2.17
MR.2.2.14.1	IM.7.2.22
MR.2.2.14.2	IM.7.3
MR.2.2.14.3	IM.7.3.1–IM.7.3.1.2
MR.2.2.14.4	scoring guideline for IM.7.7
MR.3	IM.2, IM.3.3.1, IM.7.7, IM.7.9
MR.3.1	IM.2.3
MR.3.2	IM.2.3
MR.3.2.1	IM.2.2.1
MR.3.3	IM.2.2.2
MR.3.3.1	IM.7.10.1
MR.3.4	scoring guideline for IM.7.7.1
MR.3.4.1	IM.7.1.1
MR.3.4.2	IM.7.9
MR.3.4.2.1	IM.7.9.1
MR.3.4.2.2	IM.7.9.2
MR.3.4.2.2.1	IM.7.9.2.1
MR.3.4.3	IM.7.9.3
MR.3.4.4	scoring guideline for IM.7.9.3
MR.3.4.5	scoring guideline for IM.7.9.3
MR.3.5	IM.7.7.1
MR.3.6	IM.7.7.2
MR.3.6.1	IM.7.7.2
MR.3.6.2	IM.7.3
MR.4	LD.2.1.4
MR.4.1	LD.2.2.2
MR.4.1.1	LD.1.3.4.2.1
MR.4.2	IM.6.1
MR.4.3	IM.2.2, IM.8.1.5
MR.4.3.1	IM.8.1.5, IM.8.1.6
MR.4.3.2	IM.3.3
MR.5	PI.1 and PI.1.1

MEDICAL STAFF

The "Medical Staff" chapter has been relocated to Section 3 of this 1994 *Accreditation Manual for Hospitals* with the following two exceptions.

First, the standards related to the nine common responsibilities of all department/service leaders have been moved to the "Leadership" chapter.

Second, the standards commonly known as the "medical staff monitors" and related to the monitoring of surgical and other invasive procedures, medication use evaluation, the use of blood and blood components, risk management activities, and other review functions have been moved to the "Improving Organizational Performance'" chapter.

The standards for the medical record review function have been moved to the "Management of Information" chapter, and the standards for the pharmacy and therapeutics function have been moved to the "Treatment of Patients" chapter.

The cross-reference that follows details the movement of these standards.

1993	1994
MS.4.6.1.1.3	LD.2.1.1
MS.4.6.1.1.4	LD.2.1.2
MS.4.6.1.1.5	LD.2.1.3
MS.4.6.1.1.6	LD.2.1.4
MS.4.6.1.1.10	LD.2.1.5
MS.4.6.1.1.11	LD.2.1.6
MS.4.6.1.1.12	LD.2.1.7
MS.4.6.1.1.13	LD.2.1.8
MS.4.6.1.1.14	LD.2.1.9
MS.5.1.1	PI.4.2
MS.5.1.1.1	PI.4.2.1
MS.5.1.2	PI.3.4.2
MS.5.1.2.1	PI.3.4.2.1
MS.5.1.2.2	PI.3.4.2.1
MS.5.1.2.3	PI.3.4.2.1
MS.5.1.2.3.1	PI.3.4.1.1–PI.3.4.1.3
MS.5.1.2.3.2	PI.3
MS.5.1.2.3.2.1	PI.3
MS.5.1.2.3.3	PI.3.4.2.1
MS.5.1.2.3.4	PI.3.4.2.1
MS.5.1.2.3.4.1	PI.3.4.2.1
MS.5.1.2.4	PI.3
MS.5.1.2.5	PI.4.2, PI.4.2.1
MS.5.1.2.6	PI.5.3–PI.5.3.3
MSN.5.1.2	PI.3.4.2, PI.3.4.2.1
MSN.5.1.2.1	PI.4
MSN.5.1.2.1.1	PI.1.1
MSN.5.1.2.1.2	PI.4.1.3.1
MSN.5.1.2.1.2.1	PI.3.4.2.1

1993	1994
MSN.5.1.2.1.3	PI.3.1
MSN.5.1.2.1.4	PI.3.4
MSN.5.1.2.1.4.1	PI.3.4.1–PI.3.4.1.3
MSN.5.1.2.1.4.2	PI.3.4.1–PI.3.4.1.3
MSN.5.1.2.2	PI.5.3–PI.5.3.2
MSN.5.1.2.2.1	PI.5.3.3
MSN.5.1.2.2.2	PI.5.3.1.1
MSN.5.1.2.2.3	PI.4.2
MS.5.1.3	PI.3.4.2.2
MS.5.1.3.1	PI.1.1
MS.5.1.3.1.1	PI.3.4.2.2
MS.5.1.3.2	PI.3.4.1
MS.5.1.3.2.1	PI.3.4.1.1
MS.5.1.3.2.2	PI.3.4.1.2
MS.5.1.3.2.3	PI.3.4.1.3
MS.5.1.3.2.4	PI.3.4.1.2
MS.5.1.3.3	PI.3.4.2
MS.5.1.3.3.1	PI.1.1
MS.5.1.3.3.2	PI.4.1.2.2
MS.5.1.3.3.3	PI.3
MS.5.1.3.4	PI.3
MS.5.1.3.5	PI.4.2, PI.4.2.1
MS.5.1.3.6	PI.5.3–PI.5.3.3
MSN.5.1.3	PI.3.4.2.2
MSN.5.1.3.1	PI.3
MSN.5.1.3.1.1	PI.1.1
MSN.5.1.3.1.2	PI.3
MSN.5.1.3.1.2.1	PI.3.4.2.2
MSN.5.1.3.1.3	PI.3.1
MSN.5.1.3.1.4	PI.3.4
MSN.5.1.3.1.4.1	PI.3.4.1–PI.3.4.1.3
MSN.5.1.3.1.4.2	PI.3.4.1–PI.3.4.1.3
MSN.5.1.3.2	PI.5.3–PI.5.3.2
MSN.5.1.3.2.1	PI.5.3.3
MSN.5.1.3.2.2	PI.5.3.1.1
MSN.5.1.3.2.3	PI.4.2
MS.5.1.4	IM.3
MS.5.1.4.1	IM.3.3.1
MS.5.1.4.2	IM.3
MS.5.1.4.2.1	IM.3.3.1.1
MS.5.1.4.2.2	IM.3.3.1.2
MS.5.1.4.2.3	IM.3.2
MS.5.1.4.3	PI.5.3–PI.5.3.2
MS.5.1.5	PI.3.4.2.3
MS.5.1.5.1	PI.1.1
MS.5.1.5.2	PI.3.4.1
MS.5.1.5.2.1	PI.3.4.2.3
MS.5.1.5.2.1.1	PI.3
MS.5.1.5.2.1.1.1	PI.3
MS.5.1.5.2.1.1.2	PI.3
MS.5.1.5.2.2	PI.4.1.3.6
MS.5.1.5.2.4	PI.3.4.2.3
MS.5.1.5.2.5	PI.3.4.2.3
MS.5.1.5.3	PI.3

1993	1994
MS.5.1.5.4	PI.4.2
MS.5.1.5.5	PI.5.3–PI.5.3.3
MSN.5.1.5	PI.3.4.2.3
MSN.5.1.5.1	PI.3
MSN.5.1.5.1.1	PI.1.1
MSN.5.1.5.1.2	PI.3
MSN.5.1.5.1.2.1	PI.3.4.2.3
MSN.5.1.5.1.3	PI.3.1
MSN.5.1.5.1.4	PI.3.4
MSN.5.1.5.1.4.1	PI.3.4.1–PI.3.4.1.3
MSN.5.1.5.1.4.2	PI.3.4.1–PI.3.4.1.3
MSN.5.1.5.1.5	PI.4.1.3.6
MSN.5.1.5.2	PI.5.3–PI.5.3.2
MSN.5.1.5.2.1	PI.5.3.3
MSN.5.1.5.2.2	PI.5.3.1.1
MSN.5.1.5.2.3	PI.4.2
MSN.5.1.5.3	TX.13
MS.5.1.6	PI.3.4.2.2
MS.5.1.6.1	PI.1.1
MS.5.1.6.2	PI.3.4.2.2
MS.5.1.6.2.1	TX.13
MS.5.1.6.2.2	TX.1
MS.5.1.6.2.3	scoring guideline for TX.13
MS.5.1.6.2.4	PI.4.1.3.7
MS.5.1.7	PI.3.4.1.2
MS.5.1.7.1	PI.3.4.1.2
MS.5.1.7.1.1	PI.3.4.1.2
MS.5.1.7.1.2	PI.3.4.1.2
MS.5.1.7.1.3	PI.3.4.1.2
MS.5.1.7.1.4	PI.5.1
MS.5.1.8	PI.1.1
MS.5.1.8.1	PI.3.4.2.4
MS.5.1.8.3.4	PI.3.5.1

NUCLEAR MEDICINE SERVICES

Some of the standards in this chapter of the 1993 *Accreditation Manual for Hospitals* have been recast to focus on improving individual and organizational performance and have been moved to Sections 1 and 2 of this *Manual*. To help you identify these standards, we have printed them here in small italic type with their new standard references in bold type in parentheses. Organizations are expected to demonstrate compliance with these standards in their new context. For example, NM.1 in this chapter has been recast and moved to the "Leadership" chapter, as LD.1.3.4. This standard appears in small italic type, and the new standard reference, LD.1.3.4, appears in bold type in parentheses at the end of the standard. Organizations are expected to comply with LD.1.3.4 and will be scored for compliance in the "Leadership" chapter. Standards scored in this chapter are in normal type and have accompanying scoring scales (1 2 3 4 5 NA).

NM.1   Diagnostic and/or therapeutic nuclear medicine services are regularly and conveniently available to meet the needs of patients, as determined by the medical staff. **(LD.1.3.4)***

NM.1.1   All individuals who provide diagnostic and/or therapeutic nuclear medicine services independently, whether or not they are members of the department/service, have delineated clinical privileges for the services they provide.   1 2 3 4 5 NA

NM.1.1.1   All nuclear medicine diagnostic and/or therapeutic procedures are provided and performed in accordance with appropriate institutional licensure requirements and/or applicable law and regulation.   1 2 3 4 5 NA

NM.1.2   The director of diagnostic and/or therapeutic nuclear medicine services is a physician member of the medical staff who is qualified by education and experience in diagnostic and/or therapeutic nuclear medicine, is clinically competent, and possesses the administrative skills necessary to assure effective leadership of the department/service.   1 2 3 4 5 NA

NM.1.3   Comprehensive safety rules are developed by the director of the department/service in cooperation with the hospital's safety committee and the hospital's radiation safety committee, if one exists.   1 2 3 4 5 NA

*NM.1.4   There is a description of the means for providing diagnostic and/or therapeutic nuclear medicine services when they are not provided by the hospital. **(LD.1.3.4.2.1)***

---

*These services are not required for hospitals that provide only social rehabilitation/substance abuse services.

NM.1.5 When diagnostic and/or therapeutic nuclear medicine services are performed outside the hospital, the off-site source(s) meets the standards contained in this chapter of this Manual. (scoring guideline for LD.1.3.4.2.1)

NM.2 There are policies and procedures to assure effective management, safety, proper performance of equipment, effective communication, and quality control in the nuclear medicine department/service. (LD.2, LD.2.1.2, LD.2.1.3, LD.2.1.7)

NM.2.1 Policies and procedures are developed in cooperation with the medical staff, administration, nurse executive and other appropriate registered nurses, and, as necessary, other clinical departments/services and are implemented. (LD.3.3)

NM.2.1.1 The policies and procedures are reviewed periodically by a medical radiation physicist.

1 2 3 4 5 NA

NM.2.2 The written policies and procedures include, but need not be limited to, the following:

NM.2.2.1 Diagnostic and therapeutic nuclear medicine services performed at the request of individuals licensed to practice independently and authorized by the hospital to make such requests;

1 2 3 4 5 NA

NM.2.2.2 Prescribing of nuclear medicine (radionuclide) therapy and supervision of the course of therapy by a qualified physician;

1 2 3 4 5 NA

NM.2.2.3 A quality control program designed to minimize patient, personnel, and public risk and maximize the quality of diagnostic information; (PI.3.5, PI.3.5.2, PI.3.5.3.4)

NM.2.2.4 Implementation of PL.3 through PL.3.3.1.2 in the "Plant, Technology, and Safety Management" chapter of this *Manual* for all electrically and nonelectrically powered equipment used in the diagnosis, treatment, or monitoring of patients to assure that the equipment, wherever located in the hospital, performs properly;

1 2 3 4 5 NA

NM.2.2.5 Maintenance of records on radionuclides and radiopharmaceuticals from the point they enter the hospital to the point of administration and final disposal; (IM.8.1.3)

NM.2.2.5.1 Information in the records includes, at the least, (IM.8.1)

NM.2.2.5.1.1 the identity of the radionuclide, the date received, method of receipt, activity, identity of recipients and dates administered, and disposal. (IM.8.1.3)

NM.2.2.6 Safety policies, including

NM.2.2.6.1 the receipt, storage, transport, preparation, handling, use, and disposal of radionuclides, and

1 2 3 4 5 NA

NM.2.2.6.2 implementation of PL.1.6 through PL.1.6.4 in the "Plant, Technology, and Safety Management" chapter of this *Manual* (for the management of hazardous materials);

1 2 3 4 5 NA

NM.2.2.7 Standardizing of equipment performance, use of radiation standard sources having energies equivalent to those radionuclides used in patient studies;

1 2 3 4 5 NA

*NM.2.2.8 Provisions that a qualified physician, qualified medical radiation physicist, or other qualified individual (**PI.3, PI.3.4, PI.3.5.3.4**)*

*NM.2.2.8.1 monitor performance evaluations of diagnostic equipment on a quarterly basis, (**PI.3, PI.3.4, PI.3.5.3.4**)*

*NM.2.2.8.2 monitor doses administered to patients for acceptable agreement with prescribed doses, (**PI.3, PI.3.4, PI.3.5.3.4**)*

*NM.2.2.8.3 monitor, for validity, quantitative results obtained from procedures, and (**PI.3, PI.3.4, PI.3.5.3.4**)*

*NM.2.2.8.4 monitor absorbed doses of radiation in individual patients as requested by the director; (**PI.3, PI.3.4, PI.3.5.3.4**)*

NM.2.2.9 Guidelines for protecting personnel and patients from radiation;   1 2 3 4 5 NA

NM.2.2.10 Monitoring of staff and personnel for exposure to radiation;   1 2 3 4 5 NA

NM.2.2.11 Monitoring of receipt, storage, preparation, and use areas for radionuclide contamination;   1 2 3 4 5 NA

NM.2.2.12 Guidelines to be followed in the event of radionuclide contamination of the environment, patients, personnel, or equipment; and   1 2 3 4 5 NA

NM.2.2.13 Orientation and a safety education program for all personnel.   1 2 3 4 5 NA

*NM.3 Reports of consultations, interpretations of diagnostic studies, and radionuclide therapy procedures are included in the patient's medical record. (**scoring guideline for IM.7.2.18**)*

*NM.3.1 Requests/referrals for diagnostic and/or monitoring and/or therapeutic invasive procedures include the study or studies requested and appropriate clinical data to aid in the performance of the procedures requested. (**scoring guideline for PE.1.5**)*

NM.3.2 Only individuals with delineated clinical privileges to perform and/or interpret diagnostic and/or monitoring procedures and supervise radionuclide therapy procedures authenticate reports.   1 2 3 4 5 NA

NM.3.2.1 Individuals authenticate only those reports of procedures for which they have been granted specific clinical privileges through the medical staff privilege delineation process.   1 2 3 4 5 NA

NM.3.3 Authenticated reports are entered in the patient's medical record and, as appropriate, are filed in the department/service.   1 2 3 4 5 NA

Note: *Refer also to the "Improving Organizational Performance" chapter of this Manual.*

NOTES AND COMMENTS:

NURSING CARE

Some of the standards in this chapter of the 1993 *Accreditation Manual for Hospitals* have been recast to focus on improving individual and organizational performance and have been moved to Sections 1 and 2 of this *Manual*. To help you identify these standards, we have printed them here in small italic type with their new standard references in bold type in parentheses. Organizations are expected to demonstrate compliance with these standards in their new context. For example, NC.1.1 in this chapter has been recast and moved to the "Assessment of Patients" chapter, as PE.4.3. This standard appears in small italic type, and the new standard reference, PE.4.3, appears in bold type in parentheses at the end of the standard. Organizations are expected to comply with PE.4.3 and will be scored for compliance in the "Assessment of Patients" chapter. Standards scored in this chapter are in normal type and have accompanying scoring scales (1 2 3 4 5 NA).

The standards in this chapter apply to all settings in which nursing care is provided in the hospital. Patients receive nursing care* in various settings throughout the hospital. For example, nursing care is provided in medical-surgical nursing care units, in alcohol and other drug-dependence programs, in mental health nursing care units, in biopsychosocial and physical rehabilitation programs, in hospital-sponsored ambulatory clinics and services, in emergency services, in intensive care and other special care units, and in units in which surgical and other invasive procedures are performed.

*NC.1 Patients receive nursing care based on a documented assessment of their needs. (**scoring guideline for PE.3.1**)*

*NC.1.1 Each patient's need for nursing care related to his/her admission is assessed by a registered nurse. (**PE.4.3**)*

*NC.1.1.1 The assessment is conducted either at the time of admission or within a time frame preceding or following admission that is specified in hospital policy. (**PE.1.7.1**)*

NC.1.1.2 Aspects of data collection may be delegated by the registered nurse.   1 2 3 4 5 NA

*NC.1.1.3 Needs are reassessed when warranted by the patient's condition. (**PE.2.1**)*

*NC.1.2 Each patient's assessment includes consideration of biophysical, psychosocial, environmental, self-care, educational, and discharge planning factors. (**PE.1, PE.1.3, PE.1.4, PE.1.6**)*

---

*Nursing care *is defined in relevant state, commonwealth, or territory nurse practice acts and other applicable laws and regulations, and as permitted by the hospital in accordance with these definitions. Anesthesia or obstetric care, for example, when provided by nurses in expanded practice roles, is not defined as nursing care.*

*NC.1.2.1   When appropriate, data from the patient's significant other(s) are included in the assessment. (**scoring guideline for PE.1**)*

NC.1.3   Each patient's nursing care is based on identified nursing diagnoses and/or patient care needs and patient care standards and is consistent with the therapies of other disciplines.   1 2 3 4 5 NA

NC.1.3.1   The patient and/or significant other(s) is involved in the patient's care as appropriate.   1 2 3 4 5 NA

NC.1.3.2   Nursing staff members collaborate, as appropriate, with physicians and other clinical disciplines in making decisions regarding each patient's need for nursing care.   1 2 3 4 5 NA

*NC.1.3.3   In preparation for discharge, continuing care needs are assessed and referrals for such care are documented in the patient's medical record. (**scoring guideline for PE.1.6**)*

*NC.1.3.4   The patient's medical record includes documentation of (**IM.7.2**)*

*NC.1.3.4.1   initial assessments and reassessments; (**IM.7.2.5 and IM.7.2.15**)*

*NC.1.3.4.2   nursing diagnoses and/or patient care needs; (**IM.7.2.6**)*

*NC.1.3.4.3   interventions identified to meet the patient's nursing care needs; (**IM.7.2.11**)*

*NC.1.3.4.4   nursing care provided; (**IM.7.2.12**)*

*NC.1.3.4.5   the patient's response to, and the outcomes of, the care provided; and (**IM.7.2.17**)*

NC.1.3.4.6   the abilities of the patient and/or, as appropriate, his/her significant other(s) to manage continuing care needs after discharge.   1 2 3 4 5 NA

*NC.1.3.5   Nursing care data related to patient assessments, the nursing diagnoses and/or patient needs, nursing interventions, and patient outcomes are permanently integrated into the clinical information system (for example, the medical record). (**scoring guideline for IM.7.2.22**)*

*NC.1.3.5.1   Nursing care data can be identified and retrieved from the clinical information system. (**IM.7.10**)*

NC.2
All nursing staff members* are competent to fulfill their assigned responsibilities.   1 2 3 4 5 NA

NC.2.1   Each nursing staff member is assigned clinical and/or managerial responsibilities based on educational preparation, applicable licensing laws and regulations, and an assessment of current competence.   1 2 3 4 5 NA

NC.2.1.1   An evaluation of each nursing staff member's competence is conducted at defined intervals throughout the individual's association with the hospital.   1 2 3 4 5 NA

---

*Nursing staff members *include registered nurses, licensed practical/vocational nurses, nursing assistants, and other nursing personnel.*

NC.2.1.1.1 The evaluation includes an objective assessment of the individual's performance in delivering patient care services in accordance with patient needs.

1 2 3 4 5 NA

NC.2.1.1.2 The process for evaluating competence is defined in policy and procedure.

1 2 3 4 5 NA

NC.2.1.2 Nursing care responsibilities are assigned to a nursing staff member in accordance with

NC.2.1.2.1 the degree of supervision needed by the individual and its availability; and

1 2 3 4 5 NA

NC.2.1.2.2 the complexity and dynamics of the condition of each patient to whom the individual is to provide services and the complexity of the assessment required by each patient, including

NC.2.1.2.2.1 the factors that must be considered to make appropriate decisions regarding the provision of nursing care; and

1 2 3 4 5 NA

NC.2.1.2.2.2 the type of technology employed in providing nursing care.

1 2 3 4 5 NA

NC.2.2 The determination of a nursing staff member's current clinical competence and the assignment of nursing care responsibilities are the responsibility of registered nurses who have the clinical and managerial knowledge and experience necessary to competently make these decisions.

1 2 3 4 5 NA

NC.2.3 If a nursing staff member is assigned to more than one type of nursing unit or patient, the staff member is competent to provide nursing care to patients in each unit and/or to each type of patient.

1 2 3 4 5 NA

NC.2.4 Documented evidence of licensure and current clinical competence in assigned patient care responsibilities are reviewed and approved by the hospital before nursing personnel from an outside source(s) engage in patient care activities.

1 2 3 4 5 NA

NC.2.4.1 The performance of these nursing personnel in the hospital is evaluated.

1 2 3 4 5 NA

NC.2.4.1.1 Responsibility for this evaluation is defined in hospital policy.

1 2 3 4 5 NA

*NC.3 The nurse executive and other appropriate registered nurses develop hospitalwide patient care programs, policies, and procedures that describe how the nursing care needs of patients or patient populations are assessed, evaluated, and met. (**LD.1.3, LD.1.3.1**)*

NC.3.1 Policies and procedures, based on nursing standards of patient care and standards of nursing practice, describe and guide the nursing care provided.

1 2 3 4 5 NA

NC.3.1.1 The nurse executive has the authority and responsibility for establishing standards of nursing practice.

1 2 3 4 5 NA

NC.3.1.2 The policies, procedures, nursing standards of patient care, and standards of nursing practice are

NC.3.1.2.1 developed by the nurse executive, registered nurses, and other designated nursing staff members;

1 2 3 4 5 NA

NC.3.1.2.2 defined in writing;

1 2 3 4 5 NA

NC.3.1.2.3   approved by the nurse executive or a designee(s); and

1 2 3 4 5 NA

NC.3.1.2.4   used, as indicated, in the assessment of the quality of patient care.

1 2 3 4 5 NA

> NC.3.1.3   Review of policies and procedures includes information about the relevance of policies, procedures, nursing standards of patient care, and standards of nursing practice in actual use; ethical and legal concerns; current scientific knowledge; and findings from quality assessment and improvement activities and other evaluation mechanisms, as appropriate. **(PI.4)**

NC.3.2   Nursing staff members have a defined mechanism designed to address ethical issues in patient care.

1 2 3 4 5 NA

NC.3.2.1   When the hospital has an ethics committee or other defined structures designed to address ethical issues in patient care, nursing staff members participate.

1 2 3 4 5 NA

NC.3.3   Policies and procedures are developed in collaboration with other clinical and administrative groups, when appropriate.

1 2 3 4 5 NA

NC.3.3.1   The nurse executive, or a designee(s), participates in the hospital admissions system to coordinate patient requirements for nursing care with available nursing resources.

1 2 3 4 5 NA

NC.3.3.1.1   In making the decision when or where to admit and/or transfer a patient, consideration is given to the ability of the nursing staff to assess and meet the patient's nursing care needs.

1 2 3 4 5 NA

NC.3.4   Policies and procedures describe the mechanism used to assign nursing staff members to meet patient care needs.

1 2 3 4 5 NA

NC.3.4.1   There are sufficient qualified nursing staff members to meet the nursing care needs of patients throughout the hospital.

1 2 3 4 5 NA

NC.3.4.1.1   The criteria for employment, deployment, and assignment of nursing staff members are approved by the nurse executive.

1 2 3 4 5 NA

NC.3.4.2   Nurse staffing plans for each unit define the number and mix of nursing personnel in accordance with current patient care needs.

1 2 3 4 5 NA

NC.3.4.2.1   In designing and assessing nurse staffing plans, the hospital gives appropriate consideration to the utilization of registered nurses, licensed practical/vocational nurses, nursing assistants, and other nursing personnel and to the potential contribution these personnel can make to the delivery of efficient and effective patient care.

1 2 3 4 5 NA

NC.3.4.2.2   The staffing schedules are reviewed and adjusted as necessary to meet defined patient needs and unusual occurrences.

1 2 3 4 5 NA

NC.3.4.2.3   Appropriate and sufficient support services are available to allow nursing staff members to meet the nursing care needs of patients and their significant other(s).

1 2 3 4 5 NA

NC.3.4.2.4   Staffing levels are adequate to support participation of nursing staff members, as assigned, in committees/meetings and in educational and quality assessment and improvement activities.

1 2 3 4 5 NA

*NC.4   The hospital's plan for providing nursing care is designed to support improvement and innovation in nursing practice and is based on both the needs of the patients to be served and the hospital's mission. **(LD.1.3, LD.1.5)***

NC.4.1   The plan for nurse staffing and the provision of nursing care is reviewed in detail on an annual basis and receives periodic attention as warranted by changing patient care needs and outcomes.

1 2 3 4 5 NA

NC.4.1.1   Registered nurses prescribe, delegate, and coordinate the nursing care provided throughout the hospital.

1 2 3 4 5 NA

NC.4.1.2   Consistent standards for the provision of nursing care within the hospital are used to monitor and evaluate the quality of nursing care provided throughout the hospital.

1 2 3 4 5 NA

*NC.4.2   The appropriateness of the hospital's plan for providing nursing care to meet patient needs is reviewed as part of the established budget review process. **(LD.1.5.2)***

*NC.4.2.1   The review includes **(scoring guideline for LD.1.5.2)***

*NC.4.2.1.1   an analysis of actual staffing patterns; and **(scoring guideline for LD.1.5.2)***

*NC.4.2.1.2   findings from quality assessment and improvement activities. **(scoring guideline for LD.1.5.2)***

*NC.4.2.2   The allocation of financial and other resources is assessed to determine whether nursing care is provided appropriately, efficiently, and effectively. **(scoring guideline for LD.1.5.2)***

*NC.4.2.2.1   The allocation of financial and other resources is designed to support improvement and innovation in nursing practice. **(scoring guideline for LD.1.5.2)***

*NC.5   The nurse executive and other nursing leaders participate with leaders from the governing body, management, medical staff, and clinical areas in the hospital's decision-making structures and processes. **(LD.1.8)***

NC.5.1   Nursing services are directed by a nurse executive who is a registered nurse qualified by advanced education and management experience.

1 2 3 4 5 NA

NC.5.1.1   If the hospital utilizes a decentralized organizational structure, there is an identified nurse leader at the executive level to provide authority and accountability for, and coordination of, the nurse executive functions.

1 2 3 4 5 NA

*NC.5.1.2   When the hospital is part of a multihospital system, there is a mechanism(s) for the hospital's nurse executive to participate in policy decisions affecting patient care services at relevant levels of corporate decision making within the system. **(LD.1.1.2)***

*NC.5.1.2.1   The mechanism(s) is used to enhance the exchange of information about, as well as participation in, improving the nursing care provided to patients in the hospital. **(scoring guideline for LD.1.1.2)***

*NC.5.1.2.2   The mechanism(s) is defined in writing. **(scoring guideline for LD.1.1.2)***

*NC.5.2 The nurse executive or a designee(s) participates with leaders from the governing body, management, medical staff, and clinical areas in developing the hospital's mission, strategic plans, budgets, resource allocation, operation plans, and policies. (**LD.1.1**)*

*NC.5.2.1 The nurse executive develops the nursing budget in collaboration with other nursing leaders and other hospital personnel. (**LD.1.5**)*

*NC.5.2.2 The nurse executive and other nursing leaders participate in the ongoing review of the hospital's mission, strategic plans, and policies. (**LD.1.1**)*

*NC.5.3 The nurse executive and other nursing leaders participate with leaders from the governing body, management, medical staff, and clinical areas in planning, promoting, and conducting hospitalwide quality assessment and improvement activities. (**LD.4**)*

*NC.5.3.1 Registered nurses evaluate current nursing practice and patient care delivery models to improve the quality and efficiency of patient care. (**PI.3**)*

*NC.5.3.2 The nurse executive and other nursing leaders participate in developing and implementing mechanisms for collaboration between nursing staff members, physicians, and other clinical practitioners. (**LD.3.2.1**)*

*NC.5.4 The nurse executive and other nursing leaders are responsible for developing, implementing, and evaluating programs to promote the recruitment, retention, development, and continuing education of nursing staff members. (**LD.1.9**)*

*NC.5.4.1 The nurse executive and other nursing leaders participate in developing and implementing mechanisms for recognizing the expertise and performance of nursing staff members engaged in patient care. (**LD.1.9.1**)*

*NC.5.4.2 The nurse executive and other nursing leaders collaborate with governing body and other management and clinical leaders to develop mechanisms for promoting the educational and advancement goals of hospital staff members. (**LD.1.9.1**)*

*NC.5.5 The nurse executive or a designee(s) participates in evaluating, selecting, and integrating health care technology and information management systems that support patient care needs and the efficient utilization of nursing resources. (**IM.1.1.2**)*

*NC.5.5.1 The use of efficient interactive information management systems for nursing, other clinical (for example, dietary, pharmacy, physical therapy), and nonclinical information is facilitated wherever appropriate. (**IM.1.1.2**)*

NC.5.6 When the hospital provides clinical facilities for nursing education programs, appropriate nursing leaders collaborate with nursing educators to influence curricula, including clinical and/or managerial learning experiences.

1 2 3 4 5 NA

Note: *Reference to other nursing care requirements is made in the following chapters of this* Manual: *"Emergency Services," "Hospital-Sponsored Ambulatory Care Services," "Operative and Other Invasive Procedures," "Physical Rehabilitation Services," and "Special Care Units."*

NOTES AND COMMENTS:

ORIENTATION, TRAINING, AND EDUCATION OF STAFF

The standards in this chapter are not applicable to medical staff members.

SE.1
The organization provides an individual who is new to the organization or to a department/service with an orientation of sufficient scope and duration to inform the individual about his/her responsibilities and how to fulfill them within the organization or department/service.　　　　　1 2 3 4 5 NA

SE.1.1　An individual's orientation includes, at least, information about

　　SE.1.1.1　the organization's mission, governance, policies, and procedures;　　　　　1 2 3 4 5 NA

　　SE.1.1.2　department/service policies and procedures;　　　　　1 2 3 4 5 NA

　　SE.1.1.3　the individual's job description;　　　　　1 2 3 4 5 NA

　　SE.1.1.4　performance expectations;　　　　　1 2 3 4 5 NA

　　SE.1.1.5　the organization's plant, technology, and safety management programs and the individual's safety responsibilities;　　　　　1 2 3 4 5 NA

　　SE.1.1.6　the organization's infection control program and the individual's role in the prevention of infection; and　　　　　1 2 3 4 5 NA

　　SE.1.1.7　the organization's quality assessment and improvement activities and the individual's role in these activities.　　　　　1 2 3 4 5 NA

SE.2
The organization provides for education and training designed to maintain and improve the knowledge and skills of all personnel.　　　　　1 2 3 4 5 NA

SE.2.1　The needs identified for training and education are based on, as appropriate,

　　SE.2.1.1　the patient population served and the type and nature of care provided by the hospital and the department/service;　　　　　1 2 3 4 5 NA

　　SE.2.1.2　individual staff member needs;　　　　　1 2 3 4 5 NA

　　SE.2.1.3　information from quality assessment and improvement activities;　　　　　1 2 3 4 5 NA

　　SE.2.1.4　needs generated by advances made in health care management and health care science and technology;　　　　　1 2 3 4 5 NA

SE.2.1.5 findings from department/service performance appraisals of individuals;　　　1 2 3 4 5 NA

SE.2.1.6 findings from review activities by peers, if appropriate;　　　1 2 3 4 5 NA

SE.2.1.7 findings from the organization's plant, technology, and safety management programs; and　　　1 2 3 4 5 NA

SE.2.1.8 findings from infection control activities.　　　1 2 3 4 5 NA

SE.2.2　Learning objectives are based on performance expectations and address the knowledge, skills, and behaviors appropriate to the individual's job responsibilities and needed to maintain and improve his/her job performance.　　　1 2 3 4 5 NA

SE.2.3　The design of the education and training provided is based on effective instructional strategies to accomplish the specified learning objectives.　　　1 2 3 4 5 NA

SE.3
The effectiveness and appropriateness of orientation, training, and education provided for by the organization are evaluated through its quality assessment and improvement activities.　　　1 2 3 4 5 NA

SE.4
Each individual in the organization is competent, as appropriate to his/her responsibilities, in

SE.4.1　the knowledge and skills required to perform his/her responsibilities;　　　1 2 3 4 5 NA

SE.4.2　the effective and safe use of all equipment used in his/her activities;　　　1 2 3 4 5 NA

SE.4.3　the prevention of contamination and transfer of infection; and　　　1 2 3 4 5 NA

SE.4.4　cardiopulmonary resuscitation and other lifesaving interventions.　　　1 2 3 4 5 NA

NOTES AND COMMENTS:

PATHOLOGY AND CLINICAL LABORATORY SERVICES

Due to changes in federal regulations (CLIA-88), the Joint Commission published the *Accreditation Manual for Pathology and Clinical Laboratory Services (LSM)* in June 1993. With minor exceptions, the standards previously located in this chapter are now reflected in the *LSM* standards. If an organization provides laboratory services of moderate or high complexity, the standards in the *LSM* supersede the laboratory standards in this *Manual.* Organizations that provide only limited laboratory testing (waived testing or all testing that is referred to other organizations) should refer to the standards in this chapter for the necessary requirements.

If the organization is performing waived testing only, standards PA.2 through PA.2.6.2 will apply. If the organization performs moderate- and/or high-complexity testing, applicable standards in the *LSM* must be met.

PA.1
Pathology and clinical laboratory services and consultation are regularly and conveniently available to meet the needs of patients served by the organization, as determined by its medical staff.

1 2 3 4 5 NA

PA.1.1 Provision is made, either on the premises or in a reference/contract laboratory, for the prompt performance of adequate examinations in the fields of anatomic pathology, hematology, chemistry, microbiology, clinical microscopy, parasitology, immunohematology, serology, virology, and, as it relates to the pathology and clinical laboratory services, nuclear medicine.

1 2 3 4 5 NA

PA.1.1.1 All laboratory testing done while the patient is under the care of the organization and of a member of the medical staff is done in the organization's laboratories (including the central laboratory and any ancillary, near-patient-testing, and point-of-care-testing laboratories) or in approved reference laboratories.

1 2 3 4 5 NA

PA.1.1.2 The director(s) recommends reference laboratory services to the medical staff for acceptance through its designated mechanism.

1 2 3 4 5 NA

PA.1.1.2.1 In the absence of organized central pathology and clinical laboratory services, the medical staff establishes a mechanism designed to identify acceptable reference and/or contract laboratory services.

1 2 3 4 5 NA

PA.1.1.2.2 Such reference and contract laboratories meet the applicable federal standards for clinical laboratories.

1 2 3 4 5 NA

PA.2
Waived Testing.   1 2 3 4 5 NA

PA.2.1   Testing methods classified as waived testing under federal law and regulation meet the following requirements:

PA.2.1.1   The extent for which the test results are used in an individual's care (definitive or used only as a screen) is defined by the organization;   1 2 3 4 5 NA

PA.2.1.2   Staff responsible for test performance and those responsible for direction/supervision of the testing activity are identified; and   1 2 3 4 5 NA

PA.2.1.3   Staff performing tests have adequate, specific training and orientation to perform the tests, and demonstrate satisfactory levels of competence.   1 2 3 4 5 NA

PA.2.2   Current written policies and procedures are readily available and address   1 2 3 4 5 NA

PA.2.2.1   specimen collection;   1 2 3 4 5 NA

PA.2.2.2   specimen preservation;   1 2 3 4 5 NA

PA.2.2.3   instrument calibration;   1 2 3 4 5 NA

PA.2.2.4   quality control and remedial action;   1 2 3 4 5 NA

PA.2.2.5   equipment performance evaluation; and   1 2 3 4 5 NA

PA.2.2.6   test performance.   1 2 3 4 5 NA

PA.2.3   Quality control checks are conducted on each procedure as defined by the organization.   1 2 3 4 5 NA

PA.2.3.1   At a minimum, manufacturer's instructions are followed.   1 2 3 4 5 NA

PA.2.3.2   Appropriate quality control and test records are maintained.   1 2 3 4 5 NA

NOTES AND COMMENTS:

PATIENT AND FAMILY EDUCATION

Standards in this chapter of the 1993 *Accreditation Manual for Hospitals* have been recast to focus on improving individual and organizational performance and have been moved to Sections 1 and 2 of this *Manual*. The following cross-reference is provided for your information.

1993	1994
PF.1	PF.1
PF.1.1	PF.2
PF.1.1.1	PF.2.2
PF.1.1.1.1	PF.2.2.1
PF.1.1.1.2	PF.2.2.2
PF.1.1.1.3	PF.2.2.3
PF.1.1.1.4	PF.2.2.6
PF.1.2	PF.3

PATIENT RIGHTS

PREAMBLE

The organization respects the rights of the patient, recognizes that each patient is an individual with unique health care needs, and, because of the importance of respecting each patient's personal dignity, provides considerate, respectful care focused on the patient's individual needs.

The organization affirms the patient's right to make decisions regarding his/her medical care, including the decision to discontinue treatment, to the extent permitted by law.

The organization assists the patient in the exercise of his/her rights and informs the patient of any responsibilities incumbent on him/her in the exercise of those rights.

RI.1
The organization supports the rights of each patient.   1 2 3 4 5 NA

RI.1.1 Organizational policies and procedures describe the mechanisms by which the following rights are protected and exercised:

RI.1.1.1 The right of the patient to the hospital's reasonable response to his/her requests and needs for treatment or service, within the hospital's capacity, its stated mission, and applicable law and regulation;   1 2 3 4 5 NA

RI.1.1.2 The right of the patient to considerate and respectful care;   1 2 3 4 5 NA

RI.1.1.2.1 The care of the patient includes consideration of the psychosocial, spiritual, and cultural variables that influence the perceptions of illness.   1 2 3 4 5 NA

RI.1.1.2.2 The care of the dying patient optimizes the comfort and dignity of the patient through

RI.1.1.2.2.1 treating primary and secondary symptoms that respond to treatment as desired by the patient or surrogate decision maker;   1 2 3 4 5 NA

RI.1.1.2.2.2 effectively managing pain; and   1 2 3 4 5 NA

RI.1.1.2.2.3 acknowledging the psychosocial and spiritual concerns of the patient and the family regarding dying and the expression of grief by the patient and family.   1 2 3 4 5 NA

RI.1.1.3 The right of the patient, in collaboration with his/her physician, to make decisions involving his/her health care, including

RI.1.1.3.1 the right of the patient to accept medical care or to refuse treatment to the extent permitted by law and to be informed of the medical consequences of such refusal, and 1 2 3 4 5 NA

RI.1.1.3.2 the right of the patient to formulate advance directives and appoint a surrogate to make health care decisions on his/her behalf to the extent permitted by law. 1 2 3 4 5 NA

RI.1.1.3.2.1 The organization has in place a mechanism to ascertain the existence of and assist in the development of advance directives at the time of the patient's admission. 1 2 3 4 5 NA

RI.1.1.3.2.2 The provision of care is not conditioned on the existence of an advance directive. 1 2 3 4 5 NA

RI.1.1.3.2.3 Any advance directive(s) is in the patient's medical record and is reviewed periodically with the patient or surrogate decision maker. 1 2 3 4 5 NA

RI.1.1.4 The right of the patient to the information necessary to enable him/her to make treatment decisions that reflect his/her wishes; 1 2 3 4 5 NA

RI.1.1.4.1 A policy on informed decision making is developed by the medical staff and governing body and is consistent with any legal requirements. 1 2 3 4 5 NA

RI.1.1.5 The right of the patient to information, at the time of admission, about the hospital's 1 2 3 4 5 NA

RI.1.1.5.1 patient rights policy(ies), and 1 2 3 4 5 NA

RI.1.1.5.2 mechanism for the initiation, review, and, when possible, resolution of patient complaints concerning the quality of care; 1 2 3 4 5 NA

RI.1.1.6 The right of the patient or the patient's designated representative to participate in the consideration of ethical issues that arise in the care of the patient; 1 2 3 4 5 NA

RI.1.1.6.1 The organization has in place a mechanism(s) for the consideration of ethical issues arising in the care of patients and to provide education to caregivers and patients on ethical issues in health care. 1 2 3 4 5 NA

RI.1.1.7 The right of the patient to be informed of any human experimentation or other research/educational projects affecting his/her care or treatment; 1 2 3 4 5 NA

RI.1.1.8 The right of the patient, within the limits of law, to personal privacy and confidentiality of information; and 1 2 3 4 5 NA

RI.1.1.8.1 The patient and/or the patient's legally designated representative has access to the information contained in the patient's medical record, within the limits of the law. 1 2 3 4 5 NA

RI.1.1.9 The right of the patient's guardian, next of kin, or a legally authorized responsible person to exercise, to the extent permitted by law, the rights delineated on behalf of the patient if the patient has been adjudicated incompetent in accordance with the law, is found by his/her physician to be medically incapable of understanding the proposed treatment or procedure, is unable to communicate his/her wishes regarding treatment, or is a minor.

1 2 3 4 5 NA

RI.2
There are hospitalwide policies on the withholding of resuscitative services from patients and the forgoing or withdrawing of life-sustaining treatment.

1 2 3 4 5 NA

RI.2.1 The policies are developed in consultation with the medical staff, nursing staff, and other appropriate bodies and are adopted by the medical staff and approved by the governing body.

1 2 3 4 5 NA

RI.2.2 The policies describe

RI.2.2.1 the mechanism(s) for reaching decisions about the withholding of resuscitative services from individual patients or forgoing or withdrawing of life-sustaining treatment;

1 2 3 4 5 NA

RI.2.2.2 the mechanism(s) for resolving conflicts in decision making, should they arise; and

1 2 3 4 5 NA

RI.2.2.3 the roles of physicians and, when applicable, of nursing personnel, other appropriate staff, and family members in decisions to withhold resuscitative services or forgo or withdraw life-sustaining treatment.

1 2 3 4 5 NA

RI.2.3 The policies include provisions designed to assure that the rights of patients are respected.

1 2 3 4 5 NA

RI.2.4 The policies include the requirement that appropriate orders be written by the physician primarily responsible for the patient and that documentation be made in the patient's medical record if life-sustaining treatment is to be withdrawn or resuscitative services are to be withheld.

1 2 3 4 5 NA

RI.2.5 The policies address the use of advance directives in patient care to the extent permitted by law.

1 2 3 4 5 NA

NOTES AND COMMENTS:

PHARMACEUTICAL SERVICES

Some of the standards in this chapter of the 1993 *Accreditation Manual for Hospitals* have been recast to focus on improving individual and organizational performance and have been moved to Sections 1 and 2 of this *Manual*. To help you identify these standards, we have printed them here in small italic type with their new standard references in bold type in parentheses. Organizations are expected to demonstrate compliance with these standards in their new context. For example, PH.1.2 in this chapter has been recast and moved to the "Leadership" chapter, as LD.1.3.4. This standard appears in small italic type, and the new standard reference, LD.1.3.4, appears in bold type in parentheses at the end of the standard. Organizations are expected to comply with LD.1.3.4 and will be scored for compliance in the "Leadership" chapter. Standards scored in this chapter are in normal type and have accompanying scoring scales (1 2 3 4 5 NA).

PH.1
The hospital maintains a pharmaceutical department/service that is directed by a professionally competent and legally qualified pharmacist and is staffed by a sufficient number of competent personnel, in keeping with the size and scope of services of the hospital.

1 2 3 4 5 NA

PH.1.1 The pharmaceutical department/service is directed by a competent pharmacist who is appropriately licensed and who is responsible to the chief executive officer of the hospital or his/her designee.

1 2 3 4 5 NA

PH.1.1.1 The director is employed on a full-time or part-time basis.

1 2 3 4 5 NA

> *PH.1.2 The pharmaceutical services provided are sufficient to meet the needs of the patients, as determined by the medical staff. (**LD.1.3.4**)*

PH.1.3 When the hospital pharmaceutical department/service is decentralized, a licensed pharmacist, who is responsible to the director of the pharmaceutical department/service, supervises each satellite pharmacy or separate organizational element involved with the preparation and dispensing of drugs and with the provision of drug information and other pharmaceutical services.

1 2 3 4 5 NA

PH.1.4 The director of the pharmaceutical department/service is assisted by additional qualified pharmacists and pharmacy supportive personnel commensurate with the scope of services provided.

1 2 3 4 5 NA

PH.1.4.1 Nonpharmacist personnel work under the direct supervision of a licensed pharmacist and in such a relationship that the supervising pharmacist is fully aware of all activities involved in the preparation and dispensing of medications, including the maintenance of appropriate records.

1 2 3 4 5 NA

PH.1.5   The pharmacy is licensed as required. **(TX.5.1)**

PH.1.6   If the hospital does not have an organized pharmacy, pharmaceutical services are obtained from another hospital having such services or from a community pharmacy. **(LD.1.3.4.2)**

PH.1.6.1   Prepackaged drugs are then stored in, and distributed from, the hospital drug storage area, under the supervision of the director of the pharmaceutical department/service. **(scoring guideline for TX.13)**

PH.1.6.1.1   Prepackaged drugs obtained from pharmacies outside the hospital are identified and labeled so that recalls can be effected as necessary and the proper controls are established. **(scoring guideline for TX.13)**

PH.2
Space, equipment, and supplies are provided for the professional and administrative functions of the pharmaceutical department/service as required to promote patient safety through the proper storage, preparation, dispensing, and administration of drugs.

1 2 3 4 5 NA

PH.2.1   Hospitals with an organized pharmaceutical department/service have the necessary space, equipment, and supplies for the storage, preparation (compounding, packaging, and labeling), and dispensing of drugs. **(scoring guideline for TX.3)**

PH.2.1.1   As appropriate, this includes the preparation and dispensing of parenteral products and radiopharmaceuticals. **(scoring guidelines for TX.3, TX.14)**

PH.2.2   Drugs are stored under proper conditions of sanitation, temperature, light, moisture, ventilation, segregation, and security. **(TX.3)**

PH.2.3   For each nursing care unit, as required, properly controlled drug preparation areas are designated, and locked storage areas or locked medication carts are provided. **(TX.3)**

PH.2.4   Drug preparation areas are well lighted and are located where personnel preparing drugs for dispensing or administration will not be interrupted. **(TX.3)**

PH.2.5   The director of the pharmaceutical department/service or a qualified designee conducts at least monthly inspections of all nursing care units or other areas of the hospital where medications are dispensed, administered, or stored. **(PI.3.4.2.2)**

PH.2.5.1   A record of all such monthly inspections is maintained to verify that the following requirements are met: **(scoring guideline for TX.3)**

PH.2.5.1.1   Antiseptics, other drugs for external use, and disinfectants are stored separately from internal and injectable medications. **(scoring guideline for TX.3)**

PH.2.5.1.2   Drugs requiring special conditions for storage to assure stability are properly stored. **(scoring guideline for TX.3)**

PH.2.5.1.3   Outdated or otherwise unusable drugs are identified, and their distribution and administration are prevented. **(TX.10.2)**

PH.2.5.1.4   *The distribution and administration of controlled drugs are adequately documented by pharmacy, nursing, and other involved services or personnel and are in accordance with applicable law. (scoring guideline for TX.13)*

PH.2.5.1.5   *Any investigational drugs in use are properly stored, distributed, and controlled. (scoring guideline for TX.13)*

PH.2.5.1.6   *Emergency drugs, as approved by the medical staff, are in adequate and proper supply in the pharmacy and in designated hospital areas. (TX.8)*

PH.2.5.1.6.1   *The pharmacist is responsible both for the contents of emergency medication carts, kits, and so forth and for the inspection procedure to be used. (TX.8)*

PH.2.5.1.7   *The metric system is used for all medications. (scoring guideline for TX.3)*

PH.2.6   *There is a suitable area for the manipulation of parenteral medications. (TX.14.3)*

PH.2.7   *Up-to-date pharmaceutical reference materials are provided to furnish the pharmaceutical, medical, and nursing staffs with adequate information concerning drugs. (IM.9.2)*

PH.2.7.1   *The telephone number of the regional poison-control information center is readily available in the pharmacy for emergency reference. (IM.9.5)*

PH.3   *The scope of the pharmaceutical department/service is consistent with the medication needs of the patients, as determined by the medical staff. (LD.1.3.4)*

PH.3.1   *All drugs, chemicals, and biologicals meet national standards of quality or are clearly and accurately labeled as to contents. (TX.4)*

PH.3.1.1   *Such information is disclosed to the medical staff. (TX.4)*

PH.3.2   *All drugs are obtained and used in accordance with written policies and procedures that have been approved by the medical staff. (TX.13)*

PH.3.2.1   *The policies and procedures relate to the selection, distribution, and safe and effective use of drugs in the hospital. (TX.13)*

PH.3.2.2   *The policies and procedures are established by the combined effort of the director of the pharmaceutical department/service, the medical staff, the nursing department/service, and the administration. (TX.13)*

PH.3.3   *The medical staff, through its pharmacy and therapeutics function, determines the hospital formulary to be used. (scoring guideline for TX.1.1)*

PH.3.3.1   *Any hospital formulary or drug list is readily available to the professional staff who use it. (IM.9.6)*

PH.3.4   *There is a quality control program to monitor personnel qualifications, training, performance, equipment, and facilities for preparing, sterilizing, and labeling parenteral medications and solutions that are manufactured in the hospital. (PI.3.4.2.2)*

PH.3.4.1   *Appropriate records are maintained. (IM.8)*

PH.3.5 When any part of preparing, sterilizing, and labeling parenteral medications and solutions is performed within the hospital but not under direct pharmacy supervision, the director of the pharmaceutical department/service is responsible for providing written guidelines and for approving the procedure to assure that all pharmaceutical requirements are met. **(LD.2.1.2, LD.2.1.3, LD.2.1.7)**

PH.3.6 The director of the pharmaceutical department/service is responsible for maintaining and keeping available the medical staff– approved stock of antidotes and other emergency drugs, both in the pharmacy and in patient care areas. **(TX.8)**

PH.3.7 The director of the pharmaceutical department/service is responsible for maintaining records of the transactions of the pharmacy as required by applicable law and as necessary to maintain adequate control and accountability of all drugs. **(IM.8.1.1)**

PH.3.7.1 This includes a system of controls and records for the requisitioning and dispensing of pharmaceutical supplies to nursing care units and to other departments/services of the hospital. **(IM.8.1.1)**

PH.3.8 The director of the pharmaceutical department/service is responsible for maintaining a means of identifying the signatures of all practitioners authorized to use the pharmaceutical services for ambulatory care patient prescriptions, as well as a listing of their Drug Enforcement Administration numbers. **(IM.8.1.1.1, IM.8.1.1.2)**

PH.3.9 The pharmaceutical department/service provides drug monitoring services in keeping with each patient's needs, consonant with available resources. **(TX.12)**

PH.3.9.1 These may include, but need not be limited to, the following:

PH.3.9.1.1 The maintenance of a medication record or drug profile for each patient, which is based on available drug history and current therapy and includes the name, age, and weight of the patient, the current diagnosis (or diagnoses), the current drug therapy, any drug allergies or sensitivities, and other pertinent information related to the patient's drug regimen; and **(TX.6–TX.6.1)**

PH.3.9.1.2 A review of the patient's drug regimen for any potential interactions, interferences, or incompatibilities prior to dispensing drugs to the patient. **(TX.6–TX.6.1)**

PH.4 Written policies and procedures that pertain to the intrahospital drug distribution system are developed by the director of the pharmaceutical department/service in concert with the medical staff and, as appropriate, with representatives of other disciplines. **(scoring guideline for TX.13)**

PH.4.1 Drug preparation and dispensing are restricted to a licensed pharmacist or to his/her designee, who is under the direct supervision of the pharmacist. **(scoring guidelines for TX.5–TX.5.2)**

PH.4.1.1 A pharmacist reviews the prescriber's order, or a direct copy thereof, before the initial dose of medication is dispensed (with the exception of emergency orders when time does not permit). **(TX.4.2)**

PH.4.1.1.1 In cases when the medication order is written when the pharmacy is closed or the pharmacist is otherwise unavailable, the medication order is reviewed by the pharmacist as soon thereafter as possible, preferably within 24 hours. **(scoring guideline for TX.7)**

PH.4.2   Written policies and procedures that are essential for patient safety and for the control, accountability, and intrahospital distribution of drugs are enforced. **(TX.13)**

PH.4.2.1   The policies and procedures include, but need not be limited to, the following: **(TX.13)**

PH.4.2.1.1   All drugs, including those provided for ambulatory care patients or home care patients, are labeled adequately, including the addition of appropriate accessory or cautionary statement as well as the expiration date when applicable. **(TX.4.1)**

PH.4.2.1.2   Discontinued and outdated drugs, and containers with worn, illegible, or missing labels, are returned to the pharmacy for proper disposition. **(TX.10.2, scoring guideline for TX.3)**

PH.4.2.1.3   Only a pharmacist, or authorized pharmacy personnel under the direction and supervision of a pharmacist, dispenses medications, makes labeling changes, or transfers medications to different containers. **(TX.2)**

PH.4.2.1.4   Only prepackaged drugs are removed from the pharmacy when a pharmacist is not available. **(scoring guideline for TX.7)**

PH.4.2.1.4.1   Such drugs are removed only by a designated registered nurse or a physician and only in amounts sufficient for immediate therapeutic needs. **(scoring guideline for TX.7)**

PH.4.2.1.5   A drug-recall procedure that can be implemented readily includes provisions for documenting the results. **(TX.10)**

PH.4.2.1.6   Drug product defects are reported in accordance with the Food and Drug Administration Quality Reporting System or the United States Pharmaceutical Corporation Drug Product Reporting Program. **(TX.10.3)**

PH.4.2.1.7   Sample drugs brought into the hospital are controlled through the pharmaceutical department/service. **(scoring guideline for TX.13)**

PH.5   Written policies and procedures governing the safe administration of drugs and biologicals are developed by the medical staff in cooperation with the pharmaceutical department/service, the nursing department/service, and, as necessary, representatives of other disciplines. **(TX.13)**

PH.5.1   Written policies and procedures governing the safe administration of drugs are enforced. **(TX.13)**

PH.5.2   Written policies and procedures include, but need not be limited to, the following: **(TX.13)**

PH.5.2.1   Drugs are administered only on the order of a member of the medical staff, an authorized member of the house staff, or another individual who has been granted clinical privileges to write such orders. **(TX.2)**

PH.5.2.1.1   Verbal orders for drugs are accepted only by personnel so designated in the medical staff rules and regulations and are authenticated by the prescribing practitioner within the stated period of time. **(IM.7.8.1)**

PH.5.2.2 All medications are administered by or under the supervision of appropriately licensed personnel in accordance with applicable law and regulation governing such acts and in accordance with the approved medical staff rules and regulations. **(TX.11.3)**

PH.5.2.3 There is an automatic cancellation of standing drug orders when a patient undergoes surgery. **(scoring guideline for TX.13)**

PH.5.2.3.1 Automatic stop orders for drugs are otherwise determined by the medical staff and are stated in medical staff rules and regulations. **(scoring guideline for TX.13)**

PH.5.2.4 Cautionary measures for the safe admixture of parenteral products are developed. **(TX.14)**

PH.5.2.5 Drugs to be administered are verified with the prescribing practitioner's orders and are properly prepared for administration. **(TX.11.1)**

PH.5.2.5.1 The patient is identified prior to drug administration. **(TX.11.2)**

PH.5.2.5.2 Each dose of medication administered is recorded properly in the patient's medical record. **(IM.7.2.20)**

PH.5.2.6 Medication errors and adverse drug reactions are reported immediately in accordance with written procedures. **(TX.12.2)**

PH.5.2.6.1 This requirement includes notification of the practitioner who ordered the drug. **(scoring guideline for TX.12.4)**

PH.5.2.6.2 An entry of the medication administered and/or the drug reaction is properly recorded in the patient's medical record. **(IM.7.2.20)**

PH.5.2.6.3 Hospitals report any unexpected or significant adverse reactions promptly to the Food and Drug Administration and to the manufacturer. **(TX.12.2.2.1)**

PH.5.2.7 Drugs brought into the hospital by patients are not administered unless the drugs have been identified by the attending physician, another responsible prescribing practitioner, or a pharmacist (preferably the hospital pharmacist) and unless there is a written order from the practitioner responsible for the patient to administer the drugs. **(TX.11.4)**

PH.5.2.7.1 If the drugs are not to be used during the patient's hospitalization, they are packaged and sealed and either given to the patient's family or stored and returned to the patient at the time of discharge, provided such action is approved by the practitioner responsible for the patient. **(scoring guideline for TX.11.4)**

PH.5.2.8 Self-administration of medications by patients is permitted on a specific written order by the authorized prescribing practitioner and in accordance with established hospital policy. **(TX.11.4)**

PH.5.2.9 Investigational drugs are properly labeled and stored and are used only under the direct supervision of the authorized principal investigator. **(TX.11.6)**

PH.5.2.9.1 Such investigational drugs are approved by an appropriate medical staff committee. **(TX.11.6.1)**

PH.5.2.9.2 Investigational drugs are administered in accordance with an approved protocol that includes any requirements for a patient's appropriate informed consent. **(TX.11.6.2, TX.11.6.3)**

PH.5.2.9.3 On approval of the principal investigator, registered nurses may administer investigational drugs after they have been given and have demonstrated an understanding of basic pharmacologic information about the drugs. **(TX.11.6.4)**

PH.5.2.10 In the interest of minimizing errors, the use of abbreviations is discouraged and the use of the leading decimal point is avoided. **(scoring guideline for IM.5.1)**

PH.5.2.11 Each practitioner who prescribes medication must clearly state the administration times or the time interval between doses. **(TX.4)**

PH.5.2.11.1 The use of "prn" and "on call" with medication orders is qualified. **(TX.4)**

PH.5.2.12 Drugs prescribed for ambulatory care patient use in continuity with hospital care are released to patients upon discharge, only after they are labeled for such use under the supervision of the pharmacist and only on written order of the authorized prescribing practitioner. **(scoring guideline for TX.4.1)**

PH.5.2.12.1 Each drug released to a patient on discharge is recorded in the medical record. **(IM.7.2.21)**

Note: *Refer also to the following chapters of this Manual: "Alcoholism and Other Drug-Dependence Services," "Emergency Services," "Hospital-Sponsored Ambulatory Care Services," "Improving Organizational Performance," "Infection Control," "Management of Information," "Medical Staff," "Nuclear Medicine Services," "Nursing Care," "Operative and Other Invasive Procedures," "Plant, Technology, and Safety Management," "Respiratory Care Services," and "Special Care Units."*

Notes and Comments:

PHYSICAL REHABILITATION SERVICES

Some of the standards in this chapter of the 1993 *Accreditation Manual for Hospitals* have been recast to focus on improving individual and organizational performance and have been moved to Sections 1 and 2 of this *Manual*. To help you identify these standards, we have printed them here in small italic type with their new standard references in bold type in parentheses. Organizations are expected to demonstrate compliance with these standards in their new context. For example, RH.1.1.1 in this chapter has been recast and moved to the "Leadership" chapter, as LD.1.7. This standard appears in small italic type, and the new standard references, LD.1.7, appears in bold type in parentheses at the end of the standard. Organizations are expected to comply with LD.1.7 and will be scored for compliance in the "Leadership" chapter. Standards scored in this chapter are in normal type and have accompanying scoring scales (1 2 3 4 5 NA).

This chapter describes the nature of services in programs or units that promote the restoration of the functional abilities of individuals with physical, cognitive, and/or sensoriperceptual impairment. The care of individuals whose primary problem is mental illness or substance abuse is not addressed in this chapter.

An organized rehabilitation service may be provided singly (as an individual service), in combination, or as part of a comprehensive physical rehabilitation program or unit. The range of rehabilitation services offered is determined by the hospital and may include, but need not be limited to, the following: audiology, creative arts therapies, dental, dietetic, educational, occupational therapy, physical therapy, prosthetic and/or orthotic, psychological, recreational therapy, rehabilitation engineering, rehabilitation medicine, rehabilitation nursing, social work, speech-language pathology, and vocational rehabilitation services. The standards pertaining to these services are located in RH.2.

Any physical rehabilitation service, whether provided singly, in combination, or as part of a comprehensive physical rehabilitation program or unit, must meet the provisions of RH.1 and RH.4 as well as relevant portions of RH.2. When rehabilitation services are provided as part of a comprehensive physical rehabilitation program or unit, the provisions of RH.3 must also be met.

In order to provide comprehensive physical rehabilitation services, a program or unit meets the most frequently encountered physical, psychological, and social needs of patients. A comprehensive physical rehabilitation program or unit directly provides, at a minimum, rehabilitation medicine, rehabilitation nursing, social work, occupational therapy, physical therapy, and speech-language pathology services. In addition, when the population served frequently needs any other service listed in RH.2, a comprehensive unit or program directly provides such services.

Comprehensive physical rehabilitation services, whether provided on an inpatient or outpatient basis, must meet all the provisions of RH.1 and RH.3 and relevant portions of RH.2. The only exceptions are that comprehensive physical outpatient rehabilitation services are not required to meet RH.3, RH.3.2, or those standards that specify compliance activity to inpatient services only.

If, in addition to other services, a hospital provides comprehensive rehabilitation services and desires to have its program designated as such by the Joint Commission, a rehabilitation physician will be added to the survey team for this purpose; this requires an added fee. However, in a freestanding rehabilitation hospital, the rehabilitation physician will replace the physician surveyor and this does not entail additional cost. The rehabilitation physician will be able to assist in the review of comprehensive physical rehabilitation programs or units by providing on-site consultation and education related to current rehabilitation care.

RH.1

Organized physical rehabilitation services* are available and are based on an assessment of patient needs, are provided by competent professionals, and are delivered in accordance with a written plan for treatment.†

1 2 3 4 5 NA

RH.1.1   The following requirements are met in the organization of the physical rehabilitation service or services:

> *RH.1.1.1   There is a description of the scope of services provided;* **(LD.1.7)**
>
> *RH.1.1.2   Administrative direction of each physical rehabilitation service is provided by a qualified individual;* **(LD.2.2.2)**
>
> *RH.1.1.2.1   An administrative director assumes only those clinical responsibilities for which he/she has been determined to be competent;* **(LD.2.2.2.1)**

RH.1.1.3   Each patient's general medical condition is the responsibility of a qualified physician member of the medical staff;

1 2 3 4 5 NA

RH.1.1.4   Medical staff participation in the delivery of physical rehabilitation services is provided by a qualified physician member of the medical staff who is knowledgeable about rehabilitation medicine by reason of training and experience;

1 2 3 4 5 NA

RH.1.1.5   Each individual who provides physical rehabilitation services has been determined to be competent to provide such services by reason of education, training, experience, and demonstrated adherence to current standards of care;

1 2 3 4 5 NA

RH.1.1.5.1   There is evidence that each individual who provides physical rehabilitation services meets all applicable licensure, certification, or registration requirements.

1 2 3 4 5 NA

> *RH.1.1.6   The organizational relationship of the physical rehabilitation service or services to other hospital services is defined;* **(LD.3.1)**

RH.1.1.7   A sufficient number of qualified, competent professional and support personnel are available to meet the objectives of the service and the needs of the patient population;

1 2 3 4 5 NA

RH.1.1.8   Each physical rehabilitation service, or combination of services, has a qualified clinical director who has administrative responsibility for the delivery of patient care and for the supervision of the service or services;

1 2 3 4 5 NA

**For a definition of organized physical rehabilitation services and of the range of services that may be offered, see* physical rehabilitation services *in the Interpretation of Terms, page 275.*

†*These services are not required for hospitals that provide only psychiatric/substance abuse services.*

*RH.1.1.9 Policies and procedures describe mechanisms for effective organizational management and interdepartmental relationships and communications; **(LD.3.1, LD.3.2.1)***

*RH.1.1.9.1 Safety issues, including performance requirements and quality controls for all equipment used in the provision of patient care services, are addressed. **(PI.3.5.3)***

RH.1.1.9.2 Infection control guidelines are developed and enforced for the protection of patients, staff, and equipment.

1 2 3 4 5 NA

RH.1.1.10 Sufficient space, equipment, and facilities are available to support the clinical, educational, and administrative functions of the physical rehabilitation services that are provided;

1 2 3 4 5 NA

RH.1.1.10.1 To help assure that patient care equipment functions properly and in accordance with all federal, state, and local requirements, all electrically and nonelectrically powered equipment used in the diagnosis, treatment, or monitoring of patients meets the provisions of PL.3 in the "Plant, Technology, and Safety Management" chapter of this *Manual.*

1 2 3 4 5 NA

RH.1.1.11 Where clinical facilities are provided for the education and training of students, the roles and responsibilities of the physical rehabilitation services and of the educational program are defined in writing; and

1 2 3 4 5 NA

RH.1.1.12 Basic cardiopulmonary resuscitation is available at all times that patients are in the facility or unit.

1 2 3 4 5 NA

RH.1.1.12.1 Provision is made for the care of patients who require advanced cardiopulmonary support.

1 2 3 4 5 NA

RH.1.2 At least the following requirements are included in the process of providing for any physical rehabilitation service to patients:

RH.1.2.1 Consistent with applicable law and hospital policy, physical rehabilitation services are initiated by a physician or other qualified individual;

1 2 3 4 5 NA

*RH.1.2.2 On referral for physical rehabilitation services, a functional assessment and evaluation are performed by a qualified professional; **(PE.1.4.1)***

RH.1.2.3 A treatment plan is developed based on an evaluation that includes an assessment of functional ability appropriate to the patient;

1 2 3 4 5 NA

RH.1.2.3.1 The patient and the family participate as appropriate in the development and implementation of the treatment plan.

1 2 3 4 5 NA

RH.1.2.4 Measurable goals, which are described in functional or behavioral terms, are established for the patient and include time frames for achievement;

1 2 3 4 5 NA

RH.1.2.5 The treatment plan is designed to achieve stated goals and is developed by the referring individual, the rehabilitation services staff, and, to the extent possible, the patient and family;

1 2 3 4 5 NA

RH.1.2.6 The patient's progress and the results of treatment are assessed on a timely basis, which is at least monthly for outpatients and at least every two weeks for inpatients; and

1 2 3 4 5 NA

RH.1.2.6.1   Treatment goals are revised as appropriate. (scoring guideline for PE.2.4)

RH.1.2.7   The patient's progress and response to treatment are documented in the medical record. (IM.7.2.17)

RH.1.3   The medical record of a patient receiving physical rehabilitation services includes, at a minimum, the following information: (IM.7.2)

RH.1.3.1   The reason for referral to physical rehabilitation services or admission to the comprehensive physical rehabilitation program or unit; (IM.7.2.7)

RH.1.3.2   A summary of the patient's clinical condition; (IM.7.2.16)

RH.1.3.3   The goals of treatment and the treatment plan; (IM.7.2.8)

RH.1.3.4   Treatment and progress records, with appropriate ongoing assessments as required by the patient's condition and with a description of the perception of the patient and family toward, and their involvement in, physical rehabilitation services; and (IM.7.2.15)

RH.1.3.5   Assessment of physical rehabilitation achievement and estimates of further rehabilitation potential, entered on a timely basis, which is at least monthly. (scoring guideline for PE.2.4)

RH.2
Services provided to physically disabled patients, whether singly, in combination, or as part of a comprehensive physical rehabilitation program or unit, are delivered by, or under the direct supervision of, qualified professionals.

1 2 3 4 5 NA

RH.2.1   Occupational Therapy.*

RH.2.1.1   Occupational therapy services include, but need not be limited to, the following:

RH.2.1.1.1   The assessment and treatment of occupational performance, including (scoring guideline for PE.1.1)

RH.2.1.1.1.1   independent living skills, (scoring guideline for PE.1.1)

RH.2.1.1.1.2   prevocational/work adjustment, (scoring guideline for PE.1.1)

RH.2.1.1.1.3   educational skills, (scoring guideline for PE.1.1)

RH.2.1.1.1.4   play/leisure abilities, and (scoring guideline for PE.1.1)

RH.2.1.1.1.5   social skills; (scoring guideline for PE.1.1)

RH.2.1.1.2   The assessment and treatment of performance components, including neuromuscular, sensori-integrative, cognitive, and psychosocial skills; (scoring guideline for PE.1.1)

RH.2.1.1.3   Therapeutic interventions, adaptations, and prevention; and

1 2 3 4 5 NA

Occupational therapy services provide for goal-directed, purposeful activity to aid in the development of adaptive skills and performance capacities by individuals of all ages who have physical disabilities and related psychological impairment(s). Such therapy is designed to maximize independence, prevent further disability, and maintain health.

RH.2.1.1.4 Individualized evaluations of past and current performance, based on observations of individual or group tasks, standardized tests, record review, interviews, and/or activity histories.

1 2 3 4 5 NA

RH.2.1.2 Treatment goals are achieved through the use of selected modalities and techniques that include, but need not be limited to, the following:

1 2 3 4 5 NA

RH.2.1.2.1 Task-oriented activities, including the simulation or actual practice of work, self-care, leisure, and social skills and their components, as well as the use of creative media, games, computers, and other equipment;

1 2 3 4 5 NA

RH.2.1.2.2 Prevocational activities;

1 2 3 4 5 NA

RH.2.1.2.3 Sensorimotor activities;

1 2 3 4 5 NA

RH.2.1.2.4 Patient/family education and counseling;

1 2 3 4 5 NA

RH.2.1.2.5 As appropriate, the design, fabrication, and application of orthotic devices;

1 2 3 4 5 NA

RH.2.1.2.6 Guidance in the use of adaptive equipment and prosthetic devices;

1 2 3 4 5 NA

RH.2.1.2.7 Adaptation of the physical and social environment and the use of a therapeutic milieu;

1 2 3 4 5 NA

RH.2.1.2.8 Joint protection/body mechanics; and

1 2 3 4 5 NA

RH.2.1.2.9 Positioning.

1 2 3 4 5 NA

RH.2.1.3 Occupational therapy services staff monitor the extent to which goals are met relative to assessing and increasing the patient's functional abilities in daily living and relative to preventing further disability.

1 2 3 4 5 NA

RH.2.2 Physical Therapy.*

RH.2.2.1 Physical therapy services include, but need not be limited to, the following:

RH.2.2.1.1 *An initial physical therapy evaluation and assessment of the patient prior to the provision of services; (**scoring guideline for PE.1.1**)*

RH.2.2.1.2 The determination and development of treatment goals and plans in accordance with the diagnosis and prognosis, with a treatment program established to aim at preventing or reducing disability or pain and restoring lost function;

1 2 3 4 5 NA

RH.2.2.1.3 Therapeutic interventions that focus on posture, locomotion, strength, endurance, cardiopulmonary function, balance, coordination, joint mobility, flexibility, pain, and functional abilities in daily living skills;

1 2 3 4 5 NA

Physical therapy services provide identification, prevention, remediation, and rehabilitation of acute or prolonged physical dysfunction or pain, with emphasis on movement dysfunction. Such therapy encompasses examination and analysis of patients and the therapeutic application of physical and chemical agents, exercise, and other procedures to maximize functional independence.

RH.2.2.1.4 The application of modalities that include, but need not be limited to, heat, cold, light, air, water, sound, electricity, massage, mobilization, bronchopulmonary hygiene, and therapeutic exercise with or without assistive devices; and

1 2 3 4 5 NA

RH.2.2.1.5 *Assessment and training in locomotion, including, as appropriate, the use of orthotic, prosthetic, or assistive devices.* **(*scoring guideline for PE.1.1*)**

RH.2.2.2 *Physical therapy services staff monitor the extent to which services have met the therapeutic goals relative to the initial and all subsequent examinations, as well as the degree to which improvement occurs relative to the identified physical dysfunction or the degree to which pain associated with movement is reduced.* **(*scoring guideline for PE.2.3*)**

RH.2.3 Prosthetic and/or Orthotic Services.*

RH.2.3.1 *Prosthetic and/or orthotic services are monitored.* **(*scoring guideline for PE.2.3*)**

RH.2.3.1.1 *There is documented evidence of communication between the prosthetic and/or orthotic services specialists and the prescribing practitioner.* **(*IM.7.1*)**

RH.2.3.2 *Monitoring activities address patient satisfaction with the orthotic or prosthetic devices relative to fit and functioning.* **(*scoring guideline for PE.2.3*)**

RH.2.4 Psychological Services.†

RH.2.4.1 Psychological services include, but need not be limited to, the following:

RH.2.4.1.1 *Assessment, including psychological, vocational, and neuropsychological functioning; and* **(*scoring guideline for PE.1.1*)**

RH.2.4.1.2 Interventions, including individual and group psychotherapy, family consultation and therapy, and the design of such specialized psychological intervention programs as behavior modification, behavioral treatment regimens for patients with chronic pain, and biofeedback and relaxation procedures.

1 2 3 4 5 NA

RH.2.4.2 *Psychological services staff monitor the cognitive and emotional adaptation of the patient and family to the patient's physical disability.* **(*scoring guideline for PE.2.3*)**

RH.2.5 Recreational Therapy.‡

RH.2.5.1 Recreational therapy services provide, but need not be limited to, the following:

Prosthetic and/or orthotic services are provided by specialists who are qualified to manage the prosthetic and/or orthotic needs of disabled persons by performing examinations, participating in the prescribing of needed specialized equipment, designing and fitting such equipment, and following up to see that the equipment fits and functions properly.

†*Psychological services provided in physical rehabilitation settings focus on the patient's and family's adaptation to the patient's disability and on the assessment of psychological deficits associated with the physical disability.*

‡*In the physical rehabilitation setting, recreational and other leisure-time activity services provide for the development, maintenance, and expression of an appropriate leisure/social life-style for individuals with physical, mental, emotional, or social limitations.*

RH.2.5.1.1 An assessment of the patient's leisure, social, and recreational abilities, deficiencies, interests, barriers, life experiences, needs, and potential; and (scoring guideline for PE.1.1)

RH.2.5.1.2 Treatment services designed to improve social, emotional, cognitive, and physical functional behaviors as necessary prerequisites to future leisure/social involvement.

1 2 3 4 5 NA

RH.2.5.2 Recreational therapy services staff monitor the extent to which goals are achieved relative to the use of leisure time and the acquisition of socialization skills. (scoring guideline for PE.2.3)

RH.2.6   Rehabilitation Medicine Services.*

RH.2.6.1   Rehabilitation medicine services include, but need not be limited to, the following:

RH.2.6.1.1 An assessment of the patient's reported general medical condition, psychosocial status, and vocational history; (scoring guideline for PE.1.1)

RH.2.6.1.2 Neuromusculoskeletal and mental status examinations and, in the inpatient setting, a general medical examination; (scoring guideline for PE.1.7.1)

RH.2.6.1.3 Analyses of body movement, postural control, gait, and upper-extremity skills; (scoring guideline for PE.1.1)

RH.2.6.1.4 Examination and/or interpretation of supplemental laboratory, radiologic, electrodiagnostic, and special-procedure testing; (scoring guideline for PE.15)

RH.2.6.1.5   For inpatient services, general medical management by and liaison with the previous physician of record (when one exists) or arrangements for general medical management by another appropriately qualified physician, with specialty consultation and management provided as required by the patient's condition;

1 2 3 4 5 NA

RH.2.6.1.6 Medication prescription, monitoring, and appropriate revision; and (PI.3.4.2.2)

RH.2.6.1.7   Prescription and proscription of rehabilitation intervention commensurate with the patient's medical status and care requirements.

1 2 3 4 5 NA

RH.2.6.2 The quality and effectiveness of the patient's progress toward the achievement of rehabilitation goals and health maintenance, as well as the degree of success in preventing complications known to occur over time in the natural history of the disorder, are monitored. (PI.3.3.1)

RH.2.7   Rehabilitation Nursing Care.†

---

*Rehabilitation medicine services, performed by a physiatrist or other physician qualified by training, experience, and knowledge, provide for the identification of the nature and extent of functional disability and for the performance of diagnostic examinations to detect or confirm pathologic states that underlie, complicate, or exist concurrently with physical impairment and disabling conditions. A synthesis of all the medical and rehabilitation data pertinent to an individual is applied in the design of interventions that are electively used to prevent complications, enhance recovery, or promote adaptation to optimal levels of function, performance, and pursuit of personal life goals.

†Rehabilitation nursing care is designed to provide for the prevention of complications of physical disability, the restoration of optimal functioning, and adaptation to an altered life-style through the use of the nursing process (ie, assessment, planning, intervention, and evaluation).

RH.2.7.1   Rehabilitation nursing care includes physical and psychosocial assessments and interventions designed to meet patients' rehabilitation nursing care needs.

1 2 3 4 5 NA

> RH.2.7.2   *Rehabilitation nursing staff members monitor the degree to which the individualized nursing care goals for each patient are achieved.* **(scoring guideline for PE.2.3)**

RH.2.8   Social Work Services.*

RH.2.8.1   The scope of physical rehabilitation social work services includes, but need not be limited to, the following:

> RH.2.8.1.1   *Assessment of the patient's personal coping history and current psychosocial adaptation to his disability;* **(scoring guideline for PE.1.1)**

> RH.2.8.1.2   *Assessment of immediate and extended family members and other support persons relative to support networks;* **(scoring guideline for PE.1.1)**

> RH.2.8.1.3   *Assessment of housing, living arrangements, and stability and source of income relative to facilitating discharge plans; and* **(scoring guideline for PE.1.1)**

RH.2.8.1.4   Intervention strategies, designed to increase the effectiveness of coping, strengthen informal support systems, and facilitate continuity of care, including

1 2 3 4 5 NA

RH.2.8.1.4.1   community service linkage/referrals.

1 2 3 4 5 NA

> RH.2.8.2   *Social work services staff monitor the achievement of goals relative to discharge planning activities designed to meet the basic sustenance, shelter, transportation, and comfort needs of patients and their families.* **(scoring guideline for PE.2.3)**

RH.2.9   Speech-Language Pathology and/or Audiology Services.†

RH.2.9.1   Speech-language pathology and/or audiology services include, but need not be limited to, the following:

> RH.2.9.1.1   *Screening to identify individuals who require further evaluation to determine the presence or absence of a communicative disorder;* **(scoring guideline for PE.1.1)**

> RH.2.9.1.2   *Evaluating and diagnosing speech, language, and oral and pharyngeal sensorimotor competencies by a qualified speech-language pathologist, and evaluating and diagnosing auditory and vestibular competencies by a qualified audiologist using instrumentation such as audiometers, electroacoustic immittance equipment, evoked potential response equipment, and electronystagmographic equipment;* **(scoring guideline for PE.1.1)**

Social work services provide for assessment and intervention relative to psychosocial factors and the social context in which the physically disabled patient lives.

†*Speech-language pathology and/or audiology services provide for a continuum of services, including prevention, identification, diagnosis, consultation, and treatment of patients regarding speech, language, oral and pharyngeal sensorimotor function, hearing, and balance.*

RH.2.9.1.3 Planning, directing, and conducting habilitative, rehabilitative, and counseling programs to treat disorders of verbal and written language, voice, articulation, fluency, interactive communication, mastication, deglutition, auditory and/or visual processing and memory, cognition/communication, and assisted and/or augmentative communication treatment and devices;   1 2 3 4 5 NA

RH.2.9.1.4 Planning, directing, and conducting aural habilitation and rehabilitation programs by the audiologist; and   1 2 3 4 5 NA

RH.2.9.1.4.1 Such programs may include, but need not be limited to, the following:

RH.2.9.1.4.1.1 Selection of hearing aids and assistive listening devices;   1 2 3 4 5 NA

RH.2.9.1.4.1.2 Counseling, guidance, and auditory training;   1 2 3 4 5 NA

RH.2.9.1.4.1.3 Speech reading; and   1 2 3 4 5 NA

RH.2.9.1.4.1.4 Language habilitation.   1 2 3 4 5 NA

RH.2.9.1.5 Discharge planning by the professional to help ensure the patient understands his/her communication abilities and prognosis.   1 2 3 4 5 NA

RH.2.9.2 Speech-language and/or audiology services are monitored to determine the effectiveness of actions taken to improve patients' communication skills. (PI.3.3.1)

RH.2.10 Vocational Rehabilitation Services.*

RH.2.10.1 Vocational rehabilitation services are comprehensive and include, at a minimum, the following: 1 2 3 4 5 NA

*RH.2.10.1.1 Evaluation of physical and intellectual capacity; (**scoring guideline for PE.1.1**)*

*RH.2.10.1.2 Evaluation of interests and attitudes; (**scoring guideline for PE.1.1**)*

*RH.2.10.1.3 Evaluation of emotional and social adjustment; (**scoring guideline for PE.1.1**)*

*RH.2.10.1.4 Evaluation of work skills and capabilities; (**scoring guideline for PE.1.1**)*

*RH.2.10.1.5 Evaluation of vocational potential and objectives; and (**scoring guideline for PE.1.1**)*

*RH.2.10.1.6 Job analysis. (**scoring guideline for PE.1.1**)*

RH.2.10.2 Appropriate instruments, equipment, and methods are used under the supervision of a qualified specialist.   1 2 3 4 5 NA

RH.2.10.3 Vocational rehabilitation services staff monitor the degree to which appropriate work skills are achieved, the improvement in independent functioning relative to work-skill capability, and the achievement of vocational objectives. (PI.3.3.1)

---

*Vocational rehabilitation services provide for assessment and evaluation—through the use of testing, counseling, and other related activities—of the physically disabled patient's need for services designed to enable him/her to return to productive activity.

*RH.3   When comprehensive physical rehabilitation services are provided, they are implemented in an interdisciplinary manner in accordance with a written program description. (**LD.1.7.1, LD.3**)*

*RH.3.1   There is a written program description for the comprehensive physical rehabilitation program or unit, which includes at least the following: (**LD.1.7**)*

*RH.3.1.1   A mission statement; (**LD.1.7.1**)*

RH.3.1.2   Admission criteria and an organized admission process;   1 2 3 4 5 NA

*RH.3.1.3   A description of the means used to assess and meet the identified biological and psychosocial needs of patients admitted to the program or unit; (**PE.4**)*

*RH.3.1.4   A provision that the scope and intensity of treatment required by the patient are appropriate to the range of services offered by the program or unit, including specification of the minimum number of hours that rehabilitation programming is provided to the patient each week; (**LD.1.3.4**)*

RH.3.1.5   A mechanism designed to assure appropriate continuity of care at the time of patient admission to, and discharge from, the program or unit; and   1 2 3 4 5 NA

*RH.3.1.6   A provision for a program director who may serve as both medical and administrative director or a provision for separate administrative and medical directors, with a description of the director's or directors' responsibilities. (**LD.2.2.2**)*

RH.3.2   When inpatient comprehensive physical rehabilitation services are provided, there are contiguous designated inpatient beds in one or more organized units.   1 2 3 4 5 NA

*RH.3.3   Rehabilitation medicine services and consultation are available on a full-time basis, and the following requirements are met: (**LD.1.3.4.1, LD.1.3.4.2**)*

RH.3.3.1   Medical direction is provided by a qualified physician who is knowledgeable and skilled, by reason of training and experience, in the provision of rehabilitation medicine services;   1 2 3 4 5 NA

RH.3.3.2   For each patient in a comprehensive rehabilitation program, a physician qualified in rehabilitation through training and experience is responsible for the patient's medical rehabilitation and is identified in the medical record;   1 2 3 4 5 NA

RH.3.3.3   The treatment plan for each patient has physician participation relative to both the general medical and the rehabilitation medical needs of the patient; and   1 2 3 4 5 NA

RH.3.3.4   The rehabilitation services medical director is responsible for the quality of all rehabilitation medical services provided.   1 2 3 4 5 NA

*RH.3.4   Inpatient rehabilitation nursing care is provided 24 hours a day, 7 days a week, and the following requirements are met: (**scoring guideline for LD.1.3.4.1**)*

RH.3.4.1   Administrative direction is provided by a qualified registered nurse who is knowledgeable and skilled in the provision of rehabilitation nursing care;   1 2 3 4 5 NA

RH.3.4.2   A sufficient number of permanently assigned registered nurses who are knowledgeable and skilled in rehabilitation nursing care are available to meet the rehabilitation nursing care needs of patients; and

1 2 3 4 5 NA

RH.3.4.3   A sufficient number of other nursing staff members who are qualified to assist in the provision of rehabilitation nursing care to patients are assigned.

1 2 3 4 5 NA

RH.3.5   A sufficient number of qualified, competent therapeutic services professionals and support staff are available to meet the service needs described in the mission statement of the program.

1 2 3 4 5 NA

RH.3.6   There is a comprehensive interdisciplinary rehabilitation treatment plan for each patient, unless that patient is referred to a single service for outpatient care.

1 2 3 4 5 NA

RH.3.6.1   Each plan includes, but need not be limited to, the following:

RH.3.6.1.1   Multidisciplinary assessments of the biological and psychosocial needs of the patient, performed by qualified health care professionals;

1 2 3 4 5 NA

RH.3.6.1.2   A description of the patient's capacities, strengths, disabilities, and weaknesses;

1 2 3 4 5 NA

RH.3.6.1.3   Identification of the patient's rehabilitation goals, stated in functional, performance, and behavioral objectives relative to the performance of life tasks and capabilities;

1 2 3 4 5 NA

RH.3.6.1.4   Written criteria for termination of treatment or discharge from the program;

1 2 3 4 5 NA

RH.3.6.1.5   Participation of the patient and family, as appropriate;

1 2 3 4 5 NA

RH.3.6.1.6   Physician participation relative to both the general medical and the rehabilitation medical needs of the patient; and

1 2 3 4 5 NA

RH.3.6.1.7   Discharge planning addressed as part of goal setting early in the rehabilitation process.

1 2 3 4 5 NA

*RH.3.7   The medical record documents progress toward rehabilitation goal achievement and includes the results of the planned therapeutic interventions and the patient's responses to such interventions. (**scoring guideline for IM.7.2.8**)*

RH.3.8   Provision is made for continuity of care as part of the process of implementing the discharge plan.

1 2 3 4 5 NA

*RH.4   Monitoring and evaluation of the quality of care addresses the extent to which functional or behavioral goals, established in accordance with RH.1.2.4, are achieved by patients. (**PI.3.3.1**)*

NOTES AND COMMENTS:

PLANT, TECHNOLOGY, AND SAFETY MANAGEMENT

Some of the standards in this chapter of the 1993 *Accreditation Manual for Hospitals* have been recast to focus on improving individual and organizational performance and have been moved to Sections 1 and 2 of this *Manual*. To help you identify these standards, we have printed them here in small italic type with their new standard references in bold type in parentheses. Organizations are expected to demonstrate compliance with these standards in their new context. For example, PL.1.6.4 in this chapter has been recast and moved to the "Management of Information" chapter, as IM.8.1.2 and IM.8.1.2.1. This standard appears in small italic type, and the new standard references, IM.8.1.2 and IM.8.1.2.1, appear in bold type in parentheses at the end of the standard. Organizations are expected to comply with IM.8.1.2 and IM.8.1.2.1 and will be scored for compliance in the "Management of Information" chapter. Standards scored in this chapter are in normal type and have accompanying scoring scales (1 2 3 4 5 NA).

PL.1
There is a safety management program that is designed to provide a physical environment free of hazards and to manage staff activities to reduce the risk of human injury.

1 2 3 4 5 NA

PL.1.1 The governing body strives to assure a safe environment for patients, personnel, and visitors by requiring and supporting the establishment and maintenance of an effective safety management program (see also GB.1.18).

1 2 3 4 5 NA

PL.1.2 The safety management program is based on monitoring and evaluation of organizational experience, applicable law and regulation, and accepted practice and includes

PL.1.2.1   policies and procedures for safety in all departments/services;

1 2 3 4 5 NA

PL.1.2.2   a risk-assessment program that

PL.1.2.2.1   evaluates the impact on patient care and safety of the buildings, grounds, equipment, occupants, and internal physical systems, and

1 2 3 4 5 NA

PL.1.2.2.2   includes policies and procedures for a security management program;

1 2 3 4 5 NA

PL.1.2.3   special attention to hazards related to the ages of the patients served; and

1 2 3 4 5 NA

PL.1.2.4   policies and procedures for the timely reporting and resolution of situations that pose an immediate threat to life, health, and/or property.

1 2 3 4 5 NA

PL.1.2.4.1   The policies and procedures are approved in writing by the chief executive officer and the chief officer of the medical staff.

1 2 3 4 5 NA

PL.1.2.5   The objectives, scope, organization, and effectiveness of the safety management program are evaluated at least annually and revised as necessary.

1 2 3 4 5 NA

PL.1.3   A safety officer appointed by the chief executive officer or a designee and qualified by experience and/or education is responsible for the development, implementation, and monitoring of the safety management program.

1 2 3 4 5 NA

PL.1.3.1   The safety officer manages an ongoing hospitalwide process to collect and evaluate information about hazards and safety practices that is used to identify safety management issues to be addressed by the safety committee; the information collection and evaluation system includes

1 2 3 4 5 NA

PL.1.3.1.1   summaries of safety management, life safety management, equipment management, and utilities management deficiencies or problems, failures, user errors, and relevant published reports of hazards associated with any of these areas;

1 2 3 4 5 NA

PL.1.3.1.2   documented surveys, at least semiannually, of all areas of the facility to identify environmental hazards and unsafe practices;

1 2 3 4 5 NA

PL.1.3.1.3   a system for reporting and investigating all incidents that involve property damage, occupational illness, or patient, personnel, or visitor injury; and

1 2 3 4 5 NA

PL.1.3.1.4   summaries of actions taken as the result of other hospitalwide monitoring activities, including quality assessment and improvement and risk management.

1 2 3 4 5 NA

PL.1.4   There is a safety committee, appointed by the chief executive officer or a designee, composed of representatives of administration, clinical services, and support services.

1 2 3 4 5 NA

PL.1.4.1   The safety committee meets at least every other month to analyze identified safety management issues and to develop or approve recommendations for resolving them.

1 2 3 4 5 NA

PL.1.4.2   The safety officer works with appropriate staff to implement safety committee recommendations and to monitor the effectiveness of the changes.

1 2 3 4 5 NA

PL.1.4.2.1   The results of monitoring are reported to the safety committee.

1 2 3 4 5 NA

PL.1.4.3   Identified safety management issues and summaries of safety committee activities are communicated at least quarterly to the governing body, chief executive officer, directors of all departments/services, and those responsible for other monitoring activities, including quality assessment and improvement and risk management.

1 2 3 4 5 NA

PL.1.5   Orientation and education of personnel is provided in accordance with SE.1 through SE.4.4.

1 2 3 4 5 NA

PL.1.6   There is a hazardous materials and wastes program, designed and operated in accordance with applicable law and regulation, to identify and control hazardous materials and wastes; the program includes

1 2 3 4 5 NA

PL.1.6.1   policies, procedures, and written criteria for identifying, handling, storing, using, and disposing of hazardous materials from receipt through use and hazardous wastes from generation to final disposal;

1 2 3 4 5 NA

PL.1.6.2   education of personnel in accordance with SE.1 through SE.4.4 and, as appropriate, monitoring of personnel who manage and/or regularly come into contact with hazardous materials and/or wastes;

1 2 3 4 5 NA

PL.1.6.3   monitoring of compliance with the program's requirements; and

1 2 3 4 5 NA

> *PL.1.6.4   evaluation of the effectiveness of the program. As part of the hospitalwide information collection and evaluation system (see PL.1.3.1), a summary of the evaluation, including identified problems, failures, user errors, and relevant published information about environmental and occupational hazards, is reviewed by the safety committee.* **(IM.8.1.2, IM.8.1.2.1)**

PL.1.7   There is an emergency preparedness program designed to manage the consequences of natural disasters or other emergencies that disrupt the hospital's ability to provide care and treatment; the program includes

1 2 3 4 5 NA

PL.1.7.1   a description of the hospital's role in communitywide emergency preparedness plans;

1 2 3 4 5 NA

PL.1.7.2   information about how the hospital plans to implement specific procedures in response to environmental or man-made events;

1 2 3 4 5 NA

PL.1.7.3   provisions for the management of space, supplies, communications, and security;

1 2 3 4 5 NA

PL.1.7.4   provisions for the management of staff, including distribution and assignment of responsibilities and functions;

1 2 3 4 5 NA

PL.1.7.5   provisions for the management of patients, including scheduling of services, control of patient information, and admission, transfer, and discharge;

1 2 3 4 5 NA

PL.1.7.6   education of personnel in accordance with SE.1 through SE.4.4; and

1 2 3 4 5 NA

PL.1.7.7   semiannual implementations of the plan, either in response to an emergency or in a planned drill.

1 2 3 4 5 NA

PL.1.7.7.1   The hospital's performance during implementations of the plan is evaluated, documented, and reported to the safety committee through the hospitalwide information collection and evaluation system (see PL.1.3.1).

1 2 3 4 5 NA

PL.2
There is a life safety management program designed to protect patients, personnel, visitors, and property from fire and the products of combustion and to provide for the safe use of buildings and grounds.

1 2 3 4 5 NA

PL.2.1 Each building in which patients are housed overnight or receive treatment is in compliance with the appropriate provisions of the 1991 edition of the *Life Safety Code*® of the National Fire Protection Association (NFPA), or equivalent protection is provided and documented.*   1 2 3 4 5 NA

PL.2.1.1 A comprehensive Statement of Construction and Fire Protection, submitted to the Joint Commission, describes the structural features of fire protection of the facility.   1 2 3 4 5 NA

PL.2.1.2 When requirements of the *Life Safety Code*® and these standards or their equivalents are not met, a comprehensive plan of correction is developed.   1 2 3 4 5 NA

PL.2.1.3 When requirements for fire protection or environment and grounds safety are affected by construction, the hospital institutes and documents interim life safety measures to temporarily compensate for the hazards posed by existing life safety deficiencies.†   1 2 3 4 5 NA

PL.2.1.4 The interim life safety measures are continued and documented so that the level of life safety is not diminished in any occupied area and a safe environment is maintained throughout construction of or alteration to buildings or grounds.†   1 2 3 4 5 NA

PL.2.2 There is an ongoing program designed to assure that the buildings and grounds are suitable to the nature of the services provided and the ages and other characteristics of the patient population served.   1 2 3 4 5 NA

PL.2.2.1 New construction provides for the safe and convenient use of buildings and grounds by physically disabled individuals.   1 2 3 4 5 NA

PL.2.2.2 The hospital has specific policies for the maintenance, supervision, and safe use by patients of all grounds and equipment, including special activity areas.   1 2 3 4 5 NA

PL.2.2.3 Emergency departments/services are readily identifiable and easily accessible.   1 2 3 4 5 NA

PL.2.2.3.1 There are policies that address vehicular access to the emergency care areas.   1 2 3 4 5 NA

PL.2.2.4 Compliance with the requirements of the program is documented.   1 2 3 4 5 NA

PL.2.3 There is an ongoing program designed to establish and maintain fire safety.   1 2 3 4 5 NA

PL.2.3.1 The program is established through the following:

PL.2.3.1.1 Procedures to identify and maintain all applicable required features of fire protection to *Life Safety Code*® standards;   1 2 3 4 5 NA

Effective January 1, 1993, the Joint Commission began referencing NFPA 101®-1991, the Life Safety Code® (LSC) of the National Fire Protection Association. All facilities being surveyed will be evaluated using this edition of the LSC. Buildings for which plans were approved after January 1, 1993, will be evaluated as "new construction" under the applicable occupancy chapters of the LSC.

Life Safety Code® and NFPA 101® are registered trademarks of the National Fire Protection Association, Inc, Quincy, Mass.

†*See Appendix D, pages 249–250, for a listing of the interim life safety measures.*

PL.2.3.1.2 Procedures for inspecting, testing, and maintaining fire-alarm and fire-detection systems, including quarterly testing of all circuits and annual preventive maintenance of all components;   1 2 3 4 5 NA

PL.2.3.1.3 Procedures for inspecting and testing all automatic fire-extinguishing systems annually;   1 2 3 4 5 NA

PL.2.3.1.4 Procedures for the management of portable fire extinguishers, including guidelines for their identification, placement, and use; a quarterly inspection program; and a regular maintenance program; and   1 2 3 4 5 NA

PL.2.3.1.5 Procedures to review proposed acquisitions of bedding, window draperies and other curtains, furnishings, decorations, wastebaskets, and other equipment to identify issues related to fire safety.   1 2 3 4 5 NA

PL.2.3.2 The program is maintained through the following:

PL.2.3.2.1 As appropriate to occupancy classification, a fire-alarm or fire-detection system that on activation minimizes smoke transmission through control of designated fans and/or dampers in air-handling and smoke-management systems;   1 2 3 4 5 NA

PL.2.3.2.2 A fire plan that addresses appropriate staff response to a fire emergency and appropriate education for all personnel in accordance with SE.1 through SE.4.4; and   1 2 3 4 5 NA

PL.2.3.2.3 For all personnel on all shifts in all patient care buildings, quarterly conducting and evaluation of fire drills that test staff knowledge of the use and function of the fire-alarm systems, transmission of alarms, containment of smoke and fire, transfer to areas of refuge, fire extinguishment, assignment of specific duties, and preparation for building evacuation.   1 2 3 4 5 NA

PL.2.3.3 Compliance with the requirements of the program is documented.   1 2 3 4 5 NA

PL.2.4 The life safety management program is used to identify and document *Life Safety Code*® and fire protection deficiencies, failures, and user errors that may threaten the patient care environment during a fire.   1 2 3 4 5 NA

PL.2.4.1 When problems are identified, actions are taken to resolve them.   1 2 3 4 5 NA

PL.2.4.1.1 The actions are documented.   1 2 3 4 5 NA

PL.2.4.1.2 The actions are evaluated for effectiveness.   1 2 3 4 5 NA

PL.3
There is an equipment management program designed to assess and control the clinical and physical risks of fixed and portable equipment used for the diagnosis, treatment, monitoring, and care of patients and of other fixed and portable electrically powered equipment.   1 2 3 4 5 NA

PL.3.1 Written criteria, which include characteristics of equipment function, clinical application, maintenance requirements, and equipment incident history, are used to identify equipment to be included in the program.   1 2 3 4 5 NA

PL.3.1.1   Before a piece or type of equipment is used, it is evaluated for inclusion in the program, and the evaluation is documented.

1 2 3 4 5 NA

PL.3.2   A current, accurate, unique inventory is kept of all equipment included in the program, regardless of the equipment's ownership or purpose.

1 2 3 4 5 NA

PL.3.2.1   Each piece or type of equipment listed in the inventory has written equipment-testing procedures and user-training programs (in accordance with SE.1 through SE.4.4) designed to manage the clinical and physical risks.

1 2 3 4 5 NA

PL.3.2.1.1   Each piece of equipment is tested prior to initial use and at least annually thereafter; such testing is documented.

1 2 3 4 5 NA

PL.3.2.1.2   Orientation and education (in accordance with SE.1 through SE.4.4) of individuals who use and/or maintain the equipment are documented.

1 2 3 4 5 NA

PL.3.3   The equipment management program is used to identify and document equipment problems, failures, and user errors that have or may have an adverse effect on patient safety and/or the quality of care.

1 2 3 4 5 NA

PL.3.3.1   When problems are identified, actions are taken to resolve them.

1 2 3 4 5 NA

PL.3.3.1.1   The actions are documented.

1 2 3 4 5 NA

PL.3.3.1.2   The actions are evaluated for effectiveness.

1 2 3 4 5 NA

PL.3.4   When information is received that reasonably suggests that a medical device may have caused or contributed to the death, serious injury, or serious illness of a patient or other individual, the organization reports this information as required by the Safe Medical Devices Act of 1990.

1 2 3 4 5 NA

PL.4
There is a utilities management program designed to assure the operational reliability, assess the special risks, and respond to failures of utility systems that support the patient care environment.

1 2 3 4 5 NA

PL.4.1   Written criteria, which include utilities for life support, infection control, environmental support, and equipment support elements, are used to identify utilities to be included in the program.

1 2 3 4 5 NA

PL.4.2   There is a reliable, adequate emergency power system to provide electricity to designated areas during interruption of the normal electrical source.

1 2 3 4 5 NA

PL.4.2.1   As required by occupancy classification, the emergency power system provides electricity to at least the following:

PL.4.2.1.1   Alarm systems;

1 2 3 4 5 NA

PL.4.2.1.2   Egress illumination;

1 2 3 4 5 NA

PL.4.2.1.3   Elevators (at least one);

1 2 3 4 5 NA

PL.4.2.1.4   Emergency communication systems; and

1 2 3 4 5 NA

PL.4.2.1.5   Illumination of exit signs.

1 2 3 4 5 NA

PL.4.2.2   The emergency power system also provides electricity to the following areas, as applicable, based upon the services provided:

PL.4.2.2.1	Blood, bone, and tissue storage units;	1 2 3 4 5 NA
PL.4.2.2.2	Emergency care areas;	1 2 3 4 5 NA
PL.4.2.2.3	Medical air compressors;	1 2 3 4 5 NA
PL.4.2.2.4	Medical/surgical vacuum systems;	1 2 3 4 5 NA
PL.4.2.2.5	Newborn nurseries;	1 2 3 4 5 NA
PL.4.2.2.6	Obstetric delivery rooms;	1 2 3 4 5 NA
PL.4.2.2.7	Operating rooms;	1 2 3 4 5 NA
PL.4.2.2.8	Postoperative recovery rooms; and	1 2 3 4 5 NA
PL.4.2.2.9	Special care units.	1 2 3 4 5 NA

PL.4.3 A current, accurate, unique inventory is kept of all equipment for utility systems included in the program.

1 2 3 4 5 NA

PL.4.4 Utility system operational plans are written to help assure reliability, control risks, reduce failures, and train users and operators of the systems.

1 2 3 4 5 NA

PL.4.4.1 The hospital develops procedures and establishes intervals for the testing and maintenance of equipment for utility systems included in the program.

1 2 3 4 5 NA

PL.4.4.2 Tests and inspections that support operational reliability and manage risks are documented.

1 2 3 4 5 NA

PL.4.4.3 Orientation and education provided in accordance with SE.1 through SE.4.4 for individuals who use and/or maintain utility systems are documented.

1 2 3 4 5 NA

PL.4.5 There is a current, complete set of documents that indicates the distribution of each utility system, including controls for a partial or complete shutdown.

1 2 3 4 5 NA

PL.4.5.1 Where provided, emergency shutoff controls are labeled.

1 2 3 4 5 NA

PL.4.6 The utilities management program is used to identify and document utility problems, failures, and user errors that are or may be a threat to the patient care environment.

1 2 3 4 5 NA

PL.4.6.1 When problems are identified, actions are taken to resolve them.

1 2 3 4 5 NA

PL.4.6.1.1 The actions are documented.

1 2 3 4 5 NA

PL.4.6.1.2 The actions are evaluated for effectiveness.

1 2 3 4 5 NA

Notes and Comments:

PROFESSIONAL LIBRARY AND HEALTH INFORMATION SERVICES

Standards in this chapter of the 1993 *Accreditation Manual for Hospitals* have been recast to focus on improving individual and organizational performance and have been moved to Sections 1 and 2 of this *Manual.* The following cross-reference is provided for your information.

1993	**1994**
PR.1	IM.9.1
PR.1.1	IM.9.2
PR.1.2	IM.1.1.1
PR.1.3	IM.9.4
PR.1.3.1	IM.9.4
PR.1.4	IM.9

QUALITY ASSESSMENT AND IMPROVEMENT

Standards in this chapter of the 1993 *Accreditation Manual for Hospitals* have been recast to focus on improving individual and organizational performance and have been moved to Sections 1 and 2 of this *Manual*. The following cross-reference is provided for your information.

1993	1994
QA.1	LD.4
QA.1.1	scoring guideline for LD.4.1
QA.1.2	scoring guideline for LD.4.3
QA.1.3	LD.4.4
QA.1.3.1	LD.4.4.1
QA.1.3.2	LD.4.4.2
QA.1.3.3	LD.4.4.3
QA.1.4	LD.4.4.4
QA.1.5	LD.3.2.1
QA.1.6	LD.4.5
QA.2	PI.1
QA.2.1	PI.1.1
QA.2.1.1	PI.3.4
QA.2.1.1.1	PI.3.3, PI.3.3.2
QA.2.1.1.2	PI.3.4.2, PI.3.4.2.1
QA.2.1.1.3	PI.3.4.2, PI.3.4.2.2
QA.2.1.1.4	IM.3.3.1
QA.2.1.1.5	PI.3.4.2, PI.3.4.2.3
QA.2.1.1.6	PI.3.4.2, PI.3.4.2.2
QA.2.2	PI.3.3–PI.3.3.2
QA.2.2.1	PI.3.4
QA.2.2.2	LD.2.1, LD.2.1.6
QA.2.2.2.1	PI.1.1
QA.2.2.2.1.1	PI.3
QA.2.2.2.1.2	PI.3
QA.2.2.2.1.3	PI.3
QA.2.2.3	LD.4.2–LD.4.3
QA.2.2.3.1	LD.1.3.4.2.1
QA.2.3	PI.3.5
QA.2.3.1	PI.3.5.3
QA.2.3.2	PI.3.4.2.4
QA.2.3.3	PI.3.5.2
QA.2.4	PI.4
QA.2.4.1	PI.4
QA.2.4.2	PI.4.2
QA.3	LD.4, PI.1
QA.3.1	PI.3.2

1993	**1994**
QA.3.1.1	PI.3.4.1
QA.3.1.1.1	PI.3.4.1.1
QA.3.1.1.2	PI.3.4.1.2
QA.3.1.1.2.1	PI.3.4.1.2
QA.3.1.1.2.2	PI.3.4.1.2
QA.3.1.1.2.3	PI.3.4.1.2
QA.3.1.1.3	PI.3.4.1.3
QA.3.1.2	PI.3.4
QA.3.1.2.1	PI.4.1–PI.4.1.2.3
QA.3.1.2.1.1	PI.5.2
QA.3.1.2.1.1.1	PI.5.2.3
QA.3.1.2.1.1.2	PI.4.1, PI.4.1.1
QA.3.1.2.1.1.3	PI.2
QA.3.1.3	PI.3.1
QA.3.1.3.1	PI.3.4.1
QA.3.1.3.1.1	PI.3.4.1.1
QA.3.1.3.1.2	PI.3.4.1.2
QA.3.1.3.1.3	PI.3.4.1.3
QA.3.1.4	PI.4.1–PI.4.1.2.3
QA.3.1.4.1	PI.4.1
QA.3.1.4.1.1	PI.4.1.3.1
QA.3.1.4.1.2	PI.4.1.3
QA.3.1.4.2	PI.4.1–PI.4.1.2.3
QA.3.1.4.3	PI.4
QA.3.1.5	PI.4.1
QA.3.1.5.1	PI.4.1, PI.4.1.3
QA.3.1.5.2	PI.4
QA.3.1.5.3	PI.4, PI.4.2
QA.3.1.6	PI.5.1
QA.3.1.6.1	PI.5.1–PI.5.1.1.1
QA.3.1.6.1.1	PI.5.3.1
QA.3.1.6.2	PI.5.3.1
QA.3.1.7	IM.8
QA.3.1.7.1	IM.8
QA.3.1.7.2	IM.8
QA.4	LD.4.2
QA.4.1	LD.4.2
QA.4.2	IM.6
QA.4.2.1	PI.1.1
QA.4.2.2	IM.6.2
QA.4.2.3	IM.8.1.9
QA.4.3	PI.5.2, PI.5.2.3
QA.4.4	PI.5

RADIATION ONCOLOGY SERVICES

Some of the standards in this chapter of the 1993 *Accreditation Manual for Hospitals* have been recast to focus on improving individual and organizational performance and have been moved to Sections 1 and 2 of this *Manual.* To help you identify these standards, we have printed them here in small italic type with their new standard references in bold type in parentheses. Organizations are expected to demonstrate compliance with these standards in their new context. For example, RA.1 in this chapter has been recast and moved to the "Leadership" chapter, as LD.1.3.4. This standard appears in small italic type, and the new standard reference, LD.1.3.4, appears in bold type in parentheses at the end of the standard. Organizations are expected to comply with LD.1.3.4 and will be scored for compliance in the "Leadership" chapter. Standards scored in this chapter are in normal type and have accompanying scoring scales (1 2 3 4 5 NA).

> *RA.1   Radiation oncology services are available to meet the needs of patients, as determined by the medical staff.* (**LD.1.3.4**)*

RA.1.1   All individuals who provide radiation oncology services independently have delineated clinical privileges for the services they provide.   1 2 3 4 5 NA

RA.1.2   The director of the radiation oncology department/service is a physician member of the medical staff who is qualified by education and experience in radiation oncology, is clinically competent, and possesses the administrative skills necessary to assure effective leadership of the service.   1 2 3 4 5 NA

RA.1.3   Comprehensive safety rules are developed by the director of the department/service in cooperation with the hospital's safety committee and the hospital's radiation safety committee, if one exists.   1 2 3 4 5 NA

> *RA.1.4   There is a description of the means for providing radiation oncology services when they are not directly provided by the hospital. (**LD.1.3.4.2.1**)*

> *RA.1.5   When radiation oncology procedures are provided outside the hospital, the off-site source(s) meets the standards contained in this chapter of this* Manual. *(**LD.1.3.4.2.1**)*

> *RA.2   There are policies and procedures to assure effective management, safety, proper performance of equipment, effective communication, and quality control in the radiation oncology department/service. (**LD.2, LD.2.1.2, LD.2.1.3, LD.2.1.7**)*

---

*These services are not required for hospitals that provide only social rehabilitation/substance abuse services. When the hospital does not provide radiation oncology services, the off-site source(s) to and from which the patient is transported for treatment is approved by the medical staff.

RA.2.1 Policies and procedures are developed in cooperation with the medical staff, administration, nurse executive and other appropriate registered nurses, and, as necessary, other clinical departments/services and are implemented. (LD.3.3)

RA.2.1.1 The policies and procedures are reviewed periodically by a medical radiation physicist.

1 2 3 4 5 NA

RA.2.2 The written policies and procedures include, but need not be limited to, the following:

RA.2.2.1 Radiation oncology consultation services performed at the request of individuals authorized by the hospital to make such requests;

1 2 3 4 5 NA

RA.2.2.2 A quality control program designed to minimize patient, personnel, and public risks and maximize the quality of therapy; (PI.3.4.1.2, PI.3.5.2)

RA.2.2.3 Implementation of PL.3 through PL.3.3.1.2 in the "Plant, Technology, and Safety Management" chapter of this *Manual* for all electrically and nonelectrically powered equipment used in the treatment or monitoring of patients to assure that the equipment, wherever located in the hospital, performs properly;

1 2 3 4 5 NA

RA.2.2.4 Provisions that a qualified physician, qualified medical radiation physicist, or other qualified individual (PI.3, PI.3.5, PI.3.5.3.5)

RA.2.2.4.1 monitor performance evaluations of treatment equipment at least monthly, (PI.3, PI.3.5, PI.3.5.3.5)

RA.2.2.4.2 monitor each patient for the prescribed dose(s) distribution to an acceptable degree of accuracy and precision, and (PI.3, PI.3.5, PI.3.5.3.5)

RA.2.2.4.3 monitor therapy machines, radiation sources, and simulators for proper working order; (PI.3, PI.3.5, PI.3.5.3.5)

RA.2.2.5 With respect to radiation hazards from equipment, adherence to the recommendations of currently recognized and reliable authority on radiation hazards, such as the National Council on Radiation Protection and Measurements, and any requirements of appropriate licensing agencies or other government bodies;

1 2 3 4 5 NA

RA.2.2.6 Provisions for the safe use, removal, handling, and storage of radium, and other radioactive elements, as well as their disintegration products;

1 2 3 4 5 NA

RA.2.2.6.1 Refer to PL.1.6 through PL.1.6.4 in the "Plant, Technology, and Safety Management" chapter of this *Manual.*

1 2 3 4 5 NA

RA.2.2.7 Guidelines for protecting personnel and patients from radiation;

1 2 3 4 5 NA

RA.2.2.8 The monitoring of staff and personnel for exposure to radiation;

1 2 3 4 5 NA

RA.2.2.9 Guidelines developed in consultation with the infection control committee for the protection of staff, patients, and equipment; and

1 2 3 4 5 NA

RA.2.2.10 Orientation and a safety education program for all personnel.

1 2 3 4 5 NA

RA.3 Reports of consultations and summaries of radiation oncology procedures are included in the patient's medical record. (scoring guideline for IM.7.2.18)

RA.3.1 Requests/referrals for diagnostic and/or monitoring and/or therapeutic invasive procedures include the study or studies requested and appropriate clinical data to aid in the performance of the procedures requested. **(scoring guideline for PE.1.5)**

RA.3.2 Only individuals with delineated clinical privileges in radiation oncology provide consultations, prescribe and supervise treatment procedures, and summarize and authenticate the reports on therapeutic procedures.   1 2 3 4 5 NA

RA.3.3 Authenticated reports are entered in the patient's medical record and, as appropriate, are filed in the department/service.   1 2 3 4 5 NA

RA.3.4 Unless otherwise justified, the medical record of a patient receiving radiation oncology therapy reflects a histologically substantiated diagnosis. **(IM.7.2.6)**

NOTES AND COMMENTS:

RESPIRATORY CARE SERVICES

Some of the standards in this chapter of the 1993 *Accreditation Manual for Hospitals* have been recast to focus on improving individual and organizational performance and have been moved to Sections 1 and 2 of this *Manual*. To help you identify these standards, we have printed them here in small italic type with their new standard references in bold type in parentheses. Organizations are expected to demonstrate compliance with these standards in their new context. For example, RP.1 in this chapter has been recast and moved to the "Leadership" chapter, as LD.1.3.4, LD.2, and LD.2.1.2. This standard appears in small italic type, and the new standard references, LD.1.3.4, LD.2, and LD.2.1.2, appear in bold type in parentheses at the end of the standard. Organizations are expected to comply with LD.1.3.4, LD.2, and LD.2.1.2 and will be scored for compliance in the "Leadership" chapter. Standards scored in this chapter are in normal type and have accompanying scoring scales (1 2 3 4 5 NA).

Hospitals that provide any degree of respiratory care services, either from within the hospital or from an off-site source, are evaluated for compliance with all applicable requirements of this chapter of this *Manual*. Hospitals that provide continuous ventilatory support to patients are evaluated for compliance with all requirements of this chapter of this *Manual*. A respiratory intensive care unit is evaluated for compliance with the requirements of this chapter and with the requirements of the "Special Care Units" chapter of this *Manual*.

*RP.1   Respiratory care services that meet the needs of patients, as determined by the medical staff, are available at all times; are well organized, properly directed, and appropriately integrated with other units and departments of the hospital; and are staffed in a manner commensurate with the scope of services offered. (**LD.1.3.4, LD.2, LD.2.1.2**)*

*RP.1.1   The relationship of the respiratory care department/service to other units and departments of the hospital is specified within the overall hospital organizational plan. (**LD.3.1**)*

*RP.1.2   The scope of the diagnostic and therapeutic respiratory care services provided to inpatients, ambulatory care patients, and home care patients is defined in writing. (**LD.1.7.1.2**)*

RP.1.2.1   There are written guidelines for the transfer or referral of patients who require respiratory care services that are not provided by the hospital.

1 2 3 4 5 NA

*RP.1.3   Pulmonary function studies and blood gas analysis capability are appropriate for the level of respiratory care services provided and are readily available to meet the needs of patients. (**LD.1.3.4, LD.1.3.4.1**)*

*RP.1.4   When respiratory care services are provided to any extent from outside the hospital, the source(s) is approved by the medical staff through its designated mechanism and (**LD.1.3.4.2.1**)*

RP.1.4.1   *provides services whenever needed; (LD.1.3.4)*

RP.1.4.2   meets all safety requirements;   1 2 3 4 5 NA

RP.1.4.3   *abides by all pertinent rules and regulations of the hospital and the medical staff; (LD.1.7)*

RP.1.4.4   *documents the quality control measures to be implemented; and (PI.3.4)*

RP.1.4.5   meets all applicable requirements of this and related chapters of this *Manual.*   1 2 3 4 5 NA

RP.1.5   Medical direction of the respiratory care department/service is provided by a physician member of the active medical staff who has special interest and knowledge in the diagnosis, treatment, and assessment of respiratory problems.   1 2 3 4 5 NA

RP.1.5.1   Whenever possible, this physician is qualified by special training and/or experience in the management of acute and chronic respiratory problems.   1 2 3 4 5 NA

RP.1.5.2   The physician director or his/her qualified designee is available to provide any required respiratory care consultation, particularly on patients receiving continuous ventilatory or oxygenation support.   1 2 3 4 5 NA

RP.1.6   Respiratory care services are provided by a sufficient number of qualified personnel under competent medical direction.   1 2 3 4 5 NA

RP.1.7   Respiratory care personnel provide respiratory care services commensurate with their documented training, experience, and competence.   1 2 3 4 5 NA

RP.1.8   Personnel who provide respiratory care services comply with all applicable law and regulation.   1 2 3 4 5 NA

RP.1.9   Nonphysician respiratory care personnel perform patient procedures associated with a potential hazard, including arterial puncture for obtaining blood samples, only when authorized in writing by the physician director of the respiratory care department/service acting in accordance with medical staff policy.   1 2 3 4 5 NA

RP.1.9.1   The director maintains documentation of the qualification of such personnel to perform these procedures.   1 2 3 4 5 NA

RP.2

Respiratory care services are guided by written policies and procedures.   1 2 3 4 5 NA

RP.2.1   Written policies and procedures specify the scope and conduct of patient care to be rendered in the provision of respiratory care services.   1 2 3 4 5 NA

RP.2.1.1   The policies and procedures are approved by the medical staff through its designated mechanism and are enforced.   1 2 3 4 5 NA

RP.2.2   The written policies and procedures relate to at least the following:

RP.2.2.1   Specification as to who may perform specific procedures and provide instruction, under what circumstances, and under what degree of supervision;   1 2 3 4 5 NA

RP.2.2.1.1   Such procedures include, but need not be limited to,

RP.2.2.1.1.1   cardiopulmonary resuscitation,

1 2 3 4 5 NA

RP.2.2.1.1.2   the obtaining of blood samples and their analysis,

1 2 3 4 5 NA

RP.2.2.1.1.3   pulmonary function testing,

1 2 3 4 5 NA

RP.2.2.1.1.4   therapeutic percussion and vibration,

1 2 3 4 5 NA

RP.2.2.1.1.5   bronchopulmonary drainage,

1 2 3 4 5 NA

RP.2.2.1.1.6   coughing and breathing exercises,

1 2 3 4 5 NA

RP.2.2.1.1.7   mechanical ventilatory and oxygenation support for infants, children, and adults, and

1 2 3 4 5 NA

RP.2.2.1.1.8   aerosol, humidification, and therapeutic gas administration.

1 2 3 4 5 NA

RP.2.2.2   Assembly and sequential operation of equipment and accessories to implement therapeutic regimens;

1 2 3 4 5 NA

RP.2.2.3   Steps to be taken in the event of adverse reactions, based on established criteria for the identification of undesirable side effects;

1 2 3 4 5 NA

RP.2.2.4   Procurement, handling, storage, and dispensing of therapeutic gases;

1 2 3 4 5 NA

RP.2.2.5   Pertinent safety practices, including the control of electrical, flammable, explosive, and mechanical hazards;

1 2 3 4 5 NA

RP.2.2.6   Infection control measures to minimize the possibility of contamination and the transfer of infection; and

1 2 3 4 5 NA

RP.2.2.7   Administration of medications in accordance with the physician's order and with the requirements of the "Pharmaceutical Services" chapter of this Manual. **(TX.4–TX.4.1.3)**

RP.3
The respiratory care department/service has equipment and facilities to assure the safe, effective, and timely provision of respiratory care services to patients.

1 2 3 4 5 NA

RP.3.1   Sufficient space is provided for the respiratory care department/service to

1 2 3 4 5 NA

RP.3.1.1   store, decontaminate, clean, disinfect or sterilize, maintain, and repair equipment; and

1 2 3 4 5 NA

RP.3.1.2   store supplies.

1 2 3 4 5 NA

RP.3.2   There are sufficient space and equipment to perform any pulmonary function studies or blood gas analyses provided in the hospital.

1 2 3 4 5 NA

RP.3.2.1   All requirements relating to the performance of pulmonary function studies or blood gas analyses are met regardless of which hospital department is responsible for performing them.

1 2 3 4 5 NA

RP.3.3   All equipment is calibrated and operated according to the manufacturer's specifications and is periodically inspected and maintained according to an established schedule, as part of the hospital's preventive maintenance program. **(PI.3.5.2)**

RP.3.4　Resuscitative, ventilatory, and oxygenation support equipment is available for patients of all sizes served by the hospital.　　　1　2　3　4　5　NA

> *RP.4　Respiratory care services are provided to patients in accordance with a written prescription by the physician responsible for the patient and are documented in the patient's medical record.* **(scoring guideline for IM.7.2.11)**
>
> *RP.4.1　The prescription for respiratory care specifies the type, frequency, and duration of treatment and, as appropriate, the type and dose of medication, the type of diluent, and the oxygen concentration.* **(scoring guideline for IM.7.2.20)**
>
> *RP.4.2　A written record of the prescription and any related respiratory consultation is maintained in the respiratory care department's/service's files, is incorporated into the patient's medical record, and includes the diagnosis.* **(IM.7.2.6, IM.7.2.18)**
>
> *RP.4.3　All respiratory care services provided to a patient are documented in the patient's medical record, including the type of therapy, date and time of administration, effects of therapy, and any adverse reactions.* **(IM.7.2.12)**

Note: *Refer also to related requirements in the following chapters of this* Manual: *"Improving Organizational Performance," "Infection Control," "Management of Information," "Medical Staff," "Nursing Care," "Pathology and Clinical Laboratory Services," "Pharmaceutical Services," "Plant, Technology, and Safety Management," and "Special Care Units."*

NOTES AND COMMENTS:

RESPONSIBILITIES OF DEPARTMENT/ SERVICE DIRECTORS

Standards in this chapter of the 1993 *Accreditation Manual for Hospitals* have been recast to focus on improving individual and organizational performance and have been moved to Sections 1 and 2 of this *Manual*. The following cross-reference is provided for your information.

1993	1994
RL.1	LD.2
RL.1.1	LD.2.1
RL.1.1.1	LD.2.1.1
RL.1.1.2	LD.2.1.2
RL.1.1.3	LD.2.1.3
RL.1.1.4	LD.2.1.4
RL.1.1.5	LD.2.1.5
RL.1.1.6	LD.2.1.6
RL.1.1.7	LD.2.1.7
RL.1.1.8	LD.2.1.8
RL.1.1.9	LD.2.1.9
RL.2	LD.2.1.10

SOCIAL WORK SERVICES

Some of the standards in this chapter of the 1993 *Accreditation Manual for Hospitals* have been recast to focus on improving individual and organizational performance and have been moved to Sections 1 and 2 of this *Manual.* To help you identify these standards, we have printed them here in small italic type with their new standard references in bold type in parentheses. Organizations are expected to demonstrate compliance with these standards in their new context. For example, SO.1 in this chapter has been recast and moved to the "Leadership" chapter, as LD.1.3.4, LD.2, and LD.2.1.2. This standard appears in small italic type, and the new standard references, LD.1.3.4, LD.2, and LD.2.1.2, appear in bold type in parentheses at the end of the standard. Organizations are expected to comply with LD.1.3.4, LD.2, and LD.2.1.2 and will be scored for compliance in the "Leadership" chapter. Standards scored in this chapter are in normal type and have accompanying scoring scales (1 2 3 4 5 NA).

> *SO.1 Social work services are readily available to the patient, the patient's family, and other persons significant to the patient; are well organized, properly directed, and staffed with a sufficient number of qualified individuals; and are appropriately integrated with other units and departments/services of the hospital. **(LD.1.3.4, LD.2, LD.2.1.2)***

SO.1.1 The provision of social work services is based on individual patient need and the availability of community resources.

1 2 3 4 5 NA

> *SO.1.2 Collaboration with representatives of the hospital administration, the medical staff, the nursing department/service, and other departments/services involved in direct patient care and, as appropriate, with representatives of community organizations is assured in the development and implementation of the social work department/service program. **(LD.1.3.1)***

> *SO.1.3 Social work services may be provided through various methods depending on the scope of services offered by the hospital and the resources available in the community. **(scoring guideline for LD.1.3)***

SO.1.4 When a hospital does not have a qualified social worker employed on a full-time or part-time basis, it has a designated employee to coordinate and assure the provision of social work services.

1 2 3 4 5 NA

SO.1.5 When a qualified social worker is not available on at least a regular part-time basis to direct and provide social work services, a qualified social worker provides consultation.

1 2 3 4 5 NA

> *SO.1.6 In a hospital with an organized social work department/service, a qualified social worker directs the provision of social work services. **(LD.2.2.2)***

SO.1.7 Social work services are provided by a sufficient number of qualified personnel.

1 2 3 4 5 NA

SO.1.7.1   The size of the staff is related to the scope and complexity of the hospital's services and to the social needs of the patients served.

1 2 3 4 5 NA

SO.1.8   Social work department/service personnel are currently licensed, registered, or certified as legally required.

1 2 3 4 5 NA

SO.2
To facilitate continuity of care, assistance is provided to the patient and the patient's family in adapting to the patient care plan, whether the service provided is to be continued in a home or an out-of-home care setting.

1 2 3 4 5 NA

SO.3   Social work services are guided by written policies and procedures. (LD.2.1.3)

SO.3.1   There are written policies and procedures concerning the scope and conduct of social work services. (LD.1.7.1.2)

SO.3.1.1   The policies and procedures are consistent with hospital and medical staff rules and regulations relating to patient care and medical records and with legal requirements. (LD.3.3)

SO.3.2   Social work department/service policies and procedures relate to at least the following: (LD.1.7.1)

SO.3.2.1   Type of services available; (LD.1.7.1.2)

SO.3.2.2   Identification of patients and their families requiring social work services; (scoring guideline for PE.1.1)

SO.3.2.3   Confidentiality of information;

1 2 3 4 5 NA

SO.3.2.4   Consultation and referral procedures;

1 2 3 4 5 NA

SO.3.2.5   Relationship of the department/service to other hospital services and off-site agencies;

1 2 3 4 5 NA

SO.3.2.6   Maintenance of required records, statistical information, and reports; (IM.8.1.5)

SO.3.2.7   Home environmental evaluations for attending practitioners, as requested; (scoring guideline for PE.1.1)

SO.3.2.8   Role of the social work department/service in discharge planning; and

1 2 3 4 5 NA

SO.3.2.9   Social work functions resulting from applicable law and regulation.

1 2 3 4 5 NA

SO.4   Adequate documentation of the social work services provided is included in the patient's medical record. (IM.7.2.8)

SO.4.1   When social work services are provided to a patient, clear and concise entries are made in the patient's medical record to permit regular communication with physicians, nurses, and other personnel involved in the patient's care. (IM.7.1)

Note: *Refer also to the "Improving Organizational Performance" chapter of this* Manual. *For further requirements relating to medical records, see the "Management of Information" chapter of this* Manual.

NOTES AND COMMENTS:

SPECIAL CARE UNITS

Some of the standards in this chapter of the 1993 *Accreditation Manual for Hospitals* have been recast to focus on improving individual and organizational performance and have been moved to Sections 1 and 2 of this *Manual*. To help you identify these standards, we have printed them here in small italic type with their new standard references in bold type in parentheses. Organizations are expected to demonstrate compliance with these standards in their new context. For example, SP.1 in this chapter has been recast and moved to the "Leadership" chapter, as LD.1.3.2. This standard appears in small italic type, and the new standard reference, LD.1.3.2, appears in bold type in parentheses at the end of the standard. Organizations are expected to comply with LD.1.3.2 and will be scored for compliance in the "Leadership" chapter. Standards scored in this chapter are in normal type and have accompanying scoring scales (1 2 3 4 5 NA).

Recognizing the existence of intensive care units in many hospitals, this chapter defines the requirements that are common to all such units, as well as those that are peculiar to, or particularly pertinent to, an individual unit. Individual requirements are specified for the intensive care units most frequently encountered in acute care hospitals. This does not preclude the establishment of other types of intensive care units that may be required for particular types of patient care problems.

When a hospital has elected to consolidate intensive medical/surgical care services into a center (or unit) for the critically ill, with a concentration of qualified professional staffing and supportive resources, and with patient admission by need rather than by diagnosis, this concept will be recognized, and the center (or unit) will be evaluated accordingly.

In the context of these standards, a special care unit is one that provides intensive care continuously on a 24-hour-a-day basis. Specific-purpose special care units may include, but need not be limited to, burn, cardiac, cardiovascular surgery, neonatal, and respiratory units; multipurpose special care units usually include medical-surgical intensive care units or a combination of the above. A special care unit ordinarily is not combined with a postanesthesia recovery unit.

These standards are also intended to apply to units providing chronic renal dialysis services; they do not apply to units providing acute renal dialysis services. If chronic renal dialysis services are provided on an ambulatory basis, only SP.5.4 through SP.5.4.4 apply.

*SP.1   Special care units, as appropriate for the hospital, are established for patients requiring extraordinary care on a concentrated and continuous basis. (**LD.1.3.2**)*

SP.1.1   Written criteria for patient admission to, and discharge from, a special care unit, including priority determination, are developed by the medical staff, with the participation of the nursing department/service.

1 2 3 4 5 NA

SP.2   Each special care unit is properly directed and staffed according to the nature of the special patient care needs anticipated and the scope of services offered. **(LD.2.2.1)**

SP.2.1   Each special care unit is directed by a physician member of the active medical staff who has received special training, acquired experience, and demonstrated competence in a specialty related to the care provided in the unit.

1 2 3 4 5 NA

SP.2.1.1   The director is responsible for making decisions, in consultation with the physician responsible for the patient, for the disposition of a patient when patient load exceeds optimal operational capacity. **(LD.2.2)**

SP.2.2   The activities of a multipurpose special care unit are guided by a multidisciplinary committee of the medical staff, and the chairperson or a designated member of the committee serves as director of the unit. **(LD.3.4)**

SP.2.2.1   The registered nurse assigned managerial responsibility for the special care unit participates in meetings of the multidisciplinary committee. **(LD.3.4)**

SP.2.2.2   A multidisciplinary committee meets as often as required but not less than quarterly.

1 2 3 4 5 NA

SP.2.3   Medical staff coverage meets the special care needs of the patients within the unit.

1 2 3 4 5 NA

SP.2.3.1   The medical staff, through its designated mechanism, determines the circumstances under which consultation by a qualified specialist is required.

1 2 3 4 5 NA

SP.2.4   The supervision of nursing care in the unit is provided by a designated registered nurse who has relevant education, training, and experience and who has demonstrated current competence.

1 2 3 4 5 NA

SP.2.4.1   Nursing staff members are knowledgeable about the emotional and rehabilitative aspects of the special care unit patient and are capable of applying appropriate therapeutic interventions.

1 2 3 4 5 NA

SP.2.4.2   To provide the care required, a sufficient number of permanently assigned, qualified registered nurses are on duty within the unit at all times when patients are in the unit.

1 2 3 4 5 NA

SP.2.4.2.1   Other nursing personnel who are trained and experienced in providing the type and amount of care needed by the special care patient are available and assigned, as needed.

1 2 3 4 5 NA

SP.3   The provision of patient care in special care units is guided by written policies and procedures. **(LD.2.1.3)**

SP.3.1   Written policies and procedures concerning the scope and provision of care in each special care unit are developed by the medical staff and the nursing department/service. **(LD.1.7, LD.1.7.1.2)**

SP.3.1.1   The policies and procedures are approved by the medical staff through its designated mechanism and are enforced. **(LD.3.3)**

SP.3.2   Written policies and procedures relate to at least the following:

SP.3.2.1   Admission and discharge of patients;

1 2 3 4 5 NA

SP.3.2.2   A system for informing the physician responsible for a patient
of changes in the patient's condition; *(scoring guideline for IM.7.1)*

SP.3.2.3   Explicit directions as to the location and storage of medications, supplies, and special equipment;   1 2 3 4 5 NA

SP.3.2.4   Methods for the procurement of equipment and drugs at all times;   1 2 3 4 5 NA

SP.3.2.5   Responsibility for maintaining the integrity of the emergency drug system;   1 2 3 4 5 NA

SP.3.2.6   Infection control;   1 2 3 4 5 NA

SP.3.2.7   Procedures to be followed in the event of a breakdown of essential equipment;   1 2 3 4 5 NA

SP.3.2.8   Pertinent safety practices;   1 2 3 4 5 NA

SP.3.2.9   Regulations for the control of traffic, including visitors;   1 2 3 4 5 NA

SP.3.2.10   The role of the unit in the hospital's external and internal disaster plans;   1 2 3 4 5 NA

SP.3.2.11   Specification as to who may perform special procedures, under what circumstances, and under what degree of supervision;   1 2 3 4 5 NA

SP.3.2.12   Use of standing orders; and *(scoring guidelines for IM.7.2–IM.7.2.23)*

SP.3.2.13   Protocol for handling specific emergency conditions. *(LD.2.1.3)*

SP.4
Special care units are designed and equipped to facilitate the safe and effective care of patients.   1 2 3 4 5 NA

SP.4.1   Each special care unit is organized as a physically and functionally distinct entity with controlled access.   1 2 3 4 5 NA

SP.4.2   An effective means of isolation is provided for patients suffering from communicable or infectious disease, for patients requiring protective isolation, and for disoriented or emotionally disturbed patients who require the services of the unit until placement elsewhere becomes possible.   1 2 3 4 5 NA

SP.4.2.1   An effective means of separating children from adults is provided whenever possible.   1 2 3 4 5 NA

SP.4.3   Direct or indirect visual observation by unit staff of all patients is possible from one or more vantage points.   1 2 3 4 5 NA

SP.4.4   The floor space allocated to each bed is sufficient to accommodate the equipment and personnel necessary to meet anticipated contingencies.   1 2 3 4 5 NA

SP.4.5   A direct intercommunication/alarm system is provided between the nurses' station and the patient's bedside, with connections to treatment, work, lounge, or other areas from which additional personnel may be summoned.   1 2 3 4 5 NA

SP.4.6 The equipment provided is suitable for the size of the patient being treated. 1 2 3 4 5 NA

SP.4.7 When child or adolescent patients are treated in a special care unit, there is documentation of age-appropriate care. 1 2 3 4 5 NA

SP.4.8 When not provided as part of the unit's fixed supplies, equipment, or capabilities, at least the following are readily available in the hospital for use within each special care unit:

SP.4.8.1 Oxygen and compressed air and the means of administration; 1 2 3 4 5 NA

SP.4.8.2 Mechanical ventilatory assistance equipment, including airways, manual breathing bags, and ventilators/respirators; 1 2 3 4 5 NA

SP.4.8.3 A cardiac defibrillator with synchronization capability; 1 2 3 4 5 NA

SP.4.8.4 Respiratory and cardiac monitoring equipment; 1 2 3 4 5 NA

SP.4.8.5 Thoracentesis and closed thoracostomy sets; 1 2 3 4 5 NA

SP.4.8.6 A tracheostomy set; 1 2 3 4 5 NA

SP.4.8.7 Tourniquets; 1 2 3 4 5 NA

SP.4.8.8 Vascular cutdown sets; 1 2 3 4 5 NA

SP.4.8.9 Infusion pumps; 1 2 3 4 5 NA

SP.4.8.10 Laryngoscopes and endotracheal tubes; 1 2 3 4 5 NA

SP.4.8.11 Tracheobronchial and gastric suction equipment; 1 2 3 4 5 NA

SP.4.8.12 Portable x-ray equipment; and 1 2 3 4 5 NA

SP.4.8.13 A patient weighing device for bed patients. 1 2 3 4 5 NA

SP.4.9 Life-support equipment brought from other hospital departments/services as replacement items are checked for operational readiness and safety prior to use. 1 2 3 4 5 NA

SP.4.10 An emergency cart within the unit contains appropriate drugs and equipment, as determined by the medical staff. 1 2 3 4 5 NA

SP.4.10.1 The emergency cart is checked at least on every shift and after each use by an appropriate, designated member of the hospital staff to assure that all items required for immediate patient care are in place in the cart and are in usable condition. 1 2 3 4 5 NA

*SP.4.11 Clinical laboratory services are readily available 24 hours a day. (**scoring guideline for LD.1.3.4.1**)*

*SP.4.11.1 Such laboratory services have the capability of performing all necessary laboratory tests, with timely reporting of results, including chemistries, blood gas analyses, pH levels, electrolyte determinations, and serum and urine osmolalities. (**LD.1.3.4.1**)*

*SP.4.11.1.1 Microbiology services are readily available. (**LD.1.3.4.1**)*

*SP.4.12 The unit or hospital assures that there is an adequate supply of blood to meet the needs of patients at all times. (**LD.1.3.4**)*

*SP.4.13 Diagnostic radiologic services are readily available 24 hours a day. (**scoring guideline for LD.1.3.4.1**)*

SP.4.14 Special precautions, including those related to electrical and device safety, are taken when the care of a patient requires the use of any type of electrically operated device.   1 2 3 4 5 NA

SP.4.14.1 All special care unit personnel involved in direct patient care are informed when specific patients have particular sensitivity to electrical current.   1 2 3 4 5 NA

SP.5
When a specific-purpose unit is established for the care of a specific type of diagnosis or procedure, the use of the unit is ordinarily restricted to that purpose.   1 2 3 4 5 NA

SP.5.1 Burn Unit.

SP.5.1.1 The director or other qualified physician designee in charge of the unit has special training and extensive experience in burn-patient management.   1 2 3 4 5 NA

SP.5.1.2 There is in-house physician coverage by either a staff physician or a member of the house staff assigned to the unit.   1 2 3 4 5 NA

SP.5.1.3 Nursing care is supervised by a registered nurse with training, experience, and demonstrated current competence in burn-care nursing.   1 2 3 4 5 NA

SP.5.1.4 Because of the known susceptibility of burn wounds to infection, appropriate preventive measures are taken.   1 2 3 4 5 NA

SP.5.1.5 Policies and procedures related to decreasing the risk of infection through indirect cross-contamination and direct transfer of infection are implemented.   1 2 3 4 5 NA

SP.5.1.5.1 Such policies and procedures relate to at least the following:

SP.5.1.5.1.1 Handling of contaminated instruments, dressings, soiled linen, and equipment;   1 2 3 4 5 NA

SP.5.1.5.1.2 Decontamination of personnel, equipment, and instruments;   1 2 3 4 5 NA

SP.5.1.5.1.3 Transportation of the patient outside the unit;   1 2 3 4 5 NA

SP.5.1.5.1.4 Housekeeping and cleaning schedule;   1 2 3 4 5 NA

SP.5.1.5.1.5 Solid and liquid waste systems;   1 2 3 4 5 NA

SP.5.1.5.1.6 Traffic control; and   1 2 3 4 5 NA

SP.5.1.5.1.7 Aseptic and isolation techniques.   1 2 3 4 5 NA

SP.5.1.6 If hydrotherapy is required, it is provided within the unit to reduce the risk of cross-infection and contamination to patients who are not burn patients.   1 2 3 4 5 NA

SP.5.1.7 A designated operating room is available.   1 2 3 4 5 NA

SP.5.1.8 If the use of biological membranes is a component of care provided by the unit, policies and procedures related to obtaining and storing homograft and heterograft skin are developed and implemented.   1 2 3 4 5 NA

SP.5.2 Intensive Care Unit: Cardiac, Cardiovascular Surgery, or Respiratory.

SP.5.2.1 The director or other qualified physician designee in charge of the unit has recognized special training and experience and demonstrated competence in the management of cardiac, cardiovascular surgical, or respiratory patients, as appropriate.   1 2 3 4 5 NA

  SP.5.2.1.1 Appropriate professional consultation is available at all times. (LD.1.3.4.2)

  SP.5.2.1.2 The absence of qualified house staff confers a special responsibility on the director of the unit to assure that there is sufficient medical staff coverage at all times.   1 2 3 4 5 NA

SP.5.2.2 When cardiovascular surgical patients are treated in the unit, a qualified cardiac surgeon is available as needed.   1 2 3 4 5 NA

  SP.5.2.2.1 The unit is fully prepared to manage patients in any risk group and in the age groups for which the cardiovascular surgery team is responsible.   1 2 3 4 5 NA

SP.5.2.3 Nursing care is supervised by a registered nurse who has training, experience, and documented current competence in the care and management of cardiac, cardiovascular surgical, or respiratory patients, as appropriate.   1 2 3 4 5 NA

  SP.5.2.3.1 Other nursing staff members have similar training and experience for their level of responsibility in the care and management of the specific type of patients in the unit.   1 2 3 4 5 NA

SP.5.2.4 Within the policies and procedures that govern patient care in the unit, as approved by the medical staff, the unit nursing staff is permitted to take appropriate emergency measures based on their ability to

  SP.5.2.4.1 interpret electrocardiographic information and recognize significant dysrhythmias;   1 2 3 4 5 NA

  SP.5.2.4.2 recognize abnormalities in pulmonary function tests and blood, pH, and serum electrolyte values that are significant enough to require immediate notification of a physician; and   1 2 3 4 5 NA

  SP.5.2.4.3 use knowledgeably those specific drugs required for intensive care.   1 2 3 4 5 NA

SP.5.2.5 Respiratory therapy personnel and registered nurses assigned to the unit have demonstrated competence in pulmonary physiology and in the principles of oxygen and compressed air administration.   1 2 3 4 5 NA

  SP.5.3 Intensive Care Unit: Neonatal. (scoring guidelines for PF.2–PF.2.2.7)

SP.5.3.1 The director or other qualified physician designee in charge of the neonatal intensive care unit has at least one year of recognized special training and experience, as well as demonstrated competence, in neonatology.   1 2 3 4 5 NA

SP.5.3.2 Nursing care is supervised by a registered nurse who has training, experience, and documented current competence in the nursing care of high-risk infants.   1 2 3 4 5 NA

SP.5.3.3   The nursing staff is proficient in teaching parents how to care for their infants at home.   1 2 3 4 5 NA

> SP.5.3.4   *Policies and procedures that relate to the safe conduct of all patient care activities are developed and implemented.* **(LD.2.1.2.3)**

SP.5.3.5   Equipment used to monitor vital functions has an alarm system that is operative at all times.   1 2 3 4 5 NA

> SP.5.3.6   *Opportunities are provided for parents to participate in the care of their infant, as the infant's condition permits, in order to facilitate family adjustment and continuity of care following discharge.* **(scoring guidelines for PF.2–PF.2.2.7)**

> SP.5.3.6.1   *Special procedures that need to be performed by the parents are taught prior to the infant's discharge.* **(scoring guidelines for PF.2–PF.2.2.7)**

SP.5.3.7   Transport service is provided as needed.   1 2 3 4 5 NA

SP.5.3.7.1   Such service includes the provision of trained personnel and the following equipment and supplies: 1 2 3 4 5 NA

SP.5.3.7.1.1   A transport incubator providing light, easy access, and proper temperature;   1 2 3 4 5 NA

SP.5.3.7.1.2   Emergency resuscitation equipment;   1 2 3 4 5 NA

SP.5.3.7.1.3   Sufficient oxygen supply and the means of administration;   1 2 3 4 5 NA

SP.5.3.7.1.4   Portable cardiac and temperature monitors; and   1 2 3 4 5 NA

SP.5.3.7.1.5   A ventilator.   1 2 3 4 5 NA

SP.5.4   Renal Unit.

SP.5.4.1   The director or other qualified physician designee in charge of the unit has special training and at least one year of experience in managing patients with acute renal failure and end-stage renal disease.   1 2 3 4 5 NA

> SP.5.4.1.1   *The director is responsible for, and participates in, the selection of a suitable treatment modality and dialysis setting for patients.* **(LD.2.2)**

SP.5.4.2   When transplantation services are provided, such services are under the direction of a physician who has recognized special training and at least one year of experience in the performance of renal transplantation and the care of patients with renal transplants.   1 2 3 4 5 NA

SP.5.4.3   Nursing care is supervised by a registered nurse who has training, experience, and documented current competence in the nursing care of patients with acute renal failure and end-stage renal disease and in hemodialysis technique.   1 2 3 4 5 NA

SP.5.4.4   The water used for dialysis purposes is analyzed periodically and is treated as necessary to assure that it is biologically and chemically compatible with acceptable dialysis techniques.   1 2 3 4 5 NA

> SP.5.4.4.1   *Test results are recorded and reported to the unit's medical director and registered nurse assigned managerial responsibility for the unit.* **(PI.4.1–PI.4.1.3.2)**

SP.5.4.5 Written policies are developed and implemented for every type of dialysis conducted within the renal dialysis program. (LD.2.1.1.3, PI.4.1–PI.4.1.3.2)

SP.5.4.5.1 A schedule and procedure are developed and implemented to assure sterility or cleanliness of the equipment before each dialysis. (PI.4.1–PI.4.1.3.2)

SP.5.4.5.2 Infection control measures include procedures for the prevention and control of hepatitis. (PI.4.1–PI.4.1.3.2)

Note: *Refer also to related requirements in the following chapters of this* Manual: *"Improving Organizational Performance," "Infection Control," "Management of Information," "Medical Staff," "Nursing Care," "Operative and Other Invasive Procedures," "Pathology and Clinical Laboratory Services," "Pharmaceutical Services," "Plant, Technology, and Safety Management."*

NOTES AND COMMENTS:

SURGICAL AND ANESTHESIA SERVICES

Standards in this chapter of the 1993 *Accreditation Manual for Hospitals* have been recast to focus on improving individual and organizational performance and have been moved to Sections 1 and 2 of this *Manual*. The following cross-reference is provided for your information.

1993	1994
SA.1	LD.1.3.4
SA.1.1	LD.1.7
SA.1.1.1	scoring guideline for LD.1.3.4.1
SA.1.2	MS.1.1, MS.1.1.1
SA.1.2.1	MS.2.2.1
SA.1.2.2	MS.2.2
SA.1.2.3	MS.2.4.1.3
SA.1.3	MS.4.5
SA.1.4	PE.1.8
SA.1.4.1	IM.7.4.1
SA.1.5	MS.4.5
SA.1.5.1	LD.2.1
SA.1.5.1.1	MS.4.4, MS.4.4.1
SA.1.5.1.2	LD.1.6
SA.1.5.1.2.1	LD.1.7.1, LD.1.7.1.1
SA.1.5.1.2.2	LD.2
SA.1.5.1.2.3	PI.3.4
SA.1.5.1.2.4	PI.3.4.1.2
SA.1.5.1.2.4.1	PI.3.4.1.2
SA.1.5.1.2.5	MS.6
SA.1.5.1.2.6	MS.4.9
SA.1.5.1.2.6.1	MS.4.9
SA.1.5.1.2.6.2	MS.4.9
SA.1.5.1.2.6.3	MS.4.9
SA.1.6	MS.1.1.1, MS.1.1.2
SA.1.6.1	PE.1.8.1
SA.1.6.1.1	scoring guideline for PE.1.8.1
SA.1.6.1.1.1	scoring guideline for PE.1.8.1
SA.1.6.1.1.2	scoring guideline for PE.1.8.1
SA.1.6.1.2	scoring guideline for PE.1.8.1
SA.1.6.1.2.1	scoring guideline for PE.1.8.1
SA.1.6.1.2.2	scoring guideline for PE.1.8.1
SA.1.6.1.2.3	scoring guideline for PE.1.8.1
SA.1.6.2	PE.1.8.2
SA.1.6.2.1	PE.1.8.2.1
SA.1.6.3	PE.1.8.3
SA.1.6.3.1	PE.1.8.3
SA.1.6.3.2	MS.5.1.7.1.1

1993	**1994**
SA.1.6.4	OP.4, OP.4.1
SA.1.6.4.1	scoring guidelines for OP.4, OP.4.1
SA.1.6.4.1.1	scoring guidelines for OP.4, OP.4.1
SA.1.6.4.1.2	scoring guidelines for OP.4, OP.4.1
SA.1.6.4.1.3	scoring guidelines for OP.4, OP.4.1
SA.1.6.4.1.4	scoring guidelines for OP.4, OP.4.1
SA.1.6.4.1.5	scoring guidelines for OP.4, OP.4.1
SA.1.6.4.1.6	scoring guidelines for OP.4, OP.4.1
SA.1.6.5	OP.5, PE.1.8.4
SA.1.6.5.1	OP.5, IM.7.4.3
SA.1.6.5.1.1	OP.5.1, IM.7.4.3.1
SA.1.6.5.1.2	OP.5.3, IM.7.4.3.2
SA.1.6.5.1.3	OP.5.4, IM.7.4.3.3
SA.1.6.6	OP.6.1
SA.1.6.6.1	OP.6.1.1
SA.1.6.6.1.1	IM.7.4.3.6
SA.1.6.6.1.2	IM.7.4.3.5.1
SA.1.7	NC.1.3
SA.1.7.1	NC.2
SA.1.7.1.1	NC.2
SA.1.7.2	LD.1.6
SA.1.7.3	NC.3.4.1, NC.3.4.2
SA.1.7.3.1	NC.2
SA.1.7.3.2	IM.7.4.3.4
SA.1.7.4	scoring guideline for PE.4.3
SA.1.7.5	scoring guideline for PE.3.1
SA.1.7.6	PI.3.4
SA.1.7.7	scoring guideline for LD.1.6
SA.1.8	scoring guideline for LD.1.3.4
SA.1.9	LD.2.1.4
SA.1.10	scoring guideline for LD.1.5.2
SA.1.11	IM.7.4.2
SA.1.11.1	IM.7.4.2.1
SA.2	scoring guideline for LD.1.6
SA.2.1	scoring guideline for LD.1.6
SA.2.1.1	MS.4.9
SA.2.2	HO.2.3.5
SA.3	LD.3.2.1
SA.3.1	LD.3.2.1
SA.3.1.1	LD.2.1.3
SA.3.1.1.1	LD.2.1.3
SA.3.1.1.2	LD.2.1.3
SA.3.1.1.3	LD.2.1.3
SA.3.1.2	PI.5.3–PI.5.3.2
SA.3.2	PA.6.1.1.2.3, PA.6.1.1.3
SA.3.3	PA.6.2.2–PA.6.2.3.2.9
SA.3.3.1	PA.6.2.3

1993	**1994**
SA.3.4	IC.4
SA.3.4.1	IC.5.1
SA.3.4.2	IC.5.1
SA.3.4.3	IC.5.1.1
SA.3.4.4	IC.5.1.1
SA.3.4.5	IC.5
SA.3.4.6	IC.5
SA.3.4.7	IC.4
SA.3.5	LD.1.3

UTILIZATION REVIEW

Standards in this chapter of the 1993 *Accreditation Manual for Hospitals* have been recast to focus on improving individual and organizational performance and have been moved to Sections 1 and 2 of this *Manual*. The following cross-reference is provided for your information.

1993	**1994**
UR.1	LD.4.4
UR.1.1	LD.4.3
UR.1.2	LD.4
UR.1.2.1	LD.1.7
UR.1.3	LD.1.7.1
UR.1.3.1	LD.1.7.1.1, LD.1.7.1.2
UR.1.3.2	LD.1.6
UR.1.3.3	IM.2
UR.1.3.4	scoring guideline for LD.1.7.1
UR.1.3.5	PI.3, PI.3.4.2.4
UR.1.3.6	IM.7.3
UR.1.4	PI.3.4.1, PI.3.4.1.3, PI.3.4.2.4
UR.1.4.1	PI.3.4.1, PI.3.4.1.3, PI.3.4.2.4
UR.1.5	PI.3.4.1, PI.3.4.1.3, PI.3.4.2.4
UR.1.6	LD.4.3 and PI.3.4.2.4

APPENDIX A
STANDARDS APPLICABLE IN
TAILORED SURVEYS

This appendix is composed of two parts. Part 1 includes a table that identifies standards in this *Manual* that are applicable to long term care or mental retardation/developmental disabilities organizations that provide organized medical and/or surgical services to patients as a supplement to their basic mission. These selected standards are applied in conjunction with standards contained in the current edition of the *Accreditation Manual for Long Term Care* (AMLTC) or the *Accreditation Manual for Mental Health, Chemical Dependency, and Mental Retardation/Developmental Disabilities Services* (MHM).

Part 2 includes three tables that identify standards in the *MHM* that are applicable to hospitals that provide
- inpatient units for long-term hospitalization of chronically mentally ill patients;
- inpatient units for forensic psychiatric patients; or
- programs/services in other than freestanding settings for individuals who have mental retardation or other developmental disabilities.

Criteria for determining when the standards in a table are applied precede the table. Questions concerning the applicability of these standards should be directed to the Division of Accreditation Surveys at the Joint Commission.

Part 1: *AMH* Standards Applicable to Long Term Care or Mental Retardation/Developmental Disabilities Organizations

Organizations that are preparing for surveys should carefully study the following table to see which standards apply to their particular services. The footnotes contain important supplemental information. Please read all of them carefully.

Section/Chapter*	Long Term Care Organizations	Mental Retardation/ Developmental Disabilities Organizations
Section 1—Care of the Patient		
Assessment of Patients	PE.1.1, PE.1.5, PE.1.7.1, PE.1.8 through PE.1.8.4, PE.2 through PE.2.4, PE.4, PE.4.2, PE.4.3, PE.5.1 through PE.5.7, PE.6 through PE.6.3, PE.7 through PE.7.4	PE.1.7.1, PE.2.1, PE.4.3

These sections/chapters refer to those that appear in this Manual, *the* Accreditation Manual for Hospitals, Volume I.

Section/Chapter*	Long Term Care Organizations	Mental Retardation/ Developmental Disabilities Organizations
Treatment of Patients	TX.1, TX.5, TX.5.1, TX.8, TX.13	TX.1, TX.13
Operative and Other Invasive Procedures†	OP.1, OP.4, OP.4.1, OP.5, OP.5.1, OP.5.3, OP.5.4, OP.6.1, OP.6.1.1	
Education of Patients and Family	PF.2	

Section 2—Organizational Functions

Leadership	LD.1.3, LD.1.3.1, LD.1.3.2, LD.1.3.3, LD.1.3.4 through LD.1.3.4.1.1, LD.1.5, LD.1.6, LD.1.7, LD.1.7.1, LD.2 through LD.2.1.9, LD.2.2 through LD.3.4, LD.3.4.1.1, LD.4 through LD.4.3	LD.1.3, LD.1.3.1, LD.1.3.4 through LD.1.3.4.1.1, LD.1.5, LD.1.7, LD.1.7.1, LD.2, LD.2.1, LD.2.1.2, LD.2.1.3, LD.2.1.6, LD.2.1.7, LD.2.2.2, LD.3, LD.3.1, LD.3.3, LD.3.4.1.1, LD.4.2 through LD.4.3
Management of Information	IM.2.3, IM.3, IM.3.2, IM.3.3.1 through IM.3.3.1.2, IM.7 through IM.7.2.23, IM.7.3.1, IM.7.4.1 through IM.7.4.3.4, IM.7.4.3.5.1, IM.7.4.3.6 through IM.7.6.1, IM.7.6.1.2 through IM.7.6.2, IM.7.7, IM.7.7.1, IM.7.9, IM.7.10.1, IM.8.1, IM.8.1.3, IM.8.1.6.1	IM.3, IM.3.2, IM.3.3.1 through IM.3.3.1.2, IM.7.2, IM.7.2.5, IM.7.2.6, IM.7.2.11, IM.7.2.12, IM.7.2.15, IM.7.2.17, IM.7.2.18, IM.7.4.2.2, IM.8.1, IM.8.1.3

*These sections/chapters refer to those that appear in this Manual, the Accreditation Manual for Hospitals, Volume I.
†These standards are applicable only if the organization provides the services identified in the Preamble to the "Operative and Other Invasive Procedures" chapter.

Section/Chapter*	Long Term Care Organizations	Mental Retardation/ Developmental Disabilities Organizations
Improving Organizational Performance‡	PI.1, PI.1.1, PI.3, PI.3.1, PI.3.3 through PI.3.3.2, PI.3.4 through PI.3.4.1.3, PI.3.4.2 through PI.3.5.3, PI.3.5.3.4, PI.3.5.3.5, PI.4 through PI.4.1.3.2, PI.4.1.3.6, PI.4.1.3.7, PI.4.2 through PI.4.2.2, PI.5.1, PI.5.3 through PI.5.3.3	PI.1.1, PI.3, PI.3.1, PI.3.4 through PI.3.4.1.3, PI.3.4.2 through PI.3.4.2.3, PI.3.5, PI.3.5.2, PI.3.5.3, PI.3.5.3.4, PI.3.5.3.5, PI.4, PI.4.1.2.2, PI.4.1.3.5, PI.4.1.3.7, PI.4.2, PI.4.2.1, PI.5.3 through PI.5.3.3

Section 3—Structures with Important Functions

Medical Staff	All standards	MS.5.1

Section 4—Other Department/Service-Specific Requirements

Alcoholism and Other Drug-Dependence Services§	All standards	
Diagnostic Radiology Services#	All standards	
Emergency Services**	All standards	
Governing Body	GB.1.11 through GB.1.13, GB.1.15 through GB.1.15.3, GB.1.19	
Infection Control	All standards	All standards

*These sections/chapters refer to those that appear in this Manual, the Accreditation Manual for Hospitals, Volume I.
‡PI.3.4.1.1 through PI.3.4.1.3 and PI.3.4.2 through PI.3.4.2.1 are applicable only if the organization provides surgical services.
§These standards are applicable only if the organization provides alcoholism and other drug-dependence services.
#These standards are applicable only if the organization provides organized medical or surgical services.
**These standards are applicable only if the organization provides emergency services to the community.

Section/Chapter*	Long Term Care Organizations	Mental Retardation/ Developmental Disabilities Organizations
Management and Administrative Services	MA.1.3.11 through MA.1.3.11.2, MA.1.3.4.1 through MA.1.3.4.1.1, MA.1.3.4.2 through MA.1.3.4.3.1.4, MA.1.3.4.4, MA.1.3.5, MA.1.3.5.1, MA.1.3.5.1.2, MA.1.3.10 through MA.1.3.10.2, MA.1.3.13, MA.1.3.14, MA.1.3.15, MA.1.3.15.1, MA.1.4.3.1	MA.1.3.4.2.1 through MA.1.3.5, MA.1.3.15, MA.1.3.15.1
Nuclear Medicine Services†† ‡‡	All standards	All standards
Nursing Care	NC.1.1.2, NC.1.3, NC.1.3.4.6, NC.2, NC.2.1, NC.2.1.2 through NC.2.1.2.2, NC.3.1, NC.3.4.1, NC.3.4.2	NC.1.1.2, NC.1.3, NC.1.3.4.6, NC.3.4.2, NC.3.4.2.4
Orientation, Training, and Education of Staff	SE.2.1, SE.2.1.1, SE.4, SE.4.1	
Pathology and Clinical Laboratory Services§§	All standards	
Patient Rights	RI.1 through RI.1.1.2, RI.1.1.2.1, RI.1.1.6	

These sections/chapters refer to those that appear in this Manual, the Accreditation Manual for Hospitals, Volume I.

††*These standards are applicable only if the organization provides nuclear medicine services.*

‡‡*Not required for hospitals that provide only social rehabilitation/substance abuse services.*

§§*These standards are applicable only if the organization provides limited laboratory testing (waived testing or all testing that is referred to other organizations). If the organization provides laboratory services of moderate or high complexity, the standards in the Accreditation Manual for Pathology and Clinical Laboratory Services supersede the laboratory standards in this Manual.*

Section/Chapter*	Long Term Care Organizations	Mental Retardation/ Developmental Disabilities Organizations
Physical Rehabilitation Services‡‡ ##	RH.2.2, RH.2.2.1, RH.2.2.1.2, RH.2.2.1.3, RH.2.2.1.4, RH.2.3, RH.2.6, RH.2.6.1, RH.2.6.1.5, RH.2.6.1.7, RH.2.9, RH.2.9.1, RH.2.9.1.3 through RH.2.9.1.5	RH.1.1.4, RH.2.2, RH.2.2.1, RH.2.2.1.2, RH.2.2.1.3, RH.2.2.1.4, RH.2.7, RH.2.7.1, RH.3.1.2, RH.3.1.5, RH.3.2, RH.3.3.1 through RH.3.3.4, RH.3.4.1 through RH.3.6.1.7, RH.3.8
Plant, Technology, and Safety Management	PL.1, PL.1.2.1, PL.1.7, PL.2.2, PL.4.2, PL.4.2.1.4	
Radiation Oncology Services***	All standards	All standards
Respiratory Care Services‡‡ +++	All standards	All standards
Special Care Units‡‡‡	All standards	

*These sections/chapters refer to those that appear in this Manual, the Accreditation Manual for Hospitals, Volume I.

‡‡Not required for hospitals that provide only social rehabilitation/substance abuse services.

##These standards are applicable only if the organization provides physical therapy services.

***These standards are applicable only if the organization provides radiation oncology services.

+++These standards are applicable only if the organization provides respiratory care services.

‡‡‡These standards are applicable only if the organization provides the services of special care units.

Part 2: Additional Standards for Hospitals that Provide Services to Chronically Mentally Ill Patients, Forensic Psychiatric Patients, and Mentally Retarded/Developmentally Disabled Individuals

Hospitals that are preparing for survey should carefully study the following table to see which standards are applicable to their particular services. Criteria for determining when the standards in a table are applied precede the table and should be read carefully.

Section I—Standards from the *MHM* that are applicable to hospital inpatient units for long-term hospitalization of chronically mentally ill patients

The standards in the following table are applicable when

- the unit is designed to provide primarily sustaining services on a long-term, 24-hour-a-day, 7-day-a-week hospital-inpatient basis to patients who, by virtue of the severity of their mental illness and the degree of their disability, require the protective and/or supportive environment of a hospital and psychosocial rehabilitative services;

- the median length of stay for patients residing on the hospital inpatient unit at any time is six months or longer; and
- fifty percent or more of patients residing on the hospital inpatient unit at any time are afflicted with a severe and prolonged mental illness, as evidenced by the presence of the following:
  — A diagnosis of a severe mental disorder;
  — A continuing disability resulting from the mental disorder, manifested by significant interference with primary aspects of daily life such as basic self-care, interpersonal relationships, and continuous functioning at work or school; and
  — A duration of illness exceeding six months.

Chapter	Standards
Governance and Management	GM.6.1.1.1
Planning and Evaluation	PE.1, PE.2, PE.2.14, PE.2.1.8 through PE.2.1.10, PE.2.1.12, PE.2.1.13, PE.2.1.15 through PE.2.1.15.1, PE.2.1.15.4, PE.2.3, PE.3
Patient Rights	PI.1, PI.2.1 through PI.2.1.3.6, PI.2.1.4 through PI.2.1.6, PI.3.3, PI.3.4, PI.3.4.1, PI.4.1, PI.4.1.16, PI.9.1 through PI.10.2
Patient Management	PM.4.3, PM.8, PM.8.2,
Adult Mental Health Services	AD.1 through AD.1.1, AD.3, AD.4.2, AD.5, AD.5.1 through AD.7, AD.8.1 through AD.9.1.2, AD.11, AD.12.2, AD.12.2.1 through AD.12.2.1.3, AD.12.2.1.5, AD.14 through AD.21
Pharmacy Services	PH.26 through PH.26.1.3
Rehabilitation Services	
Activity Services	RH.1 through RH.13.5
Education Services	RH.14 through RH.19.3
Speech, Language, and Hearing Services	RH.20 through RH.24
Vocational Rehabilitation Services	RH.25 through RH.28.4
Therapeutic Environment	TH.1, TH.2, TH.3 through TH.4.2, TH.6 through TH.6.13, TH.7 through TH.21

Section II—Standards from the *MHM* that are applicable to hospital inpatient units for forensic psychiatric patients

The standards in the following table are applicable when

- fifty percent or more of patients residing on the hospital inpatient unit at any time are diagnosed as having a mental illness in a DSM-III-R category; and
- fifty percent or more of patients residing in the hospital inpatient unit at any time are
  - hospitalized on an order issued in the criminal justice system, including
    - evaluation of fitness to stand trial,
    - evaluation of criminal responsibility (not guilty by reason of insanity),
    - evaluation of fitness to be sentenced,
    - other specialized evaluations to address legal issues or effect special dispositions,
    - treatment as unfit to stand trial,
    - treatment as not guilty by reason of insanity,
    - treatment as unfit to be sentenced,
    - treatment as guilty but mentally ill, and
    - subject to confinement under a special offenders program; and/or
  - hospitalized concurrently with
    - correctional incarceration for a conviction, or
    - police detention; and/or
  - minors incarcerated in a hospital inpatient unit and on an order issued in the juvenile justice system, under other than mental health law; and/or
  - directly admitted or transferred under court order from a civil hospital or facility for the mentally retarded/developmentally disabled because of uncontrolled behavior and/or the need for security not achievable in a traditional psychiatric unit.

Chapter	Standards
Forensic Services	FC.1 through FC.3.1.6
Governance and Management	GM.6.1.1.1
Planning and Evaluation	PE.1, PE.2, PE.2.1.4, PE.2.1.8 through PE.2.1.10, PE.2.1.12, PE.2.1.13, PE.2.1.15 through PE.2.1.15.1, PE.2.1.15.4, PE.2.3, PE.3
Patient Rights	PI.1, PI.2.1 through PI.2.1.3.6, PI.2.1.4 through PI.2.1.6, PI.3.3, PI.3.4, PI.3.4.1, PI.4.1, PI.4.1.16, PI.9.1 through PI.10.2
Patient Management	PM.4.3, PM.8, PM.8.2,
Adult Mental Health Services	AD.1 through AD.1.1, AD.3, AD.4.2, AD.5, AD.5.1 through AD.7, AD.8.1 through AD.9.1.2, AD.11, AD.12.2, AD.12.2.1 through AD.12.2.1.3, AD.12.2.1.5, AD.14 through AD.21
Pharmacy Services	PH.26 through PH.26.1.3

Chapter	Standards
Rehabilitation Services	
Activity Services	RH.1 through RH.13.5
Education Services	RH.14 through RH.19.3
Speech, Language, and	
Hearing Services	RH.20 through RH.24
Vocational Rehabilitation	
Services	RH.25 through RH.28.4
Therapeutic Environment	TH.1, TH.2, TH.3 through TH.4.2, TH.6 through TH.6.13, TH.7 through TH.21

Section III—Standards from the *MHM* that are applicable to programs/services for mentally retarded or other developmentally disabled individuals in other than freestanding settings

Chapter	Standards
Governance and Management	GM.6 through GM.6.1.1.1
Professional Staff Organization	PO.2.5 through PO.3.7.2
Human Resources Management	HR.1
Planning and Evaluation	All standards
Quality Assessment and Improvement	QA.1, QA.6 through QA.6.1.1, QA.6.5 through QA.6.6.2, QA.7.1 through QA.7.1.8
Research (if provided)	All standards
Patient Rights	All standards
Patient Management	All standards
Mental Retardation and Developmental Disability Services	All standards
Special Treatment Procedures	All standards

Chapter	Standards
Rehabilitation Services	
Activity Services	All standards
Education Services	RH.14 through RH.19.3
Speech, Language, and Hearing Services	RH.20 through RH.24
Vocational Rehabilitation Services	RH.26 through RH.28.4
Plant, Technology, and Safety Management (when appropriate)	PL.1 through PL.2.4.1.1, PL.4 through PL.4.6.1.1
Therapeutic Environment	All standards

APPENDIX B
STANDARDS FOR HOSPITAL-BASED BIOPSYCHOSOCIAL REHABILITATION SERVICES, PARTIAL-HOSPITALIZATION SERVICES, AND RESIDENTIAL TREATMENT SERVICES

This appendix includes standards applicable to the following hospital-based psychiatric services:

- Biopsychosocial rehabilitation services;
- Partial-hospitalization services (sometimes also called partial-day or day-treatment programs); and
- Residential treatment services.

Hospitals that offer these services will undergo a single survey conducted by a single team of specially trained surveyors. Applicable standards from this appendix will be used in conjunction with other appropriate chapters from this *Manual*. For example, in a hospital that has a psychiatric partial-hospitalization program in which nursing care is provided, the "Nursing Care" chapter is applied along with the activity services standards in section I and the standards in section II of this appendix.

The standards in section I address activity, educational, and vocational rehabilitation services. These standards apply to all hospital-based programs that provide biopsychosocial rehabilitation services to patients in psychiatric partial-hospitalization units, residential treatment programs, and/or psychiatric inpatient units that house patients for more than four days or 96 hours. These standards are not applicable to physical rehabilitation units, detoxification/substance abuse rehabilitation units, or psychiatric inpatient units that provide crisis stabilization (units that house patients for less than four days/96 hours).

Because psychiatric inpatient units, partial-hospitalization units, and residential treatment programs should, at the very least, provide activity services, the standards in section I for these services will be applied in all such settings. Because educational and vocational rehabilitation services may or may not be provided in such settings, the standards for these services are applied only when these services are provided.

The standards in sections II and/or III are applicable only when the organization provides psychiatric partial-hospitalization and/or residential treatment services, respectively.

Any questions regarding the applicability of these standards should be directed to the Division of Accreditation Surveys at the Joint Commission.

Section I—Hospital-Based Biopsychosocial Rehabilitation Services

ACTIVITY SERVICES

BI.1
There are written policies and procedures governing the provision of activity services.

1 2 3 4 5 NA

BI.2
Appropriate activities are provided to all patients during the day, in the evening, and on the weekend.

1 2 3 4 5 NA

BI.2.1   The daily activities program is planned to provide a consistent, well-structured, yet flexible framework for daily living.

1 2 3 4 5 NA

BI.2.2   Whenever possible, patients participate in planning activity services.

1 2 3 4 5 NA

BI.2.3   The activities program is reviewed and revised according to patients' changing needs.

1 2 3 4 5 NA

BI.3
When indicated, activity services are incorporated in the plan for the patient's treatment.

1 2 3 4 5 NA

BI.3.1   The medical record contains progress notes that describe the patient's response to activity services as well as other pertinent observations.

1 2 3 4 5 NA

BI.4
There are a sufficient number of staff with appropriate skills to meet patients' needs and achieve the goals of activity services.

1 2 3 4 5 NA

BI.5
Appropriate space and equipment are provided to meet patients' needs for activity services.

1 2 3 4 5 NA

EDUCATIONAL SERVICES

BI.6
If the program provides educational services, the plan for services is described in writing.

1 2 3 4 5 NA

BI.7
When educational services are provided, there is documentation in the medical record of periodic evaluations of educational achievement in relation to developmental level, chronological age, sex, special handicaps, medications, and psychotherapeutic needs.

1 2 3 4 5 NA

BI.8
Organizations that operate their own educational service have adequate staff, space, and materials to meet patients' educational needs. 1 2 3 4 5 NA

VOCATIONAL REHABILITATION SERVICES

BI.9
Patients receive counseling on their specific vocational needs, such as their vocational strengths and weaknesses, the demands of their current and future jobs, the responsibilities of holding a job, and the problems related to vocational training, placement, and employment. 1 2 3 4 5 NA

BI.10
Programs that provide vocational rehabilitation services have written policies and procedures to govern the operation of the service. 1 2 3 4 5 NA

BI.10.1 All work programs conform to applicable law and regulation. 1 2 3 4 5 NA

BI.11
Vocational services are provided according to an individualized plan for the course of the patient's treatment. 1 2 3 4 5 NA

BI.12
There is a sufficient number of appropriately qualified staff and support personnel to meet patients' needs and the goals of vocational rehabilitation services. 1 2 3 4 5 NA

QUALITY ASSESSMENT AND IMPROVEMENT

BI.13
As part of the hospital's program to assess and improve quality, the quality of biopsychosocial rehabilitation services is monitored and evaluated in accordance with QA.3 through QA.3.1.7.2 in the "Quality Assessment and Improvement" chapter of this Manual. 1 2 3 4 5 NA

Section II—Hospital-Based Partial-Hospitalization Services

PROGRAM GOALS AND OBJECTIVES

PP.1
The program formulates and specifies its goals and objectives and describes its services in a written plan so its performance can be measured. 1 2 3 4 5 NA

PP.1.1   The plan describes the services offered by the program so a frame of reference for judging the various aspects of the program's operation is available. The plan describes

1 2 3 4 5 NA

PP.1.1.1   the intake or admission process, including how the initial contact is made with the patient and the family or significant other(s);

1 2 3 4 5 NA

PP.1.1.2   the assessment and evaluation procedures provided by the program;

1 2 3 4 5 NA

PP.1.1.3   the methods used to deliver services to meet the identified clinical needs of the patients served;

1 2 3 4 5 NA

PP.1.1.4   the process for planning the course of the patient's treatment and the periodic review of therapy;

1 2 3 4 5 NA

PP.1.1.5   the discharge and postdischarge planning processes;

1 2 3 4 5 NA

PP.1.1.6   the organizational relationships of the program with the hospital's other programs, including channels of staff communication, responsibility, and authority, as well as supervisory relationships;

1 2 3 4 5 NA

PP.1.1.7   the means by which the program provides or makes arrangements for the provision of

PP.1.1.7.1   other medical, special assessment, and therapeutic services,

1 2 3 4 5 NA

PP.1.1.7.2   patient education services, whether provided by the hospital or by agreement,

1 2 3 4 5 NA

PP.1.1.7.3   emergency services and crisis intervention, and

1 2 3 4 5 NA

PP.1.1.7.4   discharge and continuing care, including postdischarge planning, when needed, that promotes continuity of care and follow-up evaluation; and

1 2 3 4 5 NA

PP.1.1.8   when a program is organized on a team or unit basis, either totally or in part, the roles and responsibilities of team members in meeting the identified clinical needs of patients and in relation to program goals.

1 2 3 4 5 NA

PP.1.2   The plan is implemented and revised as necessary in accordance with the changing needs of the patients and the community and with the program's overall objectives and goals.

1 2 3 4 5 NA

PP.2
Within the scope of its activities, the program has enough appropriately qualified health care professional, administrative, and support staff available to adequately assess and address the patients' identified clinical needs.

1 2 3 4 5 NA

QUALITY ASSESSMENT AND IMPROVEMENT

PP.3
As part of the hospital's program to assess and improve quality, the quality of partial-hospitalization services is monitored and evaluated in accordance with QA.3 through QA.3.1.7.2 in the "Quality Assessment and Improvement" chapter of this Manual.

1 2 3 4 5 NA

Section III—Hospital-Based Residential Treatment Services

PROGRAM GOALS AND OBJECTIVES

RT.1
The program formulates and specifies its goals and objectives and describes its services in a written plan so its performance can be measured.

1 2 3 4 5 NA

RT.1.1 The plan describes the services offered by the program so a frame of reference for judging the various aspects of the program's operation is available. The plan describes

1 2 3 4 5 NA

RT.1.1.1 the intake or admission process, including how the initial contact is made with the patient and the family or significant other(s);

1 2 3 4 5 NA

RT.1.1.2 the assessment and evaluation procedures provided by the program;

1 2 3 4 5 NA

RT.1.1.3 the methods used to deliver services to meet the identified clinical needs of the patients served;

1 2 3 4 5 NA

RT.1.1.4 the process for planning the course of the patient's treatment and the periodic review of therapy;

1 2 3 4 5 NA

RT.1.1.5 the discharge and postdischarge planning processes;

1 2 3 4 5 NA

RT.1.1.6 the organizational relationships of the program with the hospital's other programs, including channels of staff communication, responsibility, and authority, as well as supervisory relationships;

1 2 3 4 5 NA

RT.1.1.7 the means by which the program provides or makes arrangements for the provision of

RT.1.1.7.1 other medical, special assessment, and therapeutic services,

1 2 3 4 5 NA

RT.1.1.7.2 patient education services, whether provided by the hospital or by agreement,

1 2 3 4 5 NA

RT.1.1.7.3 emergency services and crisis intervention, and

1 2 3 4 5 NA

RT.1.1.7.4 discharge and continuing care, including postdischarge planning, when needed, that promote continuity of care and follow-up evaluation; and

1 2 3 4 5 NA

RT.1.1.8 when a program is organized on a team or unit basis, either totally or in part, the roles and responsibilities of team members in meeting the patients' identified clinical needs and in relation to program goals.

1 2 3 4 5 NA

RT.1.2 The plan is implemented and revised as necessary in accordance with the changing needs of the patients and the community and with the overall objectives and goals of the program.

1 2 3 4 5 NA

RT.2
Within the scope of its activities, the program has enough appropriately qualified health care professional, administrative, and support staff available to adequately assess and address the identified clinical needs of patients.

1 2 3 4 5 NA

THERAPEUTIC ENVIRONMENT

RT.3
The program is located, constructed, equipped, and operated to carry out its stated goals, enhance the positive self-image of patients, and preserve their human dignity.

1 2 3 4 5 NA

RT.4
The program provides and maintains an environment that meets the clinical/ social needs of patients.

1 2 3 4 5 NA

RT.5
Each building in which patients are housed overnight or receive treatment complies with the appropriate provisions of the 1991 edition of the Life Safety Code® (LSC) *of the National Fire Protection Association (NFPA), or equivalent protection is provided and documented.**

1 2 3 4 5 NA

QUALITY ASSESSMENT AND IMPROVEMENT

RT.6
As part of the hospital's program to assess and improve quality, the quality of residential treatment services is monitored and evaluated in accordance with QA.3 through QA.3.1.7.2 in the "Quality Assessment and Improvement" chapter of this Manual.

1 2 3 4 5 NA

---

*Effective January 1, 1993, the Joint Commission began referencing NFPA 101®-1991, the Life Safety Code® (LSC) *of the National Fire Protection Association. All facilities being surveyed will be evaluated using this edition of the LSC. Buildings for which plans were approved after January 1, 1993, will be evaluated as "new construction" under the applicable occupancy chapters of the LSC.*

Life Safety Code® *and* NFPA 101® *are registered trademarks of the National Fire Protection Association, Inc, Quincy, Mass.*

The standards in this appendix were effective July 1, 1990, and considered for accreditation purposes on January 1, 1991 (see the May/June 1990 issue of Joint Commission Perspectives).

APPENDIX C
JOINT COMMISSION INDICATORS FOR THE INDICATOR MONITORING SYSTEM, BETA-PHASE TESTING, AND HOSPITAL INTERNAL USE ONLY

This appendix contains three sections: (1) the indicators selected for the Joint Commission's indicator monitoring system, which begins operation in 1994; (2) the indicators currently undergoing Beta Testing in the field; and (3) other indicators recommended by the Joint Commission's Board of Commissioners for hospitals' internal use.

Certain standards in the "Improving Organizational Performance" chapter of this *Accreditation Manual for Hospitals, Volume I (AMH, Vol I)*, require hospitals to identify indicators for monitoring and improving their performance. The scoring guidelines for these standards state that hospitals should *at least consider* using any indicators the Joint Commission recommends in this Appendix. See the "Improving Organizational Performance" chapter in the 1994 *AMH, Vol II*, for complete scoring guidelines. Please contact the Joint Commission for additional information on any of these indicators.

Section I: 1994 Indicator Monitoring System Indicators

Although some Joint Commission indicator sets continue progressing through a multiyear testing phase, the anesthesia and obstetrical care indicator sets have completed this process. Based on the results of this testing and recommendations from expert task forces, the Board of Commissioners has approved the indicators in this section for the initiation in 1994 of an indicator monitoring system in which hospitals may participate on an optional basis.

Indicators will become an integral part of evaluating a health care organization's performance in a state-of-the-art accreditation process that is both valid and credible. The indicator monitoring system is an indicator-based performance monitoring system for accredited organizations that, when integrated into the accreditation process, will provide the Joint Commission with a continuous picture of organizational performance, allowing for monitoring between triennial on-site surveys. When data from the indicator monitoring system are used in the accreditation decision process (currently anticipated to begin in 1996), every accredited hospital will be required to participate in the system so that the Joint Commission's evaluations are based on measures and measurement processes that are consistent, uniformly applied, and fair across all organizations.

Beginning in 1994 hospitals can submit indicator data to the indicator database and receive comparative feedback about their performance from the Joint Commission. These data also may be used by the organization to meet the demands of patients, payers, and others who want to make informed health care decisions.

The Joint Commission will aggregate and analyze the indicator data. Comparative performance data will then be fed back to accredited organizations so they can identify trends and patterns as related to national norms. The Joint Commission will be particularly interested in whether organizations are using indicator information to assess and improve their performance.

During 1994 and 1995 hospitals will be encouraged to participate in the indicator monitoring system on an optional basis. Optional participation is intended to provide hospitals with experience in using the indicator monitoring system before indicator data begin to be used in the survey and accreditation process.

PREPARATION FOR MANDATORY PARTICIPATION

The indicators in this section will initiate the optional indicator monitoring system in 1994. Hospitals participating in beta testing have found it can take months (6–12) to institute a successful data collection system. Early involvement can assist hospitals in implementing an effective system before it is required and used in the survey and accreditation process.

Early participation in the indicator monitoring system will allow hospitals to accumulate sufficient data to measure performance, monitor trends, and receive feedback reports from the Joint Commission. It is expected that hospitals will use this information for internal performance improvement activities and benchmarking as well as to meet the requirement of IM.10 for participating in an external reference database.

The following indicators are included in the indicator monitoring system in 1994.*

1 **Focus:** Preoperative patient evaluation, intraoperative and postoperative monitoring, and timely clinical intervention

   Numerator: Patients developing a central nervous system (CNS) complication within two postprocedure days of procedures involving anesthesia* administration, subcategorized by ASA-PS class, patient age, and CNS versus non-CNS-related procedures

2 **Focus:** Preoperative patient evaluation, appropriate surgical preparation, intraoperative and postoperative monitoring, and timely clinical intervention

   Numerator: Patients developing a peripheral neurologic deficit within two postprocedure days of procedures involving anesthesia* administration

3 **Focus:** Preoperative patient evaluation, intraoperative and postoperative monitoring, and timely clinical intervention

   Numerator: Patients developing an acute myocardial infarction within two postprocedure days of procedures involving anesthesia* administration, subcategorized by ASA-PS class, patient age, and cardiac- versus noncardiac-related procedures

---

*For the indicators related to anesthesia care, the population of interest includes all patients undergoing surgical procedures involving anesthesia. Anesthesia is defined as the administration (in any setting, for any purpose, by any route) of general, spinal, or other major regional anesthesia or sedation (with or without analgesia) for which there is a reasonable expectation that, in the manner used, the sedation/analgesia will result in the loss of protective reflexes for a significant percentage of a group of patients.

4 **Focus:** Preoperative patient evaluation, intraoperative and postoperative monitoring, and timely clinical intervention

Numerator: Patients with a cardiac arrest within two postprocedure days of procedures involving anesthesia* administration, subcategorized by ASA-PS class, patient age, and cardiac- versus noncardiac-related procedures

5 **Focus:** Preoperative patient evaluation, intraoperative and postoperative monitoring, and timely clinical intervention

Numerator: Intrahospital mortality of patients within two postprocedure days of procedures involving anesthesia* administration, subcategorized by ASA-PS class and patient age

6 **Focus:** Prenatal patient evaluation, education, and treatment selection

Numerator: Patients delivered by cesarean section, subcategorized by primary and repeat cesarean section

Denominator: All deliveries

7 **Focus:** Prenatal patient evaluation, education, and treatment selection

Numerator: Patients with vaginal birth after cesarean section

Denominator: Patients delivered with a history of previous cesarean section

8 **Focus:** Prenatal patient evaluation, intrapartum monitoring, and clinical intervention

Numerator: Live-born infants with a birthweight less than 2,500 grams

Denominator: All live births

9 **Focus:** Prenatal patient evaluation, intrapartum monitoring, neonatal patient evaluation, and clinical intervention

Numerator: Live-born infants with a birthweight greater than or equal to 2,500 grams, who have at least one of the following: an Apgar score of less than 4 at 5 minutes, a requirement for admission to the neonatal intensive care unit within 1 day of delivery for greater than 24 hours, a clinically apparent seizure, or significant birth trauma

Denominator: All live-born infants with a birthweight greater than 2,500 grams

10 **Focus:** Prenatal patient evaluation, intrapartum monitoring, neonatal patient evaluation, and clinical intervention

Numerator: Live-born infants with a birthweight greater than 1,000 grams and less than 2,500 grams who have an Apgar score of less than 4 at 5 minutes

Denominator: All live-born infants with a birthweight greater than 1,000 grams and less than 2,500 grams

---

*For the indicators related to anesthesia care, the population of interest includes all patients undergoing surgical procedures involving anesthesia. Anesthesia is defined as the administration (in any setting, for any purpose, by any route) of general, spinal, or other major regional anesthesia or sedation (with or without analgesia) for which there is a reasonable expectation that, in the manner used, the sedation/analgesia will result in the loss of protective reflexes for a significant percentage of a group of patients.

Section II: Indicators Currently in Beta Testing

The following indicators are currently undergoing beta testing as part of the development and testing process for Joint Commission indicators. They are recommended for use by hospitals.*

CARDIOVASCULAR INDICATORS

Cardiovascular Patient Population: The cardiovascular indicators draw from four populations described in the following paragraphs: coronary artery bypass grafts (CABG), percutaneous transluminal coronary angioplasty (PTCA), acute myocardial infarction (MI), and congestive heart failure (CHF)

CABG Patient Population: Patients undergoing CABG excluding those with other cardiac or peripheral vascular surgical procedures performed at the time of the CABG (for example, valve replacement)

CV-1   **Indicator Focus:** Intrahospital mortality as a means of assessing multiple aspects of CABG care

Indicator (Numerator): Intrahospital mortality of patients undergoing isolated CABG procedures, subcategorized by initial or subsequent CABG procedures, emergent or nonemergent clinical status, and postoperative day and intrahospital location of death

CV-2   **Indicator Focus:** Extended postoperative stay as a means of assessing multiple aspects of CABG care

Indicator (Numerator): Patients with prolonged postoperative stay for isolated CABG procedures subcategorized by initial or subsequent CABG procedures, emergent or nonemergent procedures, and the use or nonuse of a circulatory support device

PTCA Patient Population: Patients for whom a PTCA procedure is initiated, regardless of whether a lesion is crossed or dilated

CV-3   **Indicator Focus:** Intrahospital mortality as a means of assessing multiple aspects of PTCA care

Indicator (Numerator): Intrahospital mortality of patients following PTCA subcategorized by emergent or nonemergent clinical status, postprocedure day, and intrahospital location of death

CV-4   **Indicator Focus:** Specific clinical events as a means of assessing multiple aspects of PTCA care

Indicator (Numerator): Patients undergoing nonemergent PTCA with subsequent occurrence of either an acute MI or CABG procedure within the same hospitalization

CV-5   **Indicator Focus:** Effectiveness of PTCA

Indicator (Numerator): Patients undergoing attempted or completed PTCA during which any lesion attempted is not dilated

MI Patient Population: Patients with a principal diagnosis of acute MI either on hospital discharge, emergency department (ED) transfer to another acute care facility, or death in the ED, and patients who are admitted for an acute MI or to rule out an acute MI

---

*The final wording of each indicator in this section may be subject to revision based on the results of further testing.

CV-6   **Indicator Focus:** Intrahospital mortality as a means of assessing multiple aspects of acute MI care

Indicator (Numerator): Intrahospital mortality of patients with principal discharge diagnosis of acute MI subcategorized by history of previous infarction, age, and intrahospital location of death

CV-7   **Indicator Focus:** Diagnostic accuracy and resource utilization

Indicator (Numerator): Patients admitted for acute MI, to rule out acute MI, or for unstable angina who have a discharge diagnosis of acute MI subcategorized by admission to an intensive care unit, a monitored bed, or an unmonitored bed

CHF Patient Population: Patients with a discharge diagnosis of CHF with or without specific etiologies

CV-8   **Indicator Focus:** Diagnostic accuracy

Indicator (Numerator): Patients with discharge diagnosis of CHF with documented etiology and chest x-ray substantiation of CHF

CV-9   **Indicator Focus:** Monitoring patients' response to therapy

Indicator (Numerator): Patients with a principal discharge diagnosis of CHF and with at least two determinations of patient weight and of serum sodium, potassium, blood urea nitrogen, and creatinine levels

ONCOLOGY INDICATORS

Oncology Patient Population: Inpatients admitted for initial diagnosis and/or treatment of primary lung, colon, rectal, or female breast cancer

ON-1   **Indicator Focus:** Availability of data for diagnosis and staging

Indicator (Numerator): Surgical pathology consultation reports (pathology reports) containing histological type, tumor size, status of margins, appropriate lymph node examination, assessment of invasion or extension as indicated, and AJCC/pTN classification for patients with resection for primary cancer of the lung, colon/rectum, or female breast

ON-2   **Indicator Focus:** Use of staging by managing physicians

Indicator (Numerator): Patients undergoing treatment for primary cancer of the lung, colon/rectum, or female breast with AJCC stage of tumor designated by a managing physician

ON-3   **Indicator Focus:** Effectiveness of cancer treatment

Indicator (Numerator): Survival of patients with primary cancer of the lung, colon/rectum, or female breast by stage and histologic type*

ON-4   **Indicator Focus:** Use of tests critical to diagnosis, prognosis, and clinical management

Indicator (Numerator): Female patients with invasive primary breast cancer undergoing initial biopsy or resection of a tumor larger than 1 centimeter in greatest dimension who have presence of estrogen receptor diagnostic analysis results in medical record

---

Efficient mechanisms to obtain postdischarge data will be explored only with a subset of beta-test hospitals. Ability to obtain these data during beta testing is not a requirement for participation.

ON-5   **Indicator Focus:** Use of multimodal therapy in treatment and follow-up

       Indicator (Numerator): Female patients with AJCC Stage II pathologic lymph node positive primary invasive breast cancer treated with systemic adjuvant therapy

ON-6   **Indicator Focus:** Effectiveness of preoperative diagnosis and staging

       Indicator (Numerator): Patients with non-small-cell primary lung cancer undergoing thoracotomy with complete surgical resection of tumor

ON-7   **Indicator Focus:** Specific clinical events as a means of assessing multiple aspects of surgical care for lung cancers

       Indicator (Numerator): Patients undergoing pulmonary resection for primary lung cancer with postoperative complication of empyema, bronchopleural fistula, reoperation for postoperative bleeding, mechanical ventilation greater than five days postoperatively, or intrahospital death

ON-8   **Indicator Focus:** Comprehensiveness of diagnostic workup

       Indicator (Numerator): Patients with resections of primary colorectal cancer whose preoperative evaluation by a managing physician includes examination of the entire colon, liver function tests, chest x-ray, and carcinoembryonic antigen levels

ON-9   **Indicator Focus:** Documentation of staging, prognosis, and surgical treatment

       Indicator (Numerator): Patients with resection of primary colorectal cancer whose operative reports include location of primary tumor, local extent of disease, extent of resection, and assessment of residual abdominal disease

ON-10   **Indicator Focus:** Use of treatment approaches that impact on quality of life

       Indicator (Numerator): Patients with primary rectal cancer undergoing abdominoperineal resections with 6 centimeters or more of free distal surgical margin present on specimen, as documented in surgical pathology gross description

ON-11   **Indicator Focus:** Interdisciplinary treatment and follow-up

       Indicator (Numerator): Patients with AJCC Stage II or III primary rectal cancer with documentation of referral to or treatment by a radiation or medical oncologist

TRAUMA INDICATORS

Trauma Patient Population: Patients with ICD-9-CM diagnostic code of 800 through 959.9 who either are admitted to the hospital, die in the emergency department (ED), or are transferred from the hospital or the ED to another acute care facility, excluding patients with the following isolated injuries: burns; hip fractures in the elderly; specified fractures of the face, hand, and foot; and specified eye wounds

TR-1   **Indicator Focus:** Efficiency of emergency medical services (EMS)

       Indicator (Numerator): Trauma patients with prehospital EMS scene time greater than 20 minutes

TR-2   **Indicator Focus:** Ongoing monitoring of trauma patients

Indicator (Numerator): Trauma patients with blood pressure, pulse, respiration, and Glasgow Coma Scale (GCS) documented in the ED record on arrival and hourly until inpatient admission to operating room or intensive care unit, death, or transfer to another care facility (hourly GCS needed only if altered state of consciousness)

TR-3 **Indicator Focus:** Airway management of comatose trauma patients

Indicator (Numerator): Comatose patients discharged from the ED prior to the establishment of a mechanical airway

TR-4 **Indicator Focus:** Timeliness of diagnostic testing

Indicator (Numerator): Trauma patients with diagnosis of intracranial injury and altered state of consciousness upon ED arrival receiving initial head computerized tomography scan greater than two hours after ED arrival

TR-5 **Indicator Focus:** Timeliness of surgical intervention for adult head injury

Indicator (Numerator): Trauma patients with diagnosis of extradural or subdural brain hemorrhage undergoing craniotomy greater than four hours after ED arrival (excluding intracranial pressure monitoring) subcategorized by pediatric or adult patients

TR-6 **Indicator Focus:** Timeliness of surgical intervention for orthopedic injuries

Indicator (Numerator): Trauma patients with open fractures of the long bones as a result of blunt trauma receiving initial surgical treatment greater than eight hours after ED arrival

TR-7 **Indicator Focus:** Timeliness of surgical intervention for abdominal injuries

Indicator (Numerator): Trauma patients with diagnosis of laceration of the liver or spleen requiring surgery and undergoing laparotomy greater than two hours after ED arrival, subcategorized by pediatric or adult patients

TR-8 **Indicator Focus:** Surgical decision making for abdominal gunshot wounds and/or stab wounds

Indicator (Numerator): Trauma patients undergoing laparotomy for wounds penetrating the abdominal wall subcategorized by gunshot and/or stab wounds

TR-9 **Indicator Focus:** Timeliness of patient transfers

Indicator (Numerator): Trauma patients transferred from initial receiving hospital to another acute care facility within six hours from ED arrival to ED departure

TR-10 **Indicator Focus:** Surgical decision making for orthopedic injuries

Indicator (Numerator): Adult trauma patients with femoral diaphyseal fractures treated by a nonfixation technique

TR-11 **Indicator Focus:** Clinical decision making for potentially preventable deaths

Indicator (Numerator): Intrahospital mortality of trauma patients—with one or more of the following conditions—who did not undergo a procedure for the condition: tension pneumothorax, hemoperitoneum, hemothoraces, ruptured aorta, pericardial tamponade, and epidural or subdural hemorrhage

TR-12 **Indicator Focus:** Systems necessary for obtaining autopsies for trauma victims

Indicator (Numerator): Trauma patients who expired within 48 hours of ED arrival for whom an autopsy was performed

MEDICATION USE INDICATORS

MU-1 **Indicator Focus:** Individualizing dosage

Indicator (Numerator): Inpatients older than 65 years in whom creatinine clearance has been estimated

MU-2 **Indicator Focus:** Individualizing dosage

Indicator (Numerator): Inpatients receiving parenteral aminoglycosides who have a measured aminoglycoside serum level

MU-3 **Indicator Focus:** Reviewing the order

Indicator (Numerator): New medication orders prompting consultation by the pharmacist with physician or nurse subcategorized by orders changed

MU-4 **Indicator Focus:** Timing of medication administration

Indicator (Numerator): Patients receiving intravenous prophylactic antibiotics within two hours before the first surgical incision

MU-5 **Indicator Focus:** Accuracy of medication dispensing and administration

Indicator (Numerator): Number of reported significant medication errors

MU-6 **Indicator Focus:** Informing the patient about the medication

Indicator (Numerator): Inpatients with principal and/or other diagnoses of insulin-dependent diabetes mellitus who demonstrate self-blood-glucose monitoring and self-administration of insulin before discharge or are referred for postdischarge follow-up for diabetes management

MU-7 **Indicator Focus:** Monitoring patient response

Indicator (Numerator): Inpatients receiving digoxin, theophylline, phenytoin, or lithium who have no corresponding measured drug levels or whose highest measured level exceeds a specific limit

MU-8 **Indicator Focus:** Monitoring patient response

Indicator (Numerator): Inpatients receiving warfarin or intravenous therapeutic heparin who also receive Vitamin K, protamine sulfate, or fresh frozen plasma

MU-9 **Indicator Focus:** Reporting adverse drug reactions (ADRs)

Indicator (Numerator): ADRs reported through the hospital's ADR-reporting system analyzed by method of reporting (spontaneous or retrospective medical record abstraction), type of ADR (dose related or non-dose related), and time of occurrence (before admission or during hospitalization)

MU-10 **Indicator Focus:** Reviewing complete drug regimen

Indicator (Numerator): Inpatients receiving more than one type of oral benzodiazepine simultaneously

MU-11 **Indicator Focus:** Reviewing complete drug regimen

Indicator (Numerator): Inpatients with seven or more prescribed medications on discharge

MU-12 **Indicator Focus:** Overall performance of medication use system

Indicator (Numerator): Patients younger than 25 years with a principal discharge diagnosis of bronchoconstrictive pulmonary disease, who are readmitted to the hospital or visit the emergency department within 15 days of discharge due to an exacerbation of their principal diagnosis

INFECTION CONTROL INDICATORS

IC-1 **Indicator Focus:** Surgical wound infection

Indicator (Numerator): Selected inpatient and outpatient surgical procedures complicated by a wound infection during hospitalization or postdischarge

IC-2 **Indicator Focus:** Postoperative pneumonia

Indicator (Numerator): Selected inpatient surgical procedures complicated by the onset of pneumonia during hospitalization but not beyond ten postoperative days

IC-3 **Indicator Focus:** Urinary catheter usage

Indicator (Numerator): Selected surgical procedures on inpatients who are catheterized during the perioperative period

IC-4 **Indicator Focus:** Ventilator pneumonia

Indicator (Numerator): Ventilated inpatients who develop pneumonia

IC-5 **Indicator Focus:** Postpartum endometritis

Indicator (Numerator): Inpatients who develop endometritis following cesarean section, followed until discharge

IC-6 **Indicator Focus:** Concurrent surveillance of primary bloodstream infection

Indicator (Numerator): Inpatients with a central or umbilical line who develop primary bloodstream infection

IC-7 **Indicator Focus:** Medical record abstraction of primary bloodstream infection

Indicator (Numerator): Inpatients with a central or umbilical line and primary bloodstream infection, analyzed by method of identification

IC-8 **Indicator Focus:** Employee health program

Indicator (Numerator): Hospital staff who have been immunized for measles (rubeola) or are known to be immune

HOME INFUSION THERAPY INDICATORS

Home Infusion Therapy Patient Population: Individuals for whom a home care agency has orders to administer, assess, monitor, maintain, or evaluate for infusion therapy. For the purposes of this indicator set infusion therapy includes parenteral nutrition, enteral therapy, immunotherapy/biological response modifiers, antibiotic therapy, pain management, blood products, and chemotherapy.

IT-1   **Indicator Focus:** Unscheduled inpatient admission by type of therapy

Indicator (Numerator): Patients/clients receiving home infusion therapy who have an unscheduled inpatient admission to an acute care facility, during the designated reporting period, subcategorized by reason for admission

IT-2   **Indicator Focus:** Discontinued infusion therapy by type of therapy

Indicator (Numerator): Courses of infusion therapy discontinued before prescribed completion, during the designated reporting period, subcategorized by reason for discontinuation

IT-3   **Indicator Focus:** Interruption in infusion therapy by type of therapy

Indicator (Numerator): Total number of interruptions in infusion therapy, during the designated reporting period, subcategorized by reason for interruption in therapy

IT-4   **Indicator Focus:** Prevention and surveillance of infection by type of therapy

Indicator (Numerator): Total number of suspected or confirmed catheter-related infections in patients/clients with central lines, for which the catheter is removed or antibiotics (oral or parenteral) are ordered, during the designated reporting period, subcategorized by type of central line catheter, number of lumens, and type of infection

IT-5   **Indicator Focus:** Reporting adverse drug reactions (ADRs)

Indicator (Numerator): Total number of suspected or confirmed ADRs experienced by infusion therapy patients/clients, during the designated reporting period, subcategorized by the type and severity of ADR and by drug class

IT-6   **Indicator Focus:** Patient/client monitoring and appropriate intervention

Indicator (Numerator): Patients/clients receiving total parenteral nutrition and/or enteral therapy who have an identified goal weight and are achieving or maintaining desired weight, during the designated reporting period

Section III: Additional Indicators Approved for Hospital Use

The following indicators have undergone alpha and/or beta testing in the Joint Commission indicator development and testing process and are recommended for internal hospital use only. (These indicators will not be included in the indicator monitoring system because of difficulties in collecting comparable data across organizations.)

ADDITIONAL ANESTHESIA INDICATORS

AN-A   Patients with a discharge diagnosis of fulminant pulmonary edema developed during procedures involving anesthesia administration or within one postprocedure day of a procedure's conclusion

AN-B   Patients diagnosed with an aspiration pneumonitis occurring during procedures involving anesthesia administration or within two postprocedure days of a procedure's conclusion

AN-C   Patients developing a postural headache within four postprocedure days following procedures involving spinal or epidural anesthesia administration

AN-D   Patients experiencing a dental injury during procedures involving anesthesia care

AN-E   Patients experiencing an ocular injury during procedures involving anesthesia care

AN-F   Unplanned admission of patients to the hospital within two postprocedure days following outpatient procedures involving anesthesia

AN-G   Unplanned admission of patients to an intensive care unit within two postprocedure days of procedures involving anesthesia administration and with intensive care unit stay greater than one day

ADDITIONAL OBSTETRIC INDICATORS

OB-A   Intrahospital neonatal deaths of infants with a birthweight of 750–999 grams born in a hospital with an NICU

OB-B   Maternal readmissions within 14 days of delivery

OB-C   Intrahospital maternal deaths occurring within 42 days postpartum

OB-D   Infants with a birthweight less than 1,800 grams delivered in a hospital without an NICU

OB-E   Neonates transferred from a non-NICU hospital to an NICU hospital

OB-F   Patients with excessive maternal blood loss

ADDITIONAL CARDIOVASCULAR INDICATORS

CV-A   **Indicator Focus:** Specific complication of CABG as a means of assessing the management of CABG patients

Indicator (Numerator): Patients undergoing isolated CABG procedures returning to the operating room for treatment of postoperative thoracic bleeding subcategorized by presence or absence of thrombolytic therapy received within 48 hours prior to CABG

CV-B   **Indicator Focus:** Specific complication of CABG as a means of assessing multiple aspects of CABG care

Indicator (Numerator): Intraoperative or postoperative cerebrovascular accident in patients undergoing isolated CABG procedure

CV-C   **Indicator Focus:** Effectiveness of PTCA

Indicator (Numerator): Patients with repeat PTCA of the same lesion occurring within 72 hours of the most recent PTCA subcategorized by emergent and nonemergent status of original PTCA

CV-D   **Indicator Focus:** Specific complication of PTCA as a means of assessing multiple aspects of PTCA care

Indicator (Numerator): Patients with post-PTCA complications at femoral or brachial artery insertion site subcategorized by thrombolytic therapy within 48 hours prior to PTCA

CV-E   **Indicator Focus:** Management of thrombolytic therapy in patients with acute MI

       Indicator (Numerator): Hemorrhagic complications in patients receiving thrombolytic therapy for acute MI subcategorized by complications occurring to patients prior to discharge from the institution initiating therapy and posttransfer complications occurring to patients receiving therapy prior to transfer

ADDITIONAL ONCOLOGY INDICATORS

ON-A   **Indicator Focus:** Availability of specific data needed for diagnosis

       Indicator (Numerator): Presence of a written pathology report in the medical record of the treating institution documenting the pathologic diagnosis of patients receiving initial treatment for primary lung, colorectal, or female breast cancer

ON-B   **Indicator Focus:** Symptomatic and/or palliative care

       Indicator (Numerator): Systematic initial assessment of pain for all patients hospitalized due to metastatic lung, colorectal, or female breast cancer with pain

ON-C   **Indicator Focus:** Use of clinical staging

       Indicator (Numerator): Presence of documented AJCC clinical staging in the medical record prior to the first course of therapy for female patients with primary breast cancer

ON-D   **Indicator Focus:** Use of multimodal therapy in treatment and follow-up

       Indicator (Numerator): Treatment of female patients with primary invasive AJCC clinical Stage I or II breast cancer by excisional biopsy, segmental mastectomy, or quadrantectomy without radiation therapy

ON-E   **Indicator Focus:** Use of psychosocial support for patient follow-up

       Indicator (Numerator): Referral to support or rehabilitation groups or provision of psychosocial support for female patients with primary breast cancer

ON-F   **Indicator Focus:** Patient education

       Indicator (Numerator): Patients undergoing resection for primary colorectal cancer with enterostomy present at discharge who demonstrate understanding of enterostomy care and management instructions

ADDITIONAL TRAUMA INDICATORS

TR-A   **Indicator Focus:** Communication between EMS and ED

       Indicator (Numerator): Copy of ambulance run report(s) not present with ED medical record for trauma patients transported by prehospital EMS personnel

TR-B   **Indicator Focus:** Trauma patient assessments in the emergency department

       Indicator (Numerator): Trauma patients admitted through the ED with inpatient discharge diagnosis of cervical spine injury not indicated in admission diagnosis

TR-C   **Indicator Focus:** Emergency department decision making

Indicator (Numerator): Death of trauma patients with discharge diagnosis of closed pelvic fracture who receive transfusions of greater than six units of blood

TR-D   **Indicator Focus:** Clinical decision making for surgical intervention

Indicator (Numerator): Trauma patients receiving initial abdominal, thoracic, vascular, or cranial surgery (excluding orthopedic, plastic, and hand surgery) more than 24 hours after ED arrival

TR-E   **Indicator Focus:** Use of blood products

Indicator (Numerator): Transfusion of platelets and/or fresh frozen plasma within 24 hours of ED arrival in adult trauma patients receiving less than eight units of packed red blood cells or whole blood

TR-F   **Indicator Focus:** Effectiveness of surgical intervention

Indicator (Numerator): Return of trauma patients to the operating room within 48 hours of completion of initial surgery

TR-G   **Indicator Focus:** Clinical decision making for femoral shaft fractures

Indicator (Numerator): Trauma patients with femoral diaphyseal fractures that are not associated with other injuries who do not receive physical therapy or rehabilitation therapy

APPENDIX D
INTERIM LIFE SAFETY MEASURES

Interim life safety measures (ILSM) are a series of administrative actions that must be taken to compensate temporarily for the hazards posed by existing NFPA 101®-1991 *Life Safety Code®* (*LSC*) deficiencies or construction activities.*

ILSM must be implemented in or adjacent to all construction areas and throughout buildings with existing *LSC* deficiencies. ILSM apply to all personnel, including construction workers, and they must be implemented during project development and continuously enforced through project completion.

ILSM are intended to provide a level of life safety comparable to that described in Chapters 1 through 7, 31, and the applicable occupancy chapters of the *LSC*. Each ILSM action must be documented through written policies and procedures. Except as stated below, the organization must establish frequencies for inspection, testing, training, and monitoring and evaluation.

ILSM consist of the following actions:

a. Ensuring that exits provide free and unobstructed egress. Personnel shall receive training if alternative exits must be designated. Buildings or areas under construction must maintain escape facilities for construction workers at all times. Means of egress in construction areas must be inspected daily.

b. Ensuring free and unobstructed access to emergency departments/services and for emergency forces.

c. Ensuring that fire alarm, detection, and suppression systems are not impaired. A temporary, but equivalent system shall be provided when any fire system is impaired. Temporary systems must be inspected and tested monthly.

d. Ensuring that temporary construction partitions are smoke tight and built of noncombustible or limited combustible materials that will not contribute to the development or spread of fire.

e. Providing additional fire-fighting equipment and use training for personnel.

f. Prohibiting smoking in accordance with MA.1.3.15 and in, or adjacent to, all construction areas.

g. Developing and enforcing storage, housekeeping, and debris removal practices that reduce the flammable and combustible fire load of the building to the lowest level necessary for daily operations.

h. Conducting a minimum of two fire drills per shift per quarter.

i. Increasing hazard surveillance of buildings, grounds, and equipment, with special attention to excavations, construction areas, construction storage, and field offices.

Effective January 1, 1993, the Joint Commission began referencing NFPA-101®-1991, the Life Safety Code® (LSC) of the National Fire Protection Association. All facilities being surveyed will be evaluated using this edition of the LSC. Buildings for which plans were approved after January 1, 1993, will be evaluated as "new construction" under the applicable occupancy chapters of the LSC.

Life Safety Code® and NFPA-101® are registered trademarks of the National Fire Protection Association, Inc, Quincy, Mass.

j. Training personnel when structural or compartmentation features of fire safety are compromised.

k. Conducting organizationwide safety education programs to ensure awareness of any *LSC* deficiencies, construction hazards, and these ILSM.

Note: *If questions arise concerning the implementation and use of ILSM, contact the Department of Plant and Technology Management at the Joint Commission.*

APPENDIX E ACCREDITATION AND APPEAL PROCEDURES

The application for survey and appropriate survey documents shall be completed by the organization seeking accreditation or provisional accreditation. After a survey has been conducted, the findings, survey documents, and any other relevant material or information received from any source shall be evaluated and acted upon as described in this appendix.

I. Evaluation by Joint Commission Staff

A. *Review and Determination by Joint Commission Staff*

Joint Commission staff shall review survey findings, survey documents, and any other relevant materials or information received from any source and shall, in accordance with decision rules approved by the Accreditation Committee of the Board of Commissioners,

1. determine or recommend to the Accreditation Committee that the organization receive accreditation with commendation; or

2. determine or recommend to the Accreditation Committee that the organization be accredited, with or without type I recommendations,* as described in paragraph VI of these procedures; or

3. determine or recommend to the Accreditation Committee that the organization be conditionally accredited; or

4. determine that the organization be conditionally accredited, if the organization does not challenge its survey findings in accordance with paragraph I.B; or

5. determine to recommend to the Accreditation Committee that the organization be denied accreditation; or

6. defer consideration while additional information regarding the organization's compliance status is reviewed by Joint Commission staff; or

7. determine or recommend to the Accreditation Committee that the organization be provisionally accredited in accordance with the early survey policy set forth on page xxix; or

8. determine to recommend that the organization not be provisionally accredited in accordance with the early survey policy set forth on page xxix.

---

*A type I recommendation is a recommendation or group of recommendations that determines, in part, the accreditation decision and that should receive the highest priority in the organization's plans for improvement. The organization's progress in complying with such recommendations will be monitored by the Joint Commission at stated times during the accreditation cycle through focused surveys, written progress reports, or both.

B. *Determination to Recommend Conditional Accreditation*

1. Notification to Organization of Areas of Noncompliance with Standards. If Joint Commission staff, based on survey findings, survey documents, and any other relevant materials or information received from any source, determines to recommend that the organization be conditionally accredited, except in those circumstances described in paragraph VI, it will send the organization a copy of the draft accreditation report, outlining its findings and determination. The organization may

   a. accept the findings and determination of the staff, which will promptly result in a decision to accredit conditionally; or

   b. within 20 calendar days from receipt of the report, submit to the Joint Commission any documentation of its compliance with Joint Commission standards at the time of the survey that is not reflected in the draft accreditation report, along with an explanation of why such documentation was not available for review at the time of the survey; or

   c. request the Joint Commission to resurvey one or more of the areas that led to the recommendation of conditional accreditation. If the findings of the first survey are found to be valid, there will be no change in the recommendation, and the organization will be charged for the resurvey expense. If the findings of the survey result in a recommendation to accredit, the organization will not be charged for the resurvey expense.

2. Failure to Respond by the Organization. If, within 20 calendar days from receipt of the draft accreditation report, the organization does not submit to the Joint Commission any documentation of its compliance with Joint Commission standards at the time of the survey that is not reflected in the draft accreditation report or request the Joint Commission to resurvey one or more of the areas that led to the recommendation of conditional accreditation, then the staff recommendation shall promptly result in a decision to conditionally accredit.

3. Consideration of the Organization's Response. Joint Commission staff shall review the organization's submission of additional information or resurvey findings and shall, in accordance with decision rules approved by the Accreditation Committee,

   a. recommend to the Accreditation Committee that the organization be conditionally accredited; or

   b. recommend to the Accreditation Committee that the organization be denied accreditation; or

   c. determine or recommend to the Accreditation Committee that the organization be accredited, with or without type I recommendations, as described in paragraph VI of these procedures.

C. *Determination to Recommend That Accreditation Be Denied*

1. Notification to Organization of Areas of Noncompliance with Standards. If Joint Commission staff, based on survey findings, survey documents, and any other relevant materials or information received from any source, determines, in accordance with decision rules approved by the Accreditation Committee, to recommend to the Accreditation Committee that the organization be denied accreditation, except in those circumstances described in paragraph VI and in the falsification of information policy set forth at page xxi, it will send a copy of the draft accreditation report to the organization, outlining its findings and determination. The organization may

a. accept the findings and determination of the staff; or

b. within 20 calendar days from receipt of the report, submit to the Joint Commission any documentation of its compliance with Joint Commission standards at the time of the survey that is not reflected in the draft accreditation report, along with an explanation of why such documentation was not available for review at the time of the survey; or

c. request the Joint Commission to resurvey one or more of the areas that led to the recommendation that accreditation be denied. If the findings of the first survey are found to be valid, there will be no change in the recommendation, and the organization will be charged for the resurvey expense. If the findings of the resurvey result in a recommendation to accredit or to conditionally accredit, the organization will not be charged for the resurvey expense.

2. Failure to Respond by the Organization. If, within 20 calendar days from receipt of the draft accreditation report, the organization does not submit to the Joint Commission any documentation of its compliance with Joint Commission standards at the time of the survey that is not reflected in the draft accreditation report or request the Joint Commission to resurvey one or more of the areas that led to the recommendation that accreditation be denied, then Joint Commission staff shall recommend to the Accreditation Committee that the organization be denied accreditation.

3. Consideration of the Organization's Response. Joint Commission staff shall review the organization's submission of additional information or resurvey findings and shall, in accordance with decision rules approved by the Accreditation Committee,

a. recommend to the Accreditation Committee that the organization be conditionally accredited; or

b. recommend to the Accreditation Committee that the organization be denied accreditation; or

c. determine or recommend to the Accreditation Committee that the organization be accredited, with or without type I recommendations, as described in paragraph VI of these procedures.

D. *Decisions by the President of the Joint Commission*

Anything outlined in paragraphs I.A–I.C.3 of these procedures to the contrary notwithstanding, if the survey findings identify any condition that poses a threat to public or patient safety, the president of the Joint Commission, or if the president is not available, a vice president of the Joint Commission designated by the president to do so, may promptly decide that the organization be denied accreditation. This action, and the findings that led to this action, shall be reported by telephone and in writing to the organization's chief executive officer and in writing to the authorities having jurisdiction. The president's or his/her designee's decision shall be promptly reviewed by the Accreditation Committee in accordance with paragraph II of these procedures.

II. Review by the Accreditation Committee

A. *Scope of Review*

The Accreditation Committee shall consider the decision of the president of the Joint Commission, or his/her designee, or the report and recommendation of the Joint Commission staff, and may review the survey findings, survey documents, any other relevant materials or information received from any source, including any additional information supplied by the organization in response to this information, and the findings of any resurvey.

B. *Decision*

Following such consideration and review, the Accreditation Committee shall

1. accredit the organization with commendation; or

2. accredit the organization, with or without type I recommendations, as described in paragraph VI of these procedures; or

3. conditionally accredit the organization; or

4. deny accreditation to the organization or confirm a decision by the president or his/her designee to deny accreditation; or

5. defer consideration while additional information regarding the organization's compliance status is gathered and reviewed by Joint Commission staff; or

6. order a resurvey or partial resurvey of the organization and an evaluation of the results, to the extent appropriate, by Joint Commission staff. Thereafter, Joint Commission staff shall transmit its report and recommendation to the Accreditation Committee for action, as provided in paragraph II.C of these procedures; or

7. provisionally accredit the organization; or

8. determine to not provisionally accredit the organization.

C. *Deferred Consideration*

Whenever the Accreditation Committee defers consideration pursuant to paragraph II.B.5 or II.B.6 of these procedures, Joint Commission staff shall review and report to the Accreditation Committee concerning the organization's compliance status. The Accreditation Committee may order any resurvey or partial resurvey necessary to determine such status.

Following such consideration and review, the Accreditation Committee shall

1. accredit the organization with commendation; or

2. accredit the organization, with or without type I recommendations, as described in paragraph VI of these procedures; or

3. conditionally accredit the organization; or

4. deny accreditation or confirm a decision of the president or his/her designee to deny accreditation to the organization; or

5. defer consideration while additional information regarding the organization's compliance status is gathered and reviewed by Joint Commission staff; or

6. order an additional resurvey or partial resurvey of the organization and an evaluation of the results, to the extent appropriate, by Joint Commission staff. Thereafter, Joint Commission staff shall transmit its report and recommendations to the Accreditation Committee for action, as provided in paragraph II.C of these procedures; or

7. provisionally accredit the organization; or

8. determine to not provisionally accredit the organization.

III. Conditional Accreditation

A. *Plan of Correction*

Except as provided in paragraph VI.A.2, an organization that is conditionally accredited by the Accreditation Committee, pursuant to paragraph II.B.3 or II.C.3 of these procedures, shall be required to submit a plan of correction within 30 calendar days of its receipt of notification of conditional accreditation. The plan shall outline the steps that will be taken by the organization to correct the deficiencies specified in the accreditation decision report and the time periods in which the action will be taken.

B. *Joint Commission Staff Action*

Upon submission of the plan of correction by the organization, Joint Commission staff shall,

1. if the plan of correction is not acceptable, notify the organization that it must submit a revised plan within 15 calendar days of receipt of the notification;

   a. if a second plan of correction, submitted pursuant to paragraph III.B.1, is not acceptable, recommend to the Accreditation Committee that the organization be denied accreditation; or

2. if the plan of correction is acceptable, notify the organization that a survey to determine the extent to which the deficiencies have been corrected will be conducted within approximately six months following the notification of approval of the plan, or sooner if the plan of correction indicates earlier resolution of deficiencies; or

3. if the organization fails to make the required submission of a plan of correction in response to either the first request or to the request for a revised plan of correction, recommend to the Accreditation Committee that the organization be denied accreditation.

C. *Survey to Determine Correction of Deficiencies*

Within approximately six months following Joint Commission staff's approval of the plan of correction, the Joint Commission shall conduct a survey of the organization to determine the degree to which deficiencies have been corrected.

D. *Review and Determination by Joint Commission Staff*

Joint Commission staff shall review the survey findings, survey documents, and any other relevant materials or information received from any source. In accordance with decision rules approved by the Accreditation Committee, Joint Commission staff shall

1. recommend to the Accreditation Committee that the organization be accredited, with or without type I recommendations, as described in paragraph VI of these procedures; or

2. recommend to the Accreditation Committee that the organization be denied accreditation; or

3. defer consideration while additional information regarding the organization's compliance status is gathered and reviewed by Joint Commission staff. At the conclusion of this review, one of the recommendations outlined in paragraph III.D of these procedures shall be made to the Accreditation Committee.

E. *Action by the Accreditation Committee*

Following review of the recommendations of Joint Commission staff, the Accreditation Committee shall

1. accredit the organization, with or without type I recommendations, as described in paragraph VI of these procedures; or

2. deny accreditation to the organization; or

3. defer consideration while additional information regarding the organization's compliance status is gathered and reviewed by Joint Commission staff; or

4. order a resurvey or partial resurvey of the organization and an evaluation of the results, to the extent appropriate, by Joint Commission staff. Thereafter, Joint Commission staff shall transmit its report and recommendation to the Accreditation Committee for action, as provided in paragraph III.E of these procedures.

F. *Charges to the Organization*

The full costs of the conditional accreditation process shall be paid by the organization that receives conditional accreditation.

IV. Hearings

A. *Right to a Hearing*

An organization that has been denied accreditation pursuant to paragraph II.B.4, II.C.4, or III.E.2 of these procedures is entitled to a hearing before an Appeal Hearing Panel if the Joint Commission receives the organization's written request for the hearing within 20 calendar days after the organization receives the written notice of the Accreditation Committee's decision, including confirmation of a decision by the president, or his/her designee, to deny accreditation, as provided in paragraph IV.B of these procedures. An Appeal Hearing Panel shall be composed of three impartial individuals who are chosen by the president of the Joint Commission, or his/her designee. One member of the panel will be a member of the Board of Commissioners who did not participate in or discuss the accreditation decision.

B. *Notice of Right to a Hearing*

The Joint Commission shall promptly send the organization a written report of the Accreditation Committee's decision, the basis for the decision, the organization's right to a hearing, the dates of two scheduled meetings of the Appeal Hearing Panel, and the time within which the organization must request, in writing, a hearing before one of those panels. Any request for a hearing may include a written statement of the organization's position.

C. *Notice of the Time and Place of a Hearing*

Any hearing to which an organization is entitled shall be held at the Joint Commission's headquarters except when the president of the Joint Commission, or his/her designee, determines otherwise for good cause shown. At least 20 calendar days before a hearing, the Joint Commission shall send the organization written notice of the time and place of the hearing and copies of any supplemental materials or information received from any source that the organization does not already have and that may affect any accreditation decision. The notice of the hearing shall advise the organization of the procedure to be followed at the hearing and, if feasible, of the identity and professional qualifications of the panel members.

D. *Continuance of a Hearing*

The president of the Joint Commission, or his/her designee, may continue the date of any hearing for good cause shown to the next scheduled Appeal Hearing Panel. An organization's request for such a continuance must be received by the Joint Commission in writing at least 15 calendar days before the scheduled date of the hearing.

E. *Procedure for the Conduct of a Hearing*

A hearing may be conducted with only two of the three panel members, provided one of them is the member of the Board of Commissioners. Representatives of the organization may be accompanied by legal counsel, may make oral and written presentations, and may offer information at any meeting of the Appeal Hearing Panel. The organization may request the attendance of any Joint Commission field representative who participated in the survey and who is available to appear at the hearing. Such requests must be received within at least 15 calendar days before the hearing. Presentations or information concerning actions taken by the organization subsequent to the most recent survey are not considered relevant to the validity of the original adverse decision.

F. *Adjournment of a Hearing*

After a hearing has commenced, an Appeal Hearing Panel may, if it chooses, suspend consideration for the purpose of receiving any additional information relating to the recommendation that it will make to the Board Appeal Review Committee. The panel may adjourn to another time or place, including reconvening by telephone conference, for this purpose.

G. *Report of Appeal Hearing Panel*

After a hearing has been completed, the Appeal Hearing Panel shall study the facts surrounding the original adverse decision and independently determine to recommend that the organization be accredited with or without type I recommendations, as described in paragraph VI of these procedures, or that the organization be conditionally accredited, or that accreditation be denied to the organization. The panel will submit a written report of its findings, recommendations, and the rationale for its recommendations for consideration by the Board Appeal Review Committee. The Joint Commission shall send the organization a copy of the report of the Appeal Hearing Panel at least 30 calendar days before the meeting of the Board Appeal Review Committee at which the report will be considered. The notice shall inform the organization of the date of the meeting and of the organization's right to submit written responses or comments for consideration by the Board Appeal Review Committee. Any such written responses or comments must be received by the Joint Commission at least 15 calendar days before the meeting of the Board Appeal Review Committee.

V. Review by the Board Appeal Review Committee

A. *Procedure for Review*

The report of an Appeal Hearing Panel shall be considered at the next regular meeting of the Board Appeal Review Committee, composed of three members of the Board of Commissioners. Two members will constitute a quorum. This meeting will generally be held by telephone conference, except when it is held in conjunction with meetings of the Board or Board Committee(s). The Board Appeal Review Committee shall review the report of the Appeal Hearing Panel and any written responses or comments submitted by the organization pursuant to paragraph IV.E or IV.G of these procedures and shall take one of the following actions:

1. If the Appeal Hearing Panel recommends that the organization be accredited, the Committee shall

   a. accredit the organization, with or without type I recommendations, as described in paragraph VI of these procedures, after finding that there is substantial evidence to support the recommendation; or

   b. either deny accreditation to the organization or conditionally accredit the organization after finding that there is not substantial evidence to support the recommendation.

2. If the Appeal Hearing Panel recommends that the organization be conditionally accredited, the Committee shall

   a. conditionally accredit the organization after finding that there is substantial evidence to support the recommendation; or

   b. deny accreditation to the organization after finding that there is not substantial evidence to support the recommendation; or

   c. make an independent evaluation of the report of the Appeal Hearing Panel and then decide to accredit the organization, with or without type I recommendations, as described in paragraph VI of these procedures.

3. If the Appeal Hearing Panel recommends that the organization be denied accreditation, the Committee shall

   a. deny accreditation to the organization, after finding that there is substantial evidence to support the recommendation; or

   b. make an independent evaluation of the report of the Appeal Hearing Panel and then decide to conditionally accredit or accredit the organization, with or without type I recommendations, as described in paragraph VI of these procedures.

   The action taken by the Board Appeal Review Committee shall constitute the final accreditation decision of the Joint Commission.

B. *Participation*

   No member of the Accreditation Committee or of the Appeal Hearing Panel who participated in an accreditation decision or recommendation concerning an organization shall participate in any deliberations or vote of the Board Appeal Review Committee in its review of that accreditation decision or recommendation. This provision shall not preclude any commissioner who participated in an appeal hearing as a member of the Appeal Hearing Panel from presenting and responding to questions about the report and recommendation of that Appeal Hearing Panel to the Board Appeal Review Committee.

VI. Procedure Relating to Type I Recommendations and Determination of Corrected Deficiencies

A. A decision of Joint Commission staff pursuant to paragraph I.A.2, I.B.3.c, or I.C.3.c of these procedures, of the Accreditation Committee pursuant to paragraph II.B.2, II.C.2, or III.E.1 of these procedures, or of a Board Appeal Review Committee, as provided in paragraph V.A of these procedures, to accredit an organization may be made contingent upon satisfactory correction of type I recommendations. The organization may be conditionally accredited or its accreditation may be withdrawn if it does not correct or document the correction of the specified deficiencies within the time specified in the notice of the decision to the organization. In such circumstances, the procedures for sending a draft notice and obtaining a response from the organization set out in paragraphs I.B and I.C are not applicable. Joint Commission staff, through the use of surveys or partial surveys or through other means, such as written progress reports, shall determine whether the organization has corrected the deficiencies within the time provided and shall report its findings to the organization. If Joint Commission staff determines that the organization has not corrected the deficiencies within the time provided, staff shall, as appropriate and in accordance with decision rules approved by the Accreditation Committee,

1. provide another opportunity to the organization to correct or document the correction of deficiencies, as provided in any applicable decision rules approved by the Accreditation Committee; or

2. determine that the organization be placed into conditional accreditation status with a conditional follow-up visit in approximately four months; or

3. recommend to the Accreditation Committee that the organization be denied accreditation, if certain deficiencies, specified in decision rules approved by the Accreditation Committee, have not been corrected or the correction of which have not been documented after the specified number of opportunities given to the organization to do so.

B. If Joint Commission staff determines to recommend to the Accreditation Committee that the organization be denied accreditation in accordance with paragraph VI.A.3, staff shall submit its recommendation to the Accreditation Committee for action, as provided in paragraph II.B.1 through II.B.8.

VII. Final Accreditation Decision

A. The action taken by Joint Commission staff shall constitute the final decision of the Joint Commission to

1. accredit the organization, when taken pursuant to paragraph I.A.1, I.A.2, I.B.3.c, or I.C.3.c of these procedures; or

2. conditionally accredit the organization, when taken pursuant to paragraph I.A.4 or VI.A.2 of these procedures; or

3. provisionally accredit the organization, when taken pursuant to paragraph I.A.7 of these procedures.

B. The action taken by the Accreditation Committee shall constitute the final decision of the Joint Commission to

1. accredit the organization with commendation, when taken pursuant to paragraph II.B.1 of these procedures; or

2. accredit the organization, when taken pursuant to paragraph II.B.2, II.C.2, or III.E.1 of these procedures; or

3. conditionally accredit the organization, when taken pursuant to paragraph II.B.3 or II.C.3 of these procedures; or

4. deny accreditation to the organization, when taken pursuant to paragraph II.B.4, II.C.4, III.E.2, or VI.B of these procedures, and the organization does not request a hearing pursuant to paragraph IV.A of these procedures; or

5. provisionally accredit the organization, when taken pursuant to paragraph II.B.7 of these procedures; or

6. not provisionally accredit the organization, when taken pursuant to paragraph II.B.8 of these procedures.

VIII. Status of the Organization Pending and After Appeal and Effective Date of a Final Decision

A. The accreditation status of an accredited organization shall continue in effect pending any final accreditation decision.

B. A final decision to accredit an organization shall be considered effective as of the first day after completion of the organization's survey from which the decision results.

C. A decision to deny accreditation to an organization shall become final and effective

1. as of the date of the decision made by the Board Appeal Review Committee pursuant to paragraph V of these procedures; or

2. at the expiration of the time during which an organization may, but does not, request a hearing before an Appeal Hearing Panel, pursuant to paragraph IV.A of these procedures; or

3. on receipt by the Joint Commission, before a decision to deny accreditation to the organization by the Board Appeal Review Committee, of written notification from the organization that it accepts the decision made by the Accreditation Committee, pursuant to paragraph II.B.3, II.C.3, III.E.2, or VI.B of these procedures, and thereby withdraws its appeal.

IX. Notice

Any notice required by these accreditation procedures to be given to an organization shall be addressed to the organization at its post office address as shown in Joint Commission records and shall be sent to the organization by U.S. registered mail, return receipt requested, with postage prepaid. Any notice required to be given to the Joint Commission by the organization shall be sent by the organization in the same manner and shall be addressed to the Office of the Vice President for Accreditation Surveys, Joint Commission on Accreditation of Healthcare Organizations, One Renaissance Boulevard, Oakbrook Terrace, Illinois 60181.

INTERPRETATION OF TERMS

accreditation
A determination by the Joint Commission that an eligible hospital complies substantially with applicable Joint Commission standards.

accreditation appeal
The process through which an organization that has been denied accreditation exercises its right to a hearing by an Appeals Hearing Panel followed by a review of the panel's report and recommendation by the Board of Commissioners.

Accreditation Committee
The committee of the Board of Commissioners responsible for oversight of the accreditation decision process.

accreditation cycle
The three-year term at the conclusion of which accreditation expires unless a full survey is performed.

accreditation decision
The conclusion reached regarding a hospital's status after evaluation of the results of the on-site survey, recommendations of the surveyor(s), and any other relevant information such as documentation of compliance with standards, documentation of plans to correct deficiencies, or evidence of recent improvements. The decision may be accreditation with commendation, accreditation, conditional accreditation, or not accredited.

accreditation with commendation The highest accreditation decision—awarded to a hospital that has demonstrated exemplary performance.

conditional accreditation A determination that substantial standards compliance deficiencies exist in a hospital. Findings of correction, which serve as the bases for further consideration of awarding full accreditation, must be demonstrated through a follow-up survey.

not accredited An accreditation decision that results when a hospital has been denied accreditation, when its accreditation is withdrawn by the Joint Commission, or when it withdraws from the accreditation process. This designation also describes any hospital that has never applied for accreditation.

provisional accreditation An accreditation decision that results when an organization has demonstrated substantial compliance with the selected structural standards used in the first of two surveys conducted under the early survey policy. The second survey is conducted approximately six months later to allow the organization sufficient time to demonstrate a track record of performance. Provisional accreditation status remains until the organization completes a full survey.

accreditation decision grid

The single-page display of the performance areas that summarize the standards in the *Accreditation Manual for Hospitals*. The grid format allows for the presentation of a simplified, numeric overview of a hospital's performance in each performance area.

grid element   A performance area such as infection control or safety management that receives a discrete score on the accreditation decision grid.

grid element score   A number representing the aggregated scores of individual standards in a performance area.

grid score   A number that indicates an organization's overall accreditation performance. The grid score is calculated from the grid element scores. Also referred to as the summary grid score.

accreditation duration

The three-year time period during which a hospital, found to be in substantial compliance with Joint Commission standards, is awarded accreditation. To maintain accreditation for a three-year period, satisfactory resolution of any identified issues is required.

accreditation history

An account of past accreditation decisions for a hospital. The accreditation history may be publicly disclosed by the Joint Commission on request.

Accreditation Manual for Hospitals (AMH)

A two-volume publication consisting of policies and procedures relating to hospital accreditation surveys and the delineation of current hospital standards (volume I) and corresponding scoring guidelines (volume II). Both volumes are designed for use in hospital self-assessment; volume I is the basis for the survey report forms used by surveyors during on-site surveys.

accreditation survey

An evaluation of a hospital to assess its level of compliance with applicable Joint Commission standards and to make determinations regarding its accreditation status. The survey includes evaluation of documentation of compliance provided by hospital personnel; verbal information concerning the implementation of standards, or examples of their implementation, that will enable a determination of compliance to be made; and on-site observations by surveyors. The survey also provides the opportunity for education and consultation to hospitals regarding standards compliance.

focused survey   A survey conducted during the accreditation cycle to assess the degree to which a hospital has improved its level of compliance relating to specific recommendations. The subject matter of the survey is typically an area(s) of identified deficiency in compliance; however, other performance areas may also be assessed by a surveyor(s) even though they may not be of immediate concern.

Official Accreditation Decision Report   The report resulting from the on-site assessment of a hospital that outlines identified deficiencies in standards compliance. It also outlines the nature of the accreditation decision including enumeration of type I recommendations, the implementation of which will be monitored by the Joint Commission through the conduct of focused surveys or requests for written progress reports. The report may also include other supplemental recommendations that are designed to assist the hospital in improving its performance.

survey report form The surveyor's data collection tool in which scores and documentation are recorded.

survey team The group of health care professionals who work together to perform an accreditation survey. The basic hospital survey team consists of physician, nurse, and administrator surveyors. A laboratorian and other specialist surveyors (for example, a mental health surveyor) may be added to evaluate certain services provided by a hospital.

surveyor A physician, nurse, administrator, laboratorian, or any other health care professional who meets Joint Commission surveyor selection criteria, evaluates standards compliance, and provides education and consultation regarding standards compliance to surveyed hospitals.

tailored survey A survey in which standards from more than one standards manual are used in assessing compliance; it may include using specialist surveyors appropriate to the standards selected for survey. *See also* standard, standards manual.

administration
See management and administrative services.

admitting privileges
Authority issued to those individuals who are members of the medical staff to admit patients to the hospital. Such individuals may practice only within the scope of the clinical privileges granted by the governing body.

aggregate standards compliance data
See aggregate survey data, hospital.

aggregate survey data, hospital
Information on key hospital performance areas and standards collected from surveyed hospitals and combined to produce a database that contains accumulated information concerning the standards compliance performance of those hospitals during a specified time interval.

alcoholism and other drug-dependence services
The delivery of care relating to alcoholism and other drug dependence. Standards are applied to evaluate a hospital's performance in providing alcoholism and other drug-dependence care.

ambulatory care services
See hospital-sponsored ambulatory care services.

anesthesia services
See surgical and anesthesia services.

aspects of care, important
Care activities or processes that occur frequently or affect large numbers of patients; that place patients at risk of serious consequences if not provided correctly, if incorrect care is provided, or if correct care is not provided; and/or that tend to produce problems for patients or staff. Such activities or processes are deemed most important for purposes of performance improvement activities.

authenticate
To prove authorship, for example, by written signature, identifiable initials, or computer key.

biologicals
Medicines made from living organisms and their products including, for example, serums, vaccines, antigens, and antitoxins.

blood usage review
An activity that entails measuring, assessing, and improving the ordering; distributing, handling, and dispensing; administration; and monitoring of blood and blood components.

Board of Commissioners
The governing body of the Joint Commission.

bylaws
A governance framework that establishes the roles and responsibilities of a body and its members.

cardiopulmonary resuscitation (CPR)
The administration of artificial heart and lung action in the event of cardiac and/or respiratory arrest. The two major components of cardiopulmonary resuscitation are artificial ventilation and closed-chest cardiac massage.

chief executive officer (CEO)
The individual appointed by the governing body to act on its behalf in the overall management of the hospital. Other job titles for this position include administrator, superintendent, director, executive director, president, vice president, and executive vice president.

chief executive officer exit conference
The meeting involving the surveyor(s) and the chief executive officer, the chair of the governing body, the nurse executive, the president of the medical staff, the chief operating officer, if applicable, and others, which is held at the conclusion of an on-site accreditation survey. The purpose of this meeting is the presentation by the surveyor(s) of any findings of significant standards compliance problems and the potential impact of these on the final accreditation decision and provision of the opportunity for conference participants to clarify issues.

clinical criteria
See criteria.

clinical laboratory, hospital
A facility serving a hospital that is equipped to examine material derived from the human body to provide information for use in the diagnosis, prevention, or treatment of disease for the hospital's patients; also called medical laboratory.

clinical privileges
Authorization granted by the governing body to a practitioner to provide specific patient care services in the hospital within defined limits, based on an individual practitioner's license, education, training, experience, competence, health status, and judgment.

delineation of clinical privileges The process of listing the specific clinical privileges a hospital's staff member may be granted.

clinical resume
A component of the medical record consisting of concise recapitulation of the reasons for hospitalization, the significant findings, the procedures performed, the treatment rendered, the condition of the patient on discharge, and any specific instructions given to the patient and/or family.

community-acquired infection
See infection.

competence/competency
Capacity equal to requirement, as in "the competence of a medical or professional staff member."

compliance
To act in accordance with, as in "compliance with a standard."

compliance level   A measure of the extent to which a hospital acts in accordance with a specified standard, including the following:

substantial compliance   A hospital consistently meets all major provisions of a specified standard; designated by a score 1.

significant compliance   A hospital meets most provisions of a standard; designated by a score 2.

partial compliance   A hospital meets some of the provisions of a standard; designated by a score 3.

minimal compliance   A hospital meets few of the provisions of a standard; designated by a score 4.

noncompliance   A hospital fails to meet the provisions of a standard; designated by a score 5.

not applicable   The standard does not apply to the hospital; designated by NA.

confidentiality as a patient right
A patient's right, within the law, to personal and informational privacy, including his/her patient record.

consultation
A review of a patient's problem by a second practitioner, such as a physician or other health care provider, and the rendering of an opinion and advice to the referring practitioner. In most instances, the review involves the independent examination of the patient by the consultant. The opinion and advice are not usually binding on the referring individual.

consultation in the accreditation process   Advice that is given to staff of surveyed hospitals relating to compliance with standards that are the subject of the survey.

consultation report   A potential component of the medical record consisting of a written opinion by a consultant that reflects, when appropriate, an examination of the patient and the patient's medical record(s).

continuing education

Education beyond initial professional preparation that is relevant to the type of patient care delivered in the hospital, that provides current knowledge relevant to an individual's field of practice, and that is related to findings from performance improvement activities.

continuity of care

A component of patient care quality consisting of the degree to which the care needed by a patient is coordinated among practitioners and across organizations and time.

credentialing

The process of granting authorization by the governing body to provide specific patient care and treatment services in the hospital, within defined limits, based on an individual's license, education, training, experience, competence, health status, and judgment.

credentials One or more documents given to a person to show that he/she has a right to exercise a certain position or authority.

criteria

Expected level(s) of achievement against which performance or care can be evaluated.

clinical criteria *See* guideline, practice; parameters, practice.

criteria for survey eligibility The conditions necessary for health care organizations to be surveyed for accreditation.

data

The collection of material or facts on which a discussion or an inference is based, such as data in the patient's medical record or indicator data.

data pattern An identifiable arrangement of data that suggests a design or orderly formation relative to a data set.

data trend One type of data pattern consisting of the general direction of data measurements.

delineation of clinical privileges

See clinical privileges.

dentist

An individual who has received the degree of either doctor of dental surgery or doctor of dental medicine and who is licensed to practice dentistry.

department

An organizational unit of the hospital (also called hospital department) or of the medical staff (also called clinical department). *See also* services.

diagnosis

A scientifically or medically acceptable term given to a complex of symptoms (disturbances of function or sensation of which the patient is aware), signs (disturbances the physician or another individual can detect), and findings (detected by laboratory, x-ray, or other diagnostic procedures, or responses to therapy).

diagnostic radiology services
The delivery of care pertaining to the use of radiant energy for the diagnosis of disease. Standards are applied to evaluate a hospital's performance in providing diagnostic radiology care.

medical radiation physicist, qualified An individual who is certified by the American Board of Radiology in the appropriate disciplines of radiologic physics, including diagnostic, therapeutic, and/or medical nuclear physics or an individual who demonstrates equivalent competency in these disciplines.

radiologic technologist, qualified An individual who is a graduate of a program in radiologic technology approved by the Council on Medical Education of the American Medical Association or who has the documented equivalent in education and training.

dietetic services
The delivery of care pertaining to the provision of optimal nutrition and quality foodservice for patients. Standards are applied to evaluate a hospital's performance in providing dietetic services.

dietitian, qualified An individual who is registered by the Commission on Dietetic Registration of the American Dietetic Association or who has the documented equivalent in education, training, and experience, with evidence of relevant continuing education.

director
A person who directs, controls, supervises, or manages an organization or a component thereof.

disaster plan
See emergency preparedness plan/program.

documentation
The process of recording information in the medical record and other source documents.

quality of documentation The degree to which information recorded in source documents is accurate and complete and is performed in a timely manner.

drug
Any chemical compound that may be used on or administered to persons as an aid in the diagnosis, treatment, or prevention of disease or other abnormal condition.

drug administration The act in which a prescribed dose of an identified drug is given to a patient.

drug allergies A state of hypersensitivity induced by exposure to a particular drug antigen resulting in harmful immunologic reactions on subsequent drug exposures, such as penicillin drug allergy.

drug dispensing The issuance of one or more doses of a prescribed medication by a pharmacist or other authorized person to another person responsible for administering it.

drug usage evaluation
An activity that entails measuring, assessing, and improving the prescribing/ordering; preparation and dispensing; administration; and monitoring of medications.

emergency preparedness plan/program
A component of a hospital's safety management program designed to manage the consequences of natural disasters or other emergencies that disrupt the hospital's ability to provide care and treatment.

emergency services
The delivery of emergency care to patients. Standards are applied to evaluate a hospital's performance in providing emergency care.

emergency services levels of care (I–IV) A classification, based on specific and general requirements, that describes the capability of a hospital to provide a range of emergency services for patients who need them. For example, a hospital with Level I emergency services offers comprehensive emergency care 24 hours a day with at least one physician experienced in emergency care on duty in the emergency care area and in-hospital physician coverage by members of the medical staff or by senior-level residents for at least medical, surgical, orthopedic, obstetric/gynecologic, pediatric, and anesthesia services.

equipment management
A component of a hospital's plant, technology, and safety management program designed to assess and control the clinical and physical risks of fixed and portable equipment used for the diagnosis, treatment, monitoring, and care of patients and of other fixed and portable electrically powered equipment.

evaluation
To determine the worth of or to appraise, as in "the evaluation of hospital performance."

focused survey
See accreditation survey.

function
A related group of interdependent processes that affect patient health outcomes.

key function An organizational function believed, on the basis of evidence or expert consensus, to increase the probability of desired patient outcomes.

governing body
The individual(s), group, or agency that has ultimate authority and responsibility for establishing policy, maintaining patient care quality, and providing for organizational management and planning; other names for this group include the board, board of trustees, board of governors, and board of commissioners. Standards are applied to evaluate the performance of a hospital's governing body.

governing body bylaws Rules that establish the roles and responsibilities of the governing body.

guideline, practice
Descriptive tool or standardized specification(s) for care of the typical patient in the typical situation, developed through a formal process that incorporates the best scientific evidence of effectiveness with expert opinion. Synonyms or near synonyms include clinical criteria, parameter (or practice parameter), protocol, algorithm, review criteria, preferred practice pattern, and guideline.

guideline, scoring
Descriptive tool that is used to assist hospitals in their efforts to comply with Joint Commission standards and to determine degrees of compliance. Scoring guidelines are described in the *Accreditation Manual for Hospitals, Volume II.*

health care organization
A generic term used to describe many types of organizations that provide health care services.

hospital-sponsored ambulatory care services
The delivery of care pertaining to nonemergency, adult, adolescent, and pediatric ambulatory encounters, whether performed through the clinical departments of the hospital or an organized ambulatory program, regardless of the physical location of such services (that is, within the hospital, on its campus, or at off-campus satellite facilities). Hospital-sponsored ambulatory care services are provided by one or more organizational unit(s) or components thereof of the hospital under the responsibility of the governing body; they do not include individual diagnostic studies performed by the hospital as a service or those services provided by practitioners in their offices through written agreement. Standards are applied to evaluate a hospital's performance in providing ambulatory care services.

house staff
Individuals, licensed as appropriate, who are graduates of medical, dental, osteopathic, or podiatric schools; who are appointed to a hospital professional graduate training program that is approved by a nationally recognized accrediting body approved by the U.S. Department of Education; and who participate in patient care under the direction of licensed independent practitioners of the pertinent clinical disciplines who have clinical privileges in the hospital and are members of, or are affiliated with, the medical staff.

independent practitioner
See licensed independent practitioner.

indicator
A tool used to measure, over time, an organization's performance of functions, processes, and outcomes.

infection
An illness produced by an infectious agent.

nosocomial infection An infection acquired in the hospital; also called hospital-acquired infection.

nosocomial infection rate   The ratio describing the number of patients with nosocomial infections divided by the number of patients at risk of developing nosocomial infections. Rates may be stratified by taking into account certain patient factors that may predispose a specified group of patients to an increased risk of acquiring a nosocomial infection (also called rate stratification by infection risk).

infection control

A hospital's program, including policies and procedures, for the surveillance, prevention, and control of infection. All patient care and patient care support departments/services are included in the program. Standards are applied to evaluate the quality of a hospital's infection control program.

infection control committee   A multidisciplinary group that oversees the infection control program including representatives from at least the medical staff, nursing, and administration and the person(s) directly responsible for management of infection surveillance, prevention, and control.

intensive care unit

A unit of a hospital established for patients requiring extraordinary care on a concentrated and continuous basis. *See also* special care units.

intent of standard

A brief explanation of a standard's rationale, meaning, and significance.

invasive procedure

A procedure involving puncture or incision of the skin or insertion of an instrument or foreign material into the body including, but not limited to, percutaneous aspirations and biopsies, cardiac and vascular catheterizations, endoscopies, angioplasties, and implantations and excluding venipuncture and intravenous therapy.

Joint Commission on Accreditation of Healthcare Organizations

An independent, not-for-profit organization dedicated to improving the quality of care in organized health care settings. Founded in 1951, its members are the American College of Physicians, the American College of Surgeons, the American Dental Association, the American Hospital Association, and the American Medical Association. The major functions of the Joint Commission include developing organizational standards, awarding accreditation decisions, and providing education and consultation to health care organizations.

key function

See function.

key performance area

See performance, performance area.

key process

See process.

laboratory

See pathology and clinical laboratory services.

laboratory testing, decentralized

Analytical testing performed at sites in the hospital but physically located outside the hospital's central laboratory. The testing sites are either under the jurisdiction of the organized pathology and clinical laboratory or another department/service. Examples of such testing include bedside testing and on-unit testing such as occult-blood testing, serologic screens (for example, mononucleosis or streptococcus), urine analysis, Gram stains, and glucose meter testing. For the purposes of Joint Commission standards, decentralized laboratory testing does not include testing in "satellite laboratories" under the jurisdiction of the organized pathology and clinical laboratories that perform tests such as "stat" laboratory tests or off-site hemoglobins, hematocrits, or electrolytes; all the standards in the *Accreditation Manual for Pathology and Clinical Laboratory Services* apply to such satellite laboratories. Decentralized laboratory testing also does not include "special function laboratories" such as blood gas laboratories, most sites where intraoperative testing is performed, and cytogenetic laboratories. In addition, it does not include endocrinology laboratories that are not under the jurisdiction of the organized pathology and clinical laboratory but that are sufficiently sophisticated to warrant evaluation using all the standards in the *Accreditation Manual for Pathology and Clinical Laboratory Services.*

leaders, organization

The group of individuals that set expectations, develop plans, and implement procedures to assess and improve the quality of the organization's governance, management, clinical, and support functions and processes. Leaders include at least the leaders of the governing body; the chief executive officer and other senior managers; the elected and/or appointed leaders of the medical staff and the clinical departments and other medical staff members in organization administrative positions; the nursing executive and other senior nursing leaders; and other key leaders.

leadership interview

A meeting of all surveyors present on the first day of the survey with the hospital's senior leadership to assess how the hospital's leaders work together in performance improvement activities, the roles that each of the major components of the hospital play in its management, and the extent to which the hospital meets standards requirements for communication and cooperation.

licensed independent practitioner

Any individual who is permitted by law and by the hospital to provide patient care services without direction or supervision, within the scope of the individual's license and in accordance with individually granted clinical privileges.

licensure

A legal right that is granted by a government agency in compliance with a statute governing an occupation (such as medicine or nursing) or the operation of an activity (such as in a hospital).

Life Safety Code®

A set of standards compiled and published by the National Fire Protection Association and referenced by the Joint Commission to evaluate health care organizations under its life safety management program.

life safety management program

A component of a hospital's plant, technology, and safety management program designed to protect patients, personnel, visitors, and property from fire and the products of combustion and to provide for the safe use of buildings and grounds.

management and administrative services

The activities performed to direct and conduct the affairs of an entire hospital, or components thereof, as established by policies of the hospital. Standards are applied to evaluate the quality of a hospital's management and administrative services.

medical history

A component of the medical record consisting of an account of a patient's history, obtained whenever possible from the patient; includes at least the following information: chief complaint, details of the present illness, relevant past history, and relevant inventory by body systems.

medical laboratory

See clinical laboratory, hospital.

medical radiation physicist, qualified

See diagnostic radiology services.

medical record

The account compiled by physicians and other health care professionals of a patient's medical history, present illness, findings on examination, details of treatment, and notes on progress. The medical record is the legal record of care.

medical record, complete A medical record is complete when (1) its contents reflect the diagnosis, results of diagnostic tests, therapy rendered, condition and in-hospital progress of the patient, and condition of the patient at discharge; and (2) its contents, including any required clinical resume or final progress notes, are assembled and authenticated, and all final diagnoses and any complications are recorded without the use of symbols or abbreviations.

medical record legibility The degree to which writing on a medical record can be read or deciphered.

medical record progress notes A component of the medical record consisting of a pertinent chronologic report of the patient's course.

medical record review

An activity, carried out with the cooperation of relevant departments/services, of measuring, assessing, and improving the quality of medical record documentation—that is, the degree to which medical record documentation is accurate, complete, and performed in a timely manner.

medical staff

A hospital body that has the overall responsibility for the quality of the professional services provided by individuals with clinical privileges and also the responsibility of accounting therefor to the governing body. The medical staff includes fully licensed physicians and may include other licensed individuals permitted by law and by the hospital to provide patient care services independently (that is, without clinical direction or supervision) in the hospital. Members have delineated clinical privileges that allow them to provide patient care services independently within the scope of their clinical privileges. Members and all others with individual clinical privileges are subject to medical staff and department bylaws and are subject to review as part of the hospital's performance improvement activities. Standards are applied to evaluate the quality of a hospital's medical staff performance.

medical staff bylaws A document that describes the organization, roles, and responsibilities of the medical staff. The bylaws are developed, adopted, and periodically reviewed by the medical staff and approved by the governing body.

medical staff executive committee A group of medical staff members, a majority of whom are licensed physician members of the medical staff practicing in the hospital, selected by the medical staff, or appointed in accordance with governing body bylaws, who are responsible for making specific recommendations directly to the governing body for its approval and for receiving and acting on reports and recommendations from medical staff committees, clinical departments/services, and assigned activity groups.

medical technologist
See pathology and clinical laboratory services.

medication
Any substance intended for use in the diagnosis, cure, mitigation, treatment, or prevention of disease.

mission statement
A written expression that sets forth the purpose of a hospital or a component thereof; it usually precedes the formation of goals and objectives of the hospital or a component thereof.

monitoring and evaluation
A process designed to help hospitals effectively use their quality assessment and improvement resources by focusing on high-priority quality-of-care issues. The process includes identifying the most important aspects of the care the hospital (or department/service) provides; using indicators to systematically monitor these aspects of care; evaluating the care at least when thresholds are approached or reached to identify opportunities for improvement or problems; taking action(s) to improve care or solve problems; evaluating the effectiveness of those actions; and communicating findings through established channels.

nosocomial infection
See infection.

nosocomial infection rate
See infection.

nuclear medicine services
The delivery of scientific and clinical care involving the diagnostic, therapeutic (exclusive of sealed radium sources), and investigative use of radionuclides. Standards are applied to evaluate a hospital's performance in providing nuclear medicine services.

nursing staff
Registered nurses, licensed practical/vocational nurses, nursing assistants, and other nursing personnel who perform nursing care in a health care organization.

registered nurse An individual who is qualified by an approved postsecondary program or baccalaureate or higher degree in nursing and licensed by the state, commonwealth, or territory to practice professional nursing.

occupational therapist, qualified
See physical rehabilitation services.

oral and maxillofacial surgeon, qualified

An individual who has successfully completed a postgraduate program in oral and maxillofacial surgery accredited by a nationally recognized accrediting body approved by the U.S. Department of Education.

outcome

That which results from performance (or nonperformance) of a function(s) or process(es). An outcome represents the cumulative effect of one or more processes on a patient at a defined point in time.

parameters, practice

Strategies for patient management, developed to assist practitioners in clinical decision making. Practice parameters include standards, guidelines, and other patient management strategies.

pathology and clinical laboratory services

The services that provide information on diagnosis, prevention, or treatment of disease through the examination of the structural and functional changes in tissues and organs of the body that cause or are caused by disease. Standards are applied to evaluate a hospital's performance in providing pathology and clinical laboratory services.

pattern in data

See data.

performance

The way in which an individual, group, or organization carries out or accomplishes its important functions and processes.

performance area An element of the accreditation decision grid that summarizes a standard or group of related standards. For example, infection control and safety management are two performance areas on the Hospital Accreditation Program Accreditation Decision Grid. The performance areas identified on the accreditation decision grid are considered to be the most critical to the final accreditation decision.

performance area, key A performance area that is important in the delivery of quality care. For example, infection control and safety management are key performance areas for most hospitals.

performance assessment

Involves analysis and interpretation of performance measurement data to transform it into useful information; the second segment of a performance measurement, assessment, and improvement system.

performance improvement

The continuous study and adaptation of functions and processes of a health care organization to increase the probability of achieving desired outcomes and to better meet the needs of patients and other users of services; the third segment of a performance measurement, assessment, and improvement system.

performance measure

Any device for measuring (quantifying) level of performance.

pharmaceutical services

The activities pertaining to the appropriate, safe, and effective storage, preparation, dispensing, and administration of drugs. Standards are applied to evaluate a hospital's performance in providing pharmaceutical services.

decentralized pharmaceutical services The storage, preparation, and dispensing of drugs at hospital sites physically located outside the hospital's central pharmacy; also called satellite pharmacies.

pharmacist An individual who has a degree in pharmacy and is licensed and registered to prepare, preserve, compound, and dispense drugs and chemicals.

pharmacy A place where drugs are stored and compounded or dispensed.

physical rehabilitation services

The professional and technical care that assists physically disabled persons to increase, attain, and/or maintain functional capacity. Standards are applied to evaluate a hospital's performance in providing physical rehabilitation services.

occupational therapist, qualified An individual who is a graduate of an occupational therapy program approved by a nationally recognized accreditation body and is currently certified as an occupational therapist by the American Occupational Therapy Certification Board or has the documented equivalent in training, education, and/or experience; who meets any current legal requirements of licensure or registration; and who is currently competent in the field.

physical therapist, qualified An individual who is a graduate of a physical therapy program approved by a nationally recognized accreditation body or who has the documented equivalent in training, education, and/or experience; who meets any current legal requirements of licensure or registration; and who is currently competent in the field.

physical therapist, qualified

See physical rehabilitation services.

physician

An individual who has received a degree of doctor of medicine or doctor of osteopathy and who is fully licensed to practice medicine.

physician licensure The process by which a legal jurisdiction such as a state grants permission to a physician to practice medicine after finding that she or he has met acceptable qualification standards. Licensure also involves ongoing regulation of physicians by the legal jurisdiction, including the authority to revoke or otherwise restrict a physician's license to practice.

physician member of the medical staff A doctor of medicine or doctor of osteopathy who, by virtue of education, training, and demonstrated competence, is granted medical staff membership and clinical privileges by the hospital to perform specified diagnostic or therapeutic procedures.

plan for improvement

An organization's written statement, approved by Joint Commission staff, that details the procedures to be taken to correct existing life safety deficiencies and lists the extraordinary life safety measures to be implemented to temporarily reduce the hazards associated with the deficiencies.

plan of correction, conditional accreditation

An organization's written plan, approved by Joint Commission staff, that outlines the actions the organization will take to address compliance issues that caused the Accreditation Committee to make a decision of conditional accreditation; the plan is the basis for the follow-up survey at a specified time once the plan is approved.

plant, technology, and safety management

The organizational management program designed to provide a physical environment free of hazards and to manage staff activities to reduce the risk of human injury. Standards are applied to evaluate a hospital's performance in providing plant, technology, and safety management.

podiatrist

An individual who has received the degree of doctor of podiatry medicine and who is licensed to practice podiatry.

policies and procedures

The act, method, or manner of proceeding in some process or course of action; a particular course of action or way of doing something, such as policies and procedures governing the medical staff credentialing process.

practice guideline

See guideline, practice.

practice parameter

See guideline, practice.

process

A goal-directed, interrelated series of actions, events, mechanisms, or steps.

important process A process believed, on the basis of evidence or expert consensus, to increase the probability that desired outcomes will occur.

program

An outline of work to be done or a prearranged plan or procedure, as in "the administration's program."

progress notes, medical record

See medical record.

public information interviews

The opportunity during an on-site accreditation survey for the presentation of information by the public or other interested parties, as well as by personnel and staff of the hospital undergoing survey.

quality improvement

An approach to the continuous study and improvement of the processes of providing health care services to meet the needs of patients and others. Synonyms and near synonyms include continuous quality improvement, continuous improvement, organizationwide quality improvement, performance improvement, and total quality management.

quality of care

The degree to which health services for individuals and populations increase the likelihood of desired health outcomes and are consistent with current professional knowledge. Dimensions of quality include the following: patient perspective issues, safety of the care environment, and accessibility, appropriateness, continuity, effectiveness, efficacy, efficiency, and timeliness of care.

radiation oncology services

Delivery of care pertaining to the use of radiation therapy for patients with tumors. Standards are applied to evaluate a hospital's performance in providing radiation oncology services.

radiologic technologist, qualified

See diagnostic radiology services.

registered nurse

See nursing staff.

respiratory care services

Delivery of care to provide ventilatory support and associated services for patients. Standards are applied to evaluate a hospital's performance in providing respiratory care services.

respiratory care technician, certified An individual who has been certified by the National Board for Respiratory Care after successfully completing all education, experience, and examination requirements.

respiratory therapist An individual who has successfully completed a training program accredited by the American Medical Association Committee on Allied Health Education and Accreditation in collaboration with the Joint Review Committee for Respiratory Therapy Education and is eligible to take the registry examination administered by the National Board for Respiratory Care or has the documented equivalent in training and/or experience.

respiratory therapy technician An individual who has successfully completed a training program accredited by the American Medical Association Committee on Allied Health Education and Accreditation in collaboration with the Joint Review Committee for Respiratory Therapy Education and is eligible to take the certification examination administered by the National Board for Respiratory Care or has the documented equivalent in training and/or experience.

restraint

Use of a physical or mechanical device to involuntarily restrain the movement of the whole or a portion of a patient's body as a means of controlling his/her physical activities in order to protect him/her or others from injury. Restraint differs from the use of mechanisms usually and customarily employed during medical, diagnostic, or surgical procedures that are considered a regular part of such procedures. These mechanisms include, but are not limited to, body restraint during surgery, arm restraint during intravenous administration, and temporary physical restraint prior to administration of electroconvulsive therapy. Devices used to protect the patient, such as bedrails, tabletop chairs, protective nets, helmets, or the temporary halter-type or soft-chest restraints and mechanisms such as orthopedic appliances, braces, wheelchairs, or other appliances or devices used to posturally support the patient or assist him/her in obtaining and maintaining normative bodily functioning are not considered restraint interventions.

risk management activities
Clinical and administrative activities that hospitals undertake to identify, evaluate, and reduce the risk of injury and loss to patients, personnel, visitors, and the institution itself. Standards are applied to evaluate a hospital's performance in conducting risk management activities designed to identify, evaluate, and reduce the risk of patient injury associated with care and services.

safety of care
The degree to which the hospital environment is free from hazard or danger.

safety management
A component of a hospital's plant, technology, and safety management program that combines five elements—general safety, safety education, emergency preparedness, hazardous materials and wastes, and safety devices and operational practices. Standards are applied to evaluate a hospital's performance in conducting safety management programs.

scope of care/service
Inventory of processes that make up a specified function, including activities performed by governance, managerial, clinical, and/or support personnel.

scoring guidelines
See guideline, scoring.

seclusion
The involuntary confinement of a patient alone in a room, which the patient is physically prevented from leaving, for any period of time. Seclusion does not include involuntary confinement for legally mandated but nonclinical purposes, such as confining a person facing serious criminal charges or serving a criminal sentence to a locked room.

services
Functional divisions of a hospital or of its medical staff; also, the delivery of care.

social work services
Delivery of care that assists patients and their families in addressing emotional, social, and economic stresses of illness or injury; also called social services or social work. Standards are applied to evaluate a hospital's performance in providing social work services.

social work assistant   An individual with a bachelor's degree, preferably with a social work sequence, who is given training on the job for specific assignments and responsibilities in the provision of social work services or who has the documented equivalent in education, training, and/or experience.

social worker, qualified   An individual who either has met the requirements of a graduate curriculum (leading to a master's degree) in a school of social work that is accredited by the Council on Social Work Education or has the documented equivalent in education, training, and/or experience.

special care units
Organized service areas with a concentration of qualified professional staffing and supportive resources that are established to provide intensive care continuously on a 24-hour basis to critically ill patients. Such units include general intensive care medical/surgical units and other types of units that provide specialized intensive care (for example, burn and neonatal intensive care units).

Standards are applied to evaluate a hospital's performance in providing intensive care. *See also* intensive care unit.

standard
A statement of expectation that defines the structures and processes that must be substantially in place in an organization to enhance the quality of care.

standards manuals Six Joint Commission books delineating current standards pertaining to specified types of health care organizations or services. The books are designed for use in organization self-assessment and are the basis for the survey report forms used by Joint Commission surveyors during on-site surveys. The six manuals are *Accreditation Manual for Hospitals*; *Accreditation Manual for Ambulatory Health Care*; *Accreditation Manual for Mental Health, Chemical Dependency, and Mental Retardation/Developmental Disabilities Services*; *Accreditation Manual for Long Term Care*; *Accreditation Manual for Home Care*; and *Accreditation Manual for Pathology and Clinical Laboratory Services*. *See also Accreditation Manual for Hospitals*.

summation conference
An optional conference held by surveyors, after the chief executive officer exit conference, for all hospital staff and others designed to convey general observations about the survey findings, and, on the basis of these findings, provide preliminary information about the hospital's strengths and weaknesses.

supplemental recommendation (previously known as type II recommendation or consultative recommendation)
A recommendation or group of recommendations that encompasses a standard(s) that was scored in less than substantial compliance (that is, less than a score 1) but did not result in a type I recommendation. If not resolved, a supplemental recommendation may affect a future accreditation decision. These recommendations are contained in the "Supplemental Recommendations" section of an organization's accreditation decision report.

surgical and anesthesia services
Delivery of care to any patient, in any setting, who receives, for any purpose, by any route (1) general, spinal, or other major regional anesthesia; or (2) sedation (with or without analgesia) for which there is a reasonable expectation that in the manner used the sedation/analgesia will result in the loss of protective reflexes for a significant percentage of a group of patients.

surgical case review
An activity that entails measuring, assessing, and improving the selection of the appropriate surgical or other invasive procedure; preparation of the patient for the procedure; performance of the procedure and monitoring the patient; and provision of postprocedure care.

survey team
See accreditation survey.

surveyor
See accreditation survey.

tailored survey
See accreditation survey.

threshold

The level or point at which a stimulus is strong enough to signal the need for organization response to indicator data and the beginning of the process for determining why the threshold has been approached or crossed.

timeliness of care

A performance dimension concerning the degree to which the care/intervention is provided to the patient at the time it is most beneficial or necessary.

transplantation services

Delivery of care pertaining to grafting tissues taken from the patient's own body or from another person's.

trend in data

See data.

type I recommendation

A recommendation or group of recommendations that addresses insufficient or unsatisfactory standards compliance in a specific performance area. Resolution of type I recommendations must be achieved within stipulated time frames in order for an organization to maintain its accreditation.

utilities management

A component of an organization's plant, technology, and safety management program designed to assure the operational reliability, assess the special risks, and respond to failures of utility systems that support the patient care environment. Standards are applied to evaluate a hospital's performance in utilities management.

utility systems   Hospital systems for life support, infection control, environment support, and equipment support.

utilization review

The examination and evaluation of the appropriateness of the utilization of a hospital's resources. Standards are applied to evaluate a hospital's performance in conducting utilization review.

utilization review committee   A committee designated to carry out utilization review activities.

waived tests

Tests that meet the Clinical Laboratory Improvement Act of 1988 requirements for waived tests; are cleared by the Food and Drug Administration for home use; employ methodologies that are so simple and accurate as to render the likelihood of erroneous results negligible; or pose no risk of harm to the patient if the test is performed incorrectly.

written progress report

A postsurvey activity that involves preparing a report documenting evidence that correction of a compliance problem(s) is complete. Preparing a written progress report involves summarizing, documenting, and collecting facts and other evidence that prove an organization's current compliance with the standards that caused the type I recommendation.

INDEX

This index is designed to help the user find items quickly and efficiently. The majority of entries are referenced to specific standards. Thus the user may go directly to an item within a chapter rather than scanning an entire page for the desired material. Entries that refer to the specific chapter titles still reference the page numbers for the entire chapter.

written orders for medications brought in by patients, TX.11.4

after-hours availability, TX.7

dispensation, TX.4, TX.5

emergency, ES.5.5.3, SP.3.2.5, TX.8

family education in safe use of, PF.2.2.1

formulary lists, IM.9.6, TX.1

investigational, TX.11.6

labeling, TX.4.1

legal restrictions, TX.5.1

in medical record, IM.7.2.19, IM.7.2.20, IM.7.2.21, IM.7.4.3.2

minimization of errors, TX.4.4

monitoring

    adverse effects, TX.12, TX.12.2

    collaborative assessment, TX.12.1

    communication of patient reactions, TX.12.4

    patient information in, TX.12.3

parenteral nutrition, TX.14

performance assessment, PI.3.4.2.2

pharmacist review of prescription/order, TX.4.2

policies and procedures, TX.13

preparation and storage, TX.3

recall, TX.10

record keeping, TX.9

verbal orders of, IM.7.8.1

Microbiology, PA.1.1

Microscopy, clinical, PA.1.1

Minors, in emergency services, ES.4.1.2.2

Multihospital system, organizational planning in, LD.1.1.2

National Council on Radiation Protection and Measurements, DR.2.2.5, RA.2.2.5

National Fire Protection Association (NFPA), ES.5.4, PL.1

Natural disasters, PL.1.7

Neglected patients. *See* Abused/neglected patients

Neonatal intensive care. *See under* Intensive care unit

Neonates

assessment of, PE.7

management coordination of services for, MA.1.3.4

nurseries for, PL.4.2.2.5

in respiratory care services, RP.2.2.1.1.7

rights/responsibilities of, MA.1.3.5.1

transfers, MA.1.3.13

Newborn nurseries, PL.4.2.2.5

Nonphysicans

clinical privileges of, MS.2.16.2.1

and medical records, MS.2.16.3.2, MS.2.16.3.3, MS.2.16.3.4

in respiratory care services, RP.1.9

Nosocomial infections, IC.1.3, IC.2.2.2

Nuclear medicine services, 137–139

director of

    qualifications, NM.1.2

    role in developing safety rules, NM.1.3

equipment, NM.2.2.4, NM.2.2.7

policies and procedures, NM.2.2

quality control, PI.3.5.3.4

safety, NM.1.3, NM.2, NM.2.2.6

staff

    orientation and education, NM.2.2.13

    qualifications, NM.1.1

    radiation exposure, NM.2.2.9, NM.2.2.10, NM.2.2.11, NM.2.2.12

Nursing assistants, NC.3.4.2.1

Nursing care, 141–147

access to poison control information, IM.9.5

basis for, NC.1.3

care plan, OP.3.2

collaboration with other disciplines, NC.1.3.2

committee assignments, NC.3.4.2.4

data collection, NC.1.1.2

in decentralized hospital structures, NC.5.1.1

decision making, NC.1.3.2

diagnoses, NC.1.3

director

    delegation of responsibilities, N.C.1.1.2

    description of policies and procedures, NC.3.1.1, NC.3.1.2

    participation in admissions system, NC.3.3.1

    qualifications, NC.5.1

in discharge planning, NC.1.3.4.6

documentation in medical record, IM.7.4.3.4

documentation of licensure and clinical competence, NC.2.4

in emergency services, ES.2.3

ethical concerns, NC.3.2

medical record review, IM.3.3.1.1

patients

    assessment, PE.4.3

    involvement in care, NC.1.3.1, NC.1.3.4.6, NC.3.4.2.3

    needs assessment, NC.1

    status, PE.1.3

policies and procedures

    competence, NC.2.1.1.2

    description of, NC.3.1

    staff assignments, NC.3.4

rehabilitation, RH.2.7

significant others, involvement in, NC.1.3.1, NC.1.3.4.6, NC.3.4.2.3

in special care units

    and admission/discharge, SP.1.1

    alarm system, SP.4.5

    staffing, SP.2.4

      renal unit, SP.5.3

    supervision, SP.4

staff

    assignment of responsibilities, NC.2.1

    in burn unit, SP.5.1.3

    in cardiac/cardiovascular surgery or respiratory intensive care, SP.5.2.3, SP.5.2.4, SP.5.2.5

    competence of, NC.2

    education of, NC.5.6

    evaluation of, NC.2.1.1

    in neonatal intensive care unit, SP.5.3.2, SP.5.3.3

    participation in improvement activities, NC.3.4.2.4

    plan review, NC.4.1

    in renal unit, SP.5.3

    responsibility for determining, NC.2.2

    standards, NC.3.1, NC.4.1.2

    support services, NC.3.4.2.3

    technology, NC.2.1.2.2.2

    vocational rehabilitation services, RH.3.4.2, RH.3.4.3

Nutrition. *See also* Dietetic services

in alcoholism/drug-dependence programs, AL.1.4.5

parenteral

    administration, TX.14.4

    assessment of patient rights, TX.5

    dietetic services, DT.2.2.6

    medication orders for, TX.14.2

    preparation and dispensing, TX.14.3

    therapeutic requirement, TX.14.1

Observation beds, ES.5.2